Fundamentals of Human Physiology

A Comparative Examination

Preliminary Edition

By M. Beth Zimmer

Ferris State University

Bassim Hamadeh, CEO and Publisher
Michael Simpson, Vice President of Acquisitions
Jamie Giganti, Senior Managing Editor
Miguel Macias, Graphic Designer
Mark Combes, Senior Field Acquisitions Editor
Mirasol Enriquez, Senior Project Editor
Luiz Ferreira, Senior Licensing Specialist

First published in the United States of America in 2016 by Cognella, Inc.

Trademark Notice: Product or corporate names may be trademarks or registered trademarks, and are used only for identification and explanation without intent to infringe.

Cover image copyright © Depositphotos/STYLEPICS.

Printed in the United States of America

ISBN: 978-1-62661-687-5 (pbk) / 978-1-62661-688-2 (br)

Contents

Chapter 1: What is Physiology? General Principles

Physiology is the basic understanding of how living organisms function. Since there are a wide variety of organisms, there too are a wide variety of "fields" of physiological study; cell physiology, bacterial physiology, plant physiology, animal physiology, and human physiology. Within animals and humans, the study of physiology includes our understanding of how an entire organism works, such as what happens to a body during exercise or when the body changes from an awake state to a sleep state. It includes our understanding of how a particular organ functions within the body, such as how the heart continues to beat, day after day, until death or how the kidney works to filter blood and produce urine. And the study of physiology even includes our understanding of a particular mechanism within an individual cell, such as how insulin causes a cell to increase its uptake and utilization of glucose or how a gastric cell secretes acid into the stomach. In the study of physiology, there are a basic set of unifying concepts or general principles that are important in generating a basic foundation to our understanding of the physiology of all animals, including humans

1) The study of physiology is based on the laws of chemistry and physics.
2) The structures within organisms are compartmentalized from the cellular level to organ level to the whole organism.
3) The highly organized structures and organs function together in a precise and coordinated fashion.
4) Homeostasis or the maintenance of a constant internal environment is necessary for health and survival.
5) There is communication and controlled exchange of material between cells, tissues and organs which help to maintain homeostasis.
6) The form of structures helps to determine the function of the structures.

Basic Introduction

All organisms of the animal kingdom, including humans, share these basic, unifying principles. Our understanding of the physiology of humans is based on studies and observations of not only humans but also of animals and even cells in culture. In fact, many of the general mechanisms that we know today and which are covered in any physiology textbook have been discovered using animal research. It is important that the students of science understand and appreciate the amount of information that has been gained by animal research. For example, before any drug trial is initiated in humans, the drugs were tested in animals to measure and evaluate the effect of the drug on the whole body. This textbook will introduce each organ system with an evolutionary perspective to highlight the role that animals and animal research has played in developing our understanding of human physiology as we know today.

As stated above, physiology is based on the laws of chemistry and physics. The basic principles of chemistry and physics will not be covered in this textbook and the student is advised to consult other books on chemistry and physics where needed. We will assume that the student has taken a basic physics and chemistry class and understands the fundamentals of physics and chemistry. In this textbook we will talk about proteins and interactions between proteins as well as some basic chemical equations, and we will assume that the student has had the appropriate background to fully understand and comprehend some basic concepts. This textbook will, however, review certain key principles that are important in understanding specific physiological principles as they appear in the textbook.

Anatomy is the study of the structures of the body. Gross anatomy is the study of what you can see with the naked eye, whereas microscopic anatomy, or histology, is the study of tissues and cells; that which can be observed with the microscope. This textbook will cover some anatomy as it is relevant to the understanding of physiology. For example, in the cardiovascular system it is important to understand the basic structure of the heart in order to understand how the heart functions in routing the blood into the systemic and pulmonary circulations. However, this textbook will not go into detail and describe and name all of the bones or arteries in the body. The student is directed to specific anatomy textbooks for a full understanding of human anatomy.

Physiology is the study of how the anatomical parts function. This can be at the molecular level, i.e., how a sodium channel works, to how an organ works, to how the whole organism responds to a perturbation, such as going to high altitude. The physiologist is concerned with how the body functions normally. Pathophysiology is the study of abnormal physiology and will not be covered in this textbook except to illustrate specific examples which help to understand and appreciate normal physiology. An important principle in physiology is that form helps to determine the function. This principle applies at all levels of organization, the molecule, cell, tissue, organ, organ system or whole body. For example, the specific structure of a membrane channel allows only certain sized and certain charged particles to pass through the pore of the channel; the structure of the heart only allows blood to flow in one direction; the structure of the sarcomere found within a skeletal muscle allows the muscle cell to shorten or lengthen as needed. Throughout this textbook, you will see over and over how the structure of things (organelles, cells, organs, etc...) help determine its function.

Organization of the animal or human body

The animal or human organism is a collection molecules, cells, tissues, organs and organ systems. Within the entire organism, systems function together to produce a certain function. For example the cardiovascular system (the heart along with the arteries and the veins) works together with the respiratory system (the nasal cavity and upper airways connected to the lungs) to exchanges gases at the lungs and then again at the tissues. It also works together with the digestive system to gather nutrients and distribute them throughout the body. It also works with the urinary system to gather wastes from the tissues and remove them by filtration through the kidneys.

Organ systems contain multiple organs in order to carry out their function properly. Each organ has a specific function within the body. Many organs contain functional units which perform the primary function of the particular organ. In the kidney for example, the nephron is the functional unit and is the structure which filters the blood and creates urine. Another organ, the stomach, aids in protein digestion and creates chyme, a mixture of the food we ingested and an acidic, watery solution which helps aid in digestion and absorption in other organs such as the small intestine. Each organ is made up of one or more tissues which work together to help aid in the function of that organ. In the stomach, the cells of the epithelial tissue secrete acid, enzymes, and mucus and the smooth muscle mixes the contents together. Each tissue is made up of cells and extracellular substances such as fibers and ground substance (extracellular matrix) which work together to carry out a specific function. Bone is one type of connective tissue and contains cells such as osteoblasts which secrete the extracellular organic and inorganic substances which make up the tough, hard bony structure, and osteoclasts which enzymatically degrade bones. The homeostasis of plasma calcium involves either the activation of osteoblasts to make more bone removing calcium from the blood or the degradation of bone to release calcium and increase plasma concentrations of calcium. The cell is the smallest unit of life. The human body is made up trillions of cells and contains another trillion or more additional bacterial cells living on or in the body. Cells are comprised of individual molecules such as proteins, lipids, glucose or water which are made of atoms and elements of the periodic table. Cellular physiology is a large field and is covered briefly in Chapter 2.

Introduction to Histology

Histology, or microscopic anatomy, is the study of tissues. Histologists stain tissues and observe the physical characteristics of cells and tissues with microscopes; such as the shape, size and number of cells and structures, types of nuclei, shape and appearance of extracellular material, etc... in order to help determine their function. Living tissues contain cells along with extracellular substances that are secreted by cells. Within an organism, there is a great diversity in the shape, size and number of cells and a diversity in the amount and types of extracellular substances that can be produced and secreted by cells. This diversity allows for a diverse range of tissue functions. There are, however, only four major categories of tissues in animals and they are called the primary tissues. The four primary tissues are epithelial tissue, connective tissue, muscle tissue and nervous tissue.

Epithelium

Epithelial tissue lines all of the spaces in the body. All epithelial tissue share several key characteristics.

> ➢ Epithelial tissue can be found lining all spaces or lumen; the surface of skin, tubes and cavities, as well as all invaginations of these surfaces such as exocrine glands.
> ➢ Epithelial tissue covers all surfaces and forms either a sheet or a tube-like structure.
> ➢ All epithelial tissues are highly cellular and there is very little to no extracellular substances between cells.
> ➢ Most epithelial cells are anchored to a basement membrane. The basement membrane is secreted in part by the epithelial cells as well as the connective tissue cells found beneath the epithelium, and attaches the cells to the underlying connective tissue. The basement membrane is highly permeable.
> ➢ Epithelial tissue contains no blood vessels and must rely on the underlying connective tissue for diffusion of nutrients and gases.

All epithelial tissues are characterized based on the number of cell layers and the shape of the cell that is closest to the lumen. A single layer of epithelial cells lining a lumen is called a simple epithelium whereas more than one layer of epithelial cells is called a stratified epithelium. Based on the principle that form helps determine function, observation of a thick, stratified layer of epithelial cells may indicate a protective role, whereas, an extremely thin, single layer of epithelial cells may indicate exchange of gases. There are three general shapes of epithelial cells. A squamous-shaped cell is a very flat, thin cell which appears pancake-shaped. A cuboidal-shaped cell is either a cube, circular or triangular shape and contains a centrally located nucleus with cytoplasm that is equally distributed around the nucleus. And columnar-shaped cells are tall columns or oval shaped cells, typically with an oval-shaped nucleus which sits close to the basement membrane. Observation of a cuboidal epithelial cells that contains many vesicles may indicate a secretory role; a squamous shaped cells may indicate exchange of gas and material, and columnar cells with microvilli on the luminal side of the cell may indicate absorption of material. Again the form or structure helps to determine its function.

In the body, there are 8 types of epithelium (See Figure 1.1). Six of the epithelial tissues are fairly easy to identify and are simply based on the number of layers and the shape of the cell that is closest to the lumen. A simple squamous epithelium, simple cuboidal

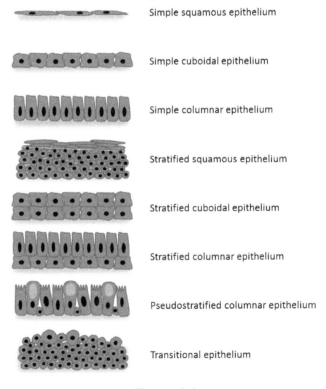

Simple squamous epithelium

Simple cuboidal epithelium

Simple columnar epithelium

Stratified squamous epithelium

Stratified cuboidal epithelium

Stratified columnar epithelium

Pseudostratified columnar epithelium

Transitional epithelium

Figure 1.1

epithelium and simple columnar epithelium are all single layered epithelial tissues that are based on the shape of the cell lining the lumen. The stratified squamous epithelium, stratified cuboidal epithelium and stratified columnar epithelium are epithelial tissues with multiple layers of cells and are named after the cell shape closest to the lumen. For example, the stratified cuboidal epithelium is typically two layers of cuboidal cells stacked on top of each other. There are two additional epithelial tissue types found in the body and they are called the pseudostratified columnar epithelium and the transitional epithelium. Pseudostratified columnar epithelium contains a single layer of cells that sit on the basement membrane, however the epithelium appears to look like there are many layers due to the types of cells lining this epithelium. There are at least 3 distinct cell shapes and sizes lining the lumen which give the appearance of a stratified epithelium. The transitional epithelium is technically a stratified epithelium and, as the name implies, changes shape or transitions from one appearance to another. Transitional epithelium lines portions of the urinary system and is exposed to extreme stretch. The epithelium can appear to have a few cell layers (2-3) or many cell layers (up to 20 or more). Epithelial tissues play important roles in many organs. The specific roles of each epithelium will be covered in detail in subsequent chapters.

Connective tissue

The name connective tissue infers that the tissue itself connects tissues to each other. Unlike epithelial tissue (and muscle and nervous tissue), connective tissue contains few cells and lots of extracellular substances. The extracellular matrix is made up of ground substance and fibers. The various types of ground substance give rise to either a fluid, collagenous, cartilaginous, or a calcified tissue appearance and the different fiber types (collagen, reticular or elastic fibers) give rise to a variety of properties that promote strength or elasticity. Connective tissue contains 4 major categories; connective tissue proper, bone, cartilage and blood (See Figure 1.2).

All connective tissue types are derived from a common precursor tissue during development called mesenchyme. The functions of connective tissue are varied because of the wide range of fiber types and the different structures of extracellular matrix. In general, connective tissue maintains the shape and structure of organs, they support and play a protective role, they provide connections, they store lipids, nutrients, and water, they help in the transport of these substances, and they are involved in immunological defense mechanisms and play a role in regeneration and healing.

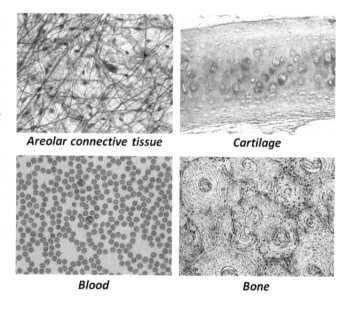

Areolar connective tissue   *Cartilage*

Blood   *Bone*

Figure 1.2

Connective tissue proper contains cells, fibers and ground substance. The cells that are actively producing and secreting the fibers and ground substance are called fibroblasts. When the cell becomes quiescent and inactive, the cell becomes a fibrocyte. Other resident cells in connective tissue proper include pericytes which are undifferentiated cells that can differentiate into a smooth muscle cell or fibroblast as needed, reticular cells which secrete reticular fibers, adipocytes which store lipids and fats, and macrophages and mast cells which are involved with immune defense mechanisms. The most common types of connective tissue proper include areolar connective tissue, dense regular connective tissue, and dense, irregular connective tissue. These tissues are found beneath epithelium and are found in most organs including skin, digestive organs, capsules of organs, tendons, etc... Other specialized types of connective tissue proper include elastic tissue, reticular tissue and adipose tissue. Elastic tissue is found in areas of high stress such as the aorta, reticular tissue is predominantly found in lymphatic and hematopoietic tissues and adipose tissue is found surrounding many organs and stores fat.

Cartilage is found in soft tissues and provides extra structural support. Cartilage is also found at joint spaces between bones and provides soft cushioning and a smooth articular surface. It is also important in the development of bone. Cartilage appears first during development and lays the framework for bone development. Cartilage is formed from cells called chondroblasts which secrete extracellular fibers and ground substance creating a strong, semi-solid matrix. The inactive cell that is encased in matrix becomes a chondrocyte and sits in a small space called a lacunae. Since there are no blood vessels running through cartilage, nutrient, waste and gas exchange takes place by diffusion of water containing dissolved solutes through the ground substance and is extremely slow. Three types of cartilage can be found in humans and is dependent upon the types and amount of fibers present; elastic cartilage, fibrocartilage and hyaline cartilage. Elastic cartilage is found in area of high stress such as the epiglottis and the ear pinna. Fibrocartilage is found in areas under extreme forces such as between the vertebrae. Hyaline cartilage is the most common cartilage in the body and can be found in joint spaces between bones, the nasal septum, the larynx, trachea and bronchi of the respiratory system.

Bone is extremely hard due to the mineralization of extracellular components and contains both organic and inorganic substances in its matrix. Like other connective tissue, bone contains cells, fibers and ground substance. During development, a cartilage framework is laid down onto which bone begins to form. Woven bone is an early form of bone in which the fibers are laid in a haphazard or disorganized manner. Woven bone is remodeled and lamellar bone takes its place. Lamellar bone is a highly organized pattern of bone formation. Each lamellae or layer of bone is laid down with its fibers oriented in opposite directions in order to confer more strength to the bone. Compact bone contains lamellar bone organized into the basic unit of bone, the osteon. The osteon contains concentric layers of bone surrounding a central canal through which blood vessels and nerves can travel. Perpendicular canals, Volkmann's canals, connect to the central canals and, together, provide a system of canals that connect the outside to the inside of bones. Osteoblasts are the cells responsible for creating and controlling the production of both woven and lamellar bone. First the cell secretes osteoid, a combination of collagen fibers and new matrix, through a process called ossification. Then precisely regulated calcification occurs. First, alkaline phosphatase is secreted from osteoblasts which precipitate calcium and phosphate ions from the blood. The osteocyte then secretes large amounts of hydroxyapatite to form crystals on the collagen fibers.

Bone is continually remodeled throughout adult life although at a very slow pace compared to other tissues of the body. During the remodeling stage or during the regulation of calcium in blood, osteocytes will break down bone by secreting an acidic solution containing lysosomal enzymes. The acid solubilizes the crystals and the enzymes break down the collagen fibers. Calcium and phosphate are released to the blood and help to elevate blood calcium levels.

Blood, the last type of connective tissue, is unusual because it contains numerous cell types floating in an aqueous medium called plasma. Plasma contains primarily water with dissolved solutes including ions, nutrients, wastes, gases, clotting factors, hormones and other blood proteins. The formed elements include the red blood cells, white blood cells and platelets. The main function of blood is to transport nutrients, wastes, gases and other substances from tissue to tissue and organ to organ. Blood also is involved in the transfer or maintenance of heat as well as play important roles in immunological defense mechanisms. Blood is covered in more detail in Chapter 6.

Figure 1.3

  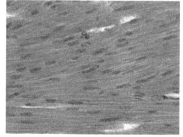

Cardiac muscle   *Skeletal muscle*   *Smooth muscle*

Muscle tissue

Contractility is a feature of all cells in the body, not only muscle cells. Contractility aids in basic cellular functions such cellular division, it allows cells to move around and migrate through tissues, and it allows cells to engulf cellular debris. Cytoskeletal proteins including actin play a role in basic cellular contractility. In muscle tissue, actin myofilaments interact with myosin myofilaments and allow them to slide past one another causing the cell to shorten. There are three types of muscle cells in the body, skeletal muscle, cardiac muscle, and smooth muscle (See Figure 1.3). All muscle cells contain actin and myosin cytoskeletal proteins which provides the basic framework necessary for contraction. However, the arrangement of cytoskeletal proteins and cellular organelles varies between the different muscle tissue types. Contractility in muscle tissue allows them to provide movement of tissues, organs and body parts. Muscle tissue is comprised largely of cells with very little fibers and extracellular matrix. There are trace amounts of connective tissue between cells and nerves innervate the muscles and help regulate their function.

Skeletal muscle cells are highly, elongated cells that develop from the fusion of many myoblasts and form a myotube in early development. The center of the myotube eventually fills in with the actin and myosin cytoskeletal proteins. These proteins are highly organized and arranged into structures called sarcomeres, the functional unit of skeletal muscle. Each muscle cell contains many nuclei located at the periphery of the cell boundary and when viewed as a longitudinal section in the light microscope, the cells seem striated or striped. These striations appear due to the precise arrangement and alignment of the sarcomeres within the center of each muscle cell. Skeletal muscles are innervated by somatic motor neurons and are under voluntary control. The physiology of skeletal muscle is covered in detail in Chapter 5.

Cardiac muscle also appears striated due to a similar arrangement of cytoskeletal proteins into functional units called sarcomeres. Cardiac muscle cells however, are relatively small and entire cell boundaries can be observed in the light microscope. Cardiac muscle cells are connected to each other through specialized interdigitated connections which contain gap junctions. This connection forms a structure in the light microscope called the intercalated disk. Cardiac muscle cells contain one or two centrally located nuclei. Cardiac muscle is found only in the heart and is innervated by the autonomic nervous system. Cardiac muscle physiology is covered in more detail in Chapter 6.

Smooth muscle does not appear striated, and therefore, is called smooth. Smooth muscle cells contain the same cytoskeletal proteins, actin and myosin, which allow the cell to contract, however, their arrangement does not create a linear, striated appearance when observing the cell in longitudinal section; i.e., there are no sarcomeres present in smooth muscle. Smooth muscle cells are small, spindle shaped cells which have a centrally located nucleus. They are also innervated and controlled by the autonomic nervous system. Smooth muscle physiology is covered in more detail in Chapter 5.

Nervous tissue

Nervous tissue is also comprised of mostly cells with little to no extracellular matrix. The nervous tissue contains two types of cells, neurons and glia (See Figure 1.4). The neurons are cells which communicate with each other and to other tissues (muscles and glands) by conducting action potentials and the glia are the supporting cells. There are different types of neurons and glia which can be found in specific places throughout the body. Nervous tissue is found within the brain and the spinal cord of the central nervous system and within the nerves, nerve plexuses, and ganglia of the peripheral nervous system. The nervous tissue is covered in detail in Chapter 3.

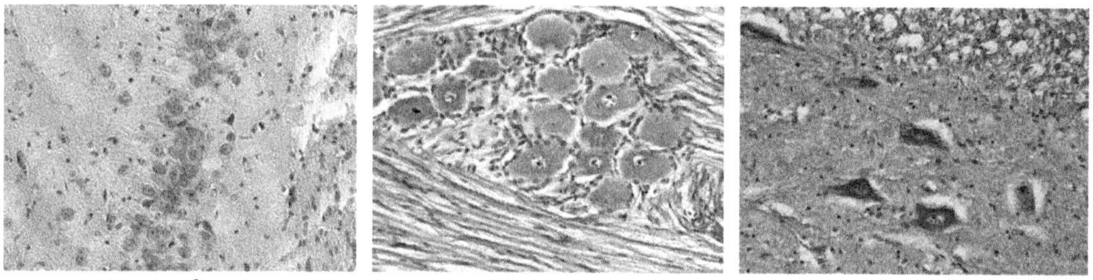

| Brain | Dorsal root ganglia | Spinal cord |

Figure 1.4

Fluid compartments

The bodies of animals are made up of ~50-65% water. How is this possible when our organs are made up of tissues that are comprised of cells and extracellular matrix? Cells contain the majority of this water in the cytosol. The intracellular fluid comprises approximately 67% of all the fluid in the body. Extracellular fluid is found in plasma (~7% of total) and the interstitial space (~26%) or the space between cells (See Figure 1.5). The extracellular fluid is constantly moving throughout the body and circulates between the capillaries and the interstitial space of tissues. Fluid movement is due to hydrostatic and osmotic forces and carries small, dissolved solutes such as ions, nutrients, wastes, gases and hormones to and from the cells of the tissues to the blood circulating in the cardiovascular system. Within tissues, water can be found in two forms, free and bound to ground substance. In connective tissue, ground substance is formed from glycoproteins, most commonly glycosaminoglycans (GAGs) to which water is attached. Most of the water in the interstitial space is in the bound state and is attached to hydroxyl, carboxyl and sulfate groups on the GAGs. Therefore, it is difficult to draw liquid out of tissues. Fluid can also move into and out of cells through special water channels called aquaporins and water is in equilibrium with the extracellular compartment. In some pathologies, excess water can be found in tissues and is called edema. This results in a greater amount of free water in the interstitial space.

Figure 1.5

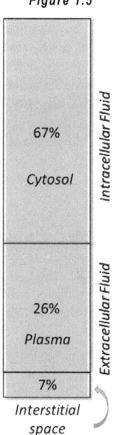

Since cells are selectively permeable, certain ions are found in higher concentrations in the extracellular or the intracellular compartments. Sodium, calcium, chloride and bicarbonate ions are found in large numbers in the extracellular compartment. Whereas, potassium, magnesium and phosphate ions are found in larger quantities in the intracellular compartment. In addition, the extracellular fluid contains more free circulating nutrients such as glucose, amino acids, and fatty acids. Once nutrients are brought into cells through specific transport mechanisms they are used for energy use or converted for storage.

Homeostasis and Control Systems

An underlying concept of physiology is the idea that the internal environment must be maintained at a relatively "constant" state. Homeostasis is the term that is applied to the tendency for the body to maintain a relatively stable internal environment even when the body is exposed to extreme changes or differences in the external environment. The concept of maintaining a constant "internal milieu" was first introduced by the French scientist, Claude Bernard in the mid to late 1800's. The American scientist, Walter Cannon, reinvented the concept of an "internal milieu" in 1913 and introduced the term, homeostasis. In simple terms, many years ago, if there was an imbalance in the internal environment, such as a dramatic change in body temperature (i.e., a fever) this would greatly increase the chance of death. Thus, maintaining a constant "internal milieu" or homeostasis was necessary for a healthy body. This idea, of course, extends well beyond body temperature and includes many things that are regulated within the body such as plasma water and ion concentrations, plasma pH, and glucose and amino acid levels, to name a few. The study of physiology is primarily concerned with how we maintain and regulate homeostasis. On the other hand, pathophysiology is focused on when the body becomes out of balance or encompasses a time when homeostasis is disturbed.

In physiology, most of the biochemical processes in the body are systems that are attempting to achieve and maintain a steady state. Steady state refers to a condition that remains stable over time, but requires constant work to achieve this stability. For example, cells are constantly running metabolic processes in order to achieve the normal steady state of a cell. In neurons, a Na^+/K^+ pump is constantly using energy (ATP) to pump ions across the plasma membrane to maintain an electrically negative internal environment; 3 Na^+ ions are pumped out of the cell and 2 K^+ ions are pumped in the cell for every molecule of ATP that is utilized. Complex biochemical reactions are steady state processes. In chemistry, to reach a state of true equilibrium, no energy is required. These reactions are usually chemical in nature (not biological) and tend to occur outside the body. However, the term equilibrium is often used in physiology and simply refers to processes that occur across some barrier and don't require energy directly.

Although homeostasis refers to the maintenance of a "constant" internal environment, homeostasis does NOT mean that a given variable does not change. It means that we are maintaining a variable within a normal range. These normal ranges are maintained by the body and hover around a particular set point. For example, most mammals maintain a relatively constant body temperature (37°C) throughout the day. This set point can change, however, depending on what the state or condition of the body. For example, body temperature is reset to a lower level during sleep and it is reset to a higher level during infections (fever).

Negative feedback systems

In order to maintain homeostasis, the body must be able to sense different types of variables, such as body temperature, and detect when these variables begin to deviate away from the set point. Once the variable moves outside of the normal range, the body must be able to respond and correct for the change. This is called a negative feedback system and is the prominent system which maintains homeostasis within organisms. Negative feedback mechanisms can occur at a cellular level, an organ level or even at the level of the whole body. For example, many cellular reactions occur through a variety of sequential steps in which a substrate is converted to an intermediate product(s), which in turn gets converted or activated to an end-product. The formation of the end-product can inhibit the first enzymatic reaction and reduce the formation of more active product. This is a classic example of a negative feedback system at a molecular or cellular level (See Figure 1.6).

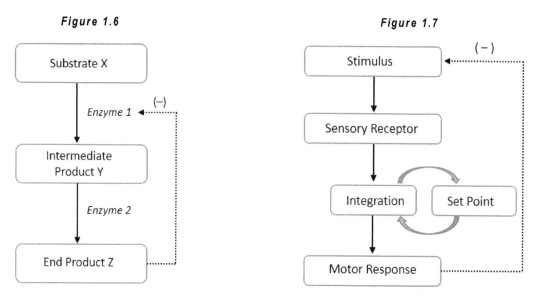

Figure 1.6

Figure 1.7

Many negative feedback mechanisms also act through a reflex mechanism or an involuntary reaction to a particular stimulus (See Figure 1.7). Reflex mechanisms require three critical components for normal function; 1) receptors that sense specific variables, 2) an integration center which compares inputs from sensory receptors to the set point and 3) an effector which responds and corrects the variable back to the normal range.

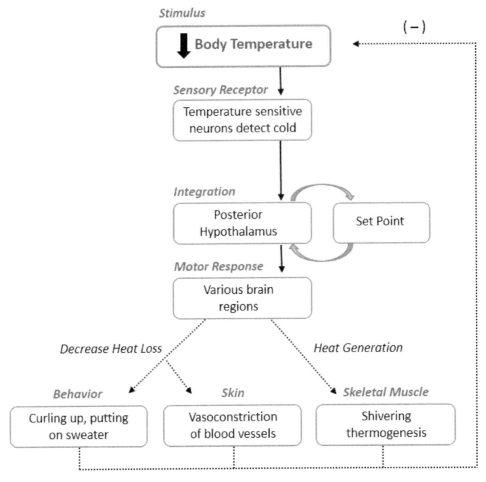

Figure 1.8

A classic example of a negative feedback system that functions as a reflex is the control of body temperature (See Figure 1.8, on the next page). Body temperature is tightly regulated around 37°C. Sensory receptors sensitive to heat and cold are found in skin and mucus membranes, as well as in the hypothalamus of the brain. These thermoreceptors sense alterations in temperature and their inputs project to the posterior hypothalamus where the signal is compared to a set point. For example, if body temperature begins to fall, several efferent or motor responses can be activated. First, behavioral changes are initiated to reduce heat loss; i.e., putting on a sweater or bundling up in a blanket or simply folding your arms in front of the body to decrease surface area and reduce exposure to the external environment. These behavioral changes may be enough to stop the reduction in heat loss. Internally, smooth muscle in the blood vessels of skin constrict to reduce blood flow to the extremities and reduce heat loss across the skin. Then, if body temperature is still too low, shivering thermogenesis can be activated where skeletal muscles contract and relax rapidly in order to actively generate heat. These efferent motor responses are initiated to attempt to correct body temperature and elevate it back to normal; i.e., a negative feedback mechanism. Negative feedback mechanisms are very common throughout the body and are the primary mechanisms initiated to maintain homeostasis.

Positive feedback systems

Positive feedback mechanisms are also present in the body which, by themselves, do not maintain homeostasis or a stable condition, but rather they lead to instability. However, there are examples where positive feedback mechanisms do play important roles in normal physiology. A positive feedback system is when a given variable deviates from a "set point," the feedback will cause the deviation to continue to get farther away from the set point. Parturition or childbirth is a classic example of a positive feedback system (See Figure 1.9). During childbirth, the head of the fetus presses down on the cervix of the mother. The cervical lining has stretch receptors which get activated and feedback to the hypothalamus in the brain. Specialized neurons in the hypothalamus will release the hormone, oxytocin into the bloodstream. Oxytocin acts on the smooth muscle of the uterus to contract and cause the fetus to further press against the cervix. This positive feedback will increase the force and number of contractions until the force of the contractions cause the birth of the infant. Once this occurs, the positive feedback mechanism is stopped because the head is no longer pressing on the cervix. In the body, positive feedback systems are not as common as negative feedback systems.

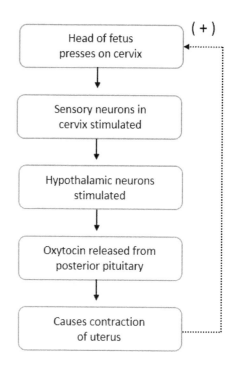

Figure 1.9

Feed-forward regulation

Another type of regulatory control mechanism is feed-forward regulation. This is a system in which the body 'anticipates' that there will be a change and the body initiates mechanisms in preparation for the change to occur. For example, this is one mechanism underlying some of the changes that occur during the onset of exercise. If a person is getting ready to exercise, mentally the person prepares, knowing roughly what that exercise will entail. Even before the person starts to exercise, sympathetic activity increases and causes cardiac output and ventilation to increase. This prepares the muscles and the cardiovascular and respiratory systems for exercise. Another example of feed-forward regulation occurs prior to eating a meal, like Thanksgiving dinner perhaps. In anticipation of a meal, your body prepares for food by increasing gastric secretions so that once the food enters the stomach, secretory enzymes and fluid is already present to begin and aid in digestion.

Homeostatic responses

Homeostasis involves a well-coordinated and regulated balance of activities occurring in cells, tissues, organs and across organ systems. In essence, the goal of homeostasis is to maintain a constant extracellular fluid composition which is in equilibrium with the intracellular fluid compartments of cells. The most critical variables, those with a very narrow range of values, are highly regulated and often regulated at the expense of other systems. For example, calcium levels in blood are critical for many cellular mechanisms. If there is not enough calcium in a diet, the body will remove calcium from bones to help regulate plasma calcium levels to maintain a constant value. This can be at the expense of the normal function of bones and can result in osteoporosis or a weakening of the bones. It is more critical to maintain calcium homeostasis in blood than to maintain the integrity of the bones.

Also, there is often redundancy in the body's systems and more than one organ or system will be able to carry out or participate in the functions required to maintain homeostasis of a given variable. For example, sodium balance is achieved by the coordinated actions of the kidneys, intestines and sweat glands. However, there is usually one organ that is critically important in the maintenance of proper homeostasis. The sweat glands only play a minor role in sodium balance and do not need to participate in order to maintain whole body homeostasis whereas the function of the kidney is vitally and critically important. Without the function of at least one kidney, the body is unable to get rid of enough waste and toxic substances which can result in severe consequences and can ultimately result in death.

Local homeostatic mechanisms require some sort of cell–to-cell communication. Communication between cells occurs by different mechanisms throughout the body. Some cells communicate indirectly by releasing some type of intercellular chemical messenger to target a specific receptor on some other cell. Other cells communicate directly by cell to cell contact mechanisms. Hormones are chemical substances that are released by endocrine glands that travel through blood and interstitial fluid to target cells in some distant location in the body. Hormones are typically used when targeting cells far away from the original source. Another type of chemical substance that is secreted by a cell is a neurotransmitter which is released by neurons to target a specific cell by a synapse. Neurotransmitters are molecules released from one neuron which travel a very short distance across the synapse to affect another neuron. Substances that are released from one cell to act on a target cell in the near vicinity is called a paracrine substance. Some substances can even act on the same cell from which it was secreted and is called an autocrine substance. In the body, some chemical substances can act as both a paracrine and an autocrine substance. For example, dopaminergic neurons release dopamine to act in a paracrine fashion to affect a target cell. If lots of dopamine is released, it can act on autoreceptors (acting in an autocrine fashion) to inhibit the production and release of dopamine (another example of a negative feedback system).

Another type of cell-to-cell communication that uses a direct method is the gap junction. Gap junctions are large channels that connect two cells together and allow substances to pass from one cell directly to another cell. Gap junctions are commonly found between smooth muscle cells, cardiac muscle cells and between neurons as well as between other types of cells (epithelium, osteocytes, etc...). In muscle cells and neurons, gap junctions help to transport ions from one cell to the next in order to spread action potentials between cells and help to coordinate the contraction of whole muscles. Gap junctions are found between some epithelial cells which help to coordinate waves of ciliary movement and gap junctions between osteocytes are involved in the transport of nutrients, gases and wastes.

Some cell-to-cell communication methods do not require intercellular chemical messengers. Some cells communicate via juxtacrine methods in which cell surface receptors interact directly with another cell's surface receptors. This type of cell-to-cell communication occurs in the immune system in which macrophages use special molecules to present antigens to helper T-cells. Juxtacrine interactions between these cells and between helper T-cells and B-cells are involved in the adaptive immune response. All of these different methods of cell-to-cell communication are involved in steps underlying various homeostatic control mechanisms.

CHAPTER 1 SUMMARY

➢ Students should understand the underlying principles and unifying concepts of physiology; 1) The study of physiology is based on the laws of chemistry and physics, 2) The structures within organisms are compartmentalized from the cellular level to organ level to the whole organism. 3) The highly organized structures and organs function together in a precise and coordinated fashion. 4) Homeostasis or the maintenance of a constant internal environment is necessary for health and survival. 5) There is communication and controlled exchange of material between cells, tissues and organs which help to maintain homeostasis. 6) The form of structures helps to determine the function of the structures.

➢ Much of what we know today regarding human physiology comes from research performed on animal models.

➢ In the body, there are many different types of cells and extracellular substances however, there are only 4 categories of primary tissue types; epithelial tissue, connective tissue, muscle tissue and nervous tissue.

➢ Homeostasis is the tendency to maintain or regulate a variable around a particular set point. Homeostasis involves the well-coordinated and regulated balance of activities occurring in cells, tissues, organs and across organ systems.

➢ Negative feedback systems work to correct any deviations from the set point and return variables back to their normal values.

➢ Positive feedback systems cause a deviation to get larger or move farther away from the set point. It does not return the variable back to normal.

➢ Cell to cell communication is necessary for control of homeostatic responses. Communication between cells can be direct or indirect.

References and Suggested Readings

Baffy G, Loscalzo J. 2014. Complexity and network dynamics in physiological adaptation: an integrated review. *Physiology and Behavior* 131:49-56.

Cooper SJ. 2008. From Claude Bernard to Walter Cannon. Emergence of the concept of homeostasis. *Appetite* 51:419-427.

Chapter 2: Cell Physiology

Every living structure is composed of a cell or cells; yeast, bacteria, plants, trees, and animals. The cell is the most basic unit of life and is quite similar amongst all living things. All cells contain an outer membrane to separate the interior of the cell from the external environment and all cells contain structures and organelles that are involved with basic cell function such as, protein synthesis, energy metabolism, secretory mechanisms, and cellular movement. The evolution of organisms has produced a wide variety of life forms and structures, however, some genes of basic cellular organization have remained throughout all life forms. Cells house the deoxynucleic acid (DNA) which encodes all of the genes that are involved with protein synthesis. This chapter will highlight some of the basic cellular features that are found in animals, including humans. We will review basic cellular function and describe mechanisms by which substances get into and out of cells. We will also cover some basic, common intracellular signaling pathways that are found throughout many cells and play important regulatory roles in cellular function.

Section 1 - Cell Structure and Function

Intracellular organelles

All cells are enclosed with a plasma membrane which separate the internal compartment from the external compartment. Most eukaryotic cells share common features which include a relatively large nucleus and various organelles (See Figure 2.1). The nucleus contains the DNA as well as some ribonucleic acid (RNA) and lots of proteins (See Figure 2.2 A, on the next page). The DNA, or the genome, of each cell in the body is identical and contains the information necessary to synthesize all of the proteins found throughout the entire body. However, cellular differentiation and specialization results in certain genes being turned on and off, such that each cell maintains a distinct phenotype and functions in a specific manner.

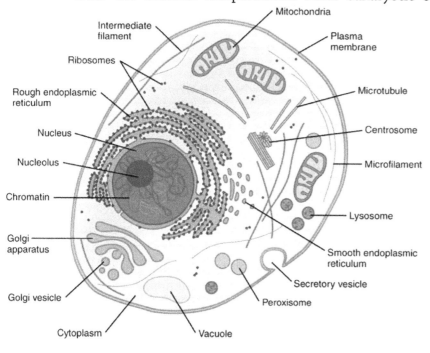

Figure 2.1

Figure 2.2 A

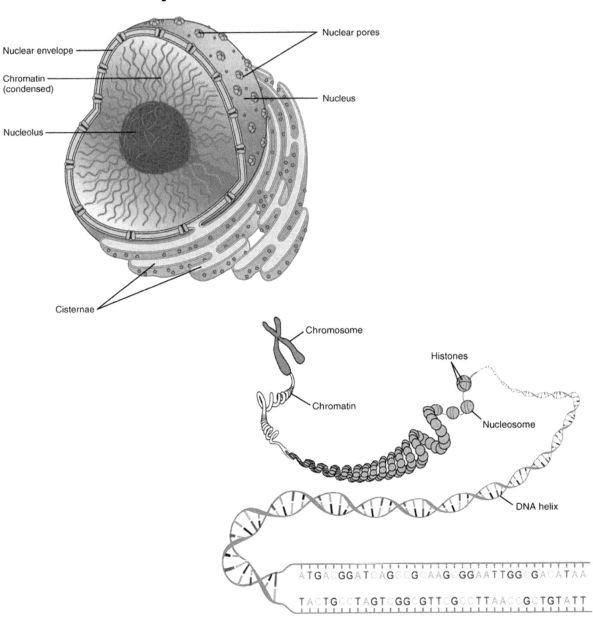

Figure 2.2 B

DNA is comprised of two strands of nucleotides coiled into a double helix (See Figure 2.2 B). Four types of nucleotides can be found in DNA: guanine (G), cysteine (C), adenine (A), and thymine (T). These four base nucleotides are joined by hydrogen bonds with its base pair on the opposite strand of DNA; G pairs with C, and A pairs with T. The specific sequence of the base pairs encode for specific proteins, much the way that individual letters grouped together create words. Three base pairs in sequence create a triplet or codon which is specific signal which designates a single amino acid. Combination of the 4 base nucleotides into triplets creates 64 possible combinations. There are, however, only 20 amino acids that are coded for. This is due to some redundancy in which multiple triplets encode for the same amino acid; for example, CCA, CCG, CCT and CCC all encode for the single amino acid glycine. There are also specific "stop" sequences (3) which denote the end of the protein structure and signal the machinery to stop adding amino acids to the protein formation.

During most of the cell cycle, the DNA is presented in a tangled mass of individual strands and are not visible as distinct structures. During cell division, the DNA replicates, condenses and becomes tightly coiled to form chromosomes. The cells of each species contains a set number of chromosomes (human = 46 chromosomes) except for the germ cells which contain half the amount of DNA (the human oocyte and sperm cells contain 23 chromosomes). The proteins found within the nucleus are first synthesized in the cytoplasm and transported back into the nucleus. The majority of the proteins in the nucleus are histones and are associated with DNA and bind directly to the DNA. They play various roles in DNA folding as well as the regulation of DNA activity. Many of the non-histones proteins are also involved in the regulation of transcription (see below). The entire nucleus is surrounded by a thin membrane called the nuclear envelope which separate the contents of the nucleus from the rest of the cell (See Figure 2.2.A). The nuclear envelope is comprised of two membranes that are continuous with the endoplasmic reticulum. The outer edge of the nuclear membrane (cytoplasmic side) has ribosomal RNA attached to it and the inner membrane is attached to the DNA located within the nucleus via proteins. The nuclear envelope contains pores which appear to regulate the movement of substances in and out of the nucleus, including ribosomal proteins.

Protein production

The production of all proteins, or protein synthesis, occurs in the cytoplasm of cells on the rough endoplasmic reticulum (RER) (See Figure 2.3). The RER appears "rough" due to ribosomes which are attached to the outer membranes of the RER and produce a studded appearance. Proteins are made on the outer membrane of RER and transported into the RER for further modification and transport. RER appears as flattened tubules throughout the cytosol of the cell.

Figure 2.3

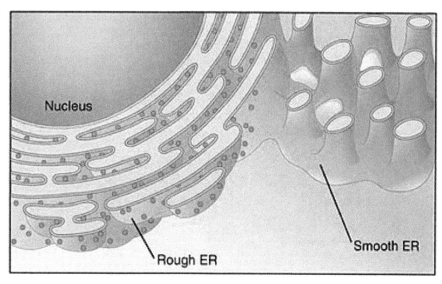

Nucleus

Rough ER

Smooth ER

Protein synthesis occurs via a series of steps that include the processes of transcription and translation (See Figure 2.4). In a cell, protein synthesis starts with transcription, a process which occurs in the nucleus as a result of the activation of a transcription factor and the formation of messenger ribonucleic acid (mRNA). All RNAs are single stranded nucleotides which includes G, C, A, and uracil (U), as opposed to T which is found in DNA. The mRNA is made by copying or transcribing a specific sequence of DNA. A specific sequence of nucleotides called the promotor acts as a starting sequence to promote transcription. RNA polymerase is an enzyme that binds to DNA at or near the promoter sequence and causes the separation of the DNA. RNA polymerase can use the individual subunits from ATP, GTP, CTP and UTP to break off two phosphate groups and attach the individual nucleotides together to create a single-stranded RNA molecule. The mRNA that is formed contains regions called exons (expression regions) and regions called introns (intervening sequences). The exons encode for the actual proteins, whereas the introns are large areas of non-coded genetic material. The specific role of the introns is not always clear, but they may play a role in the process of transcription in some cases. Before the mRNA is finished, a process called splicing must occur. Splicing removes the introns and puts the exons together to form the finished mRNA product. Splicing also occurs inside the nucleus and is accomplished with the use of a spliceosome which is made of small nuclear RNAs and proteins. Splicing can produce a single end product or multiple end products depending on which exons are attached to the final mRNA and which exons are left off.

Figure 2.4

A.

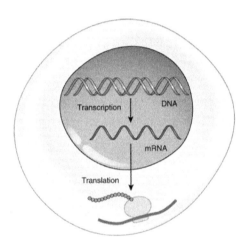

B.

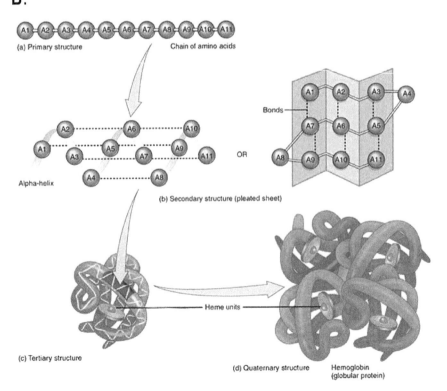

(a) Primary structure
Chain of amino acids

Bonds

OR

Alpha-helix

(b) Secondary structure (pleated sheet)

Heme units

(c) Tertiary structure

(d) Quaternary structure
Hemoglobin
(globular protein)

The mRNA passes through nuclear pores into the cytoplasm and associates with ribosomes along the RER (See Figure 2.3). Translation of the mRNA into protein occurs along the ribosome. Ribosomes are comprised of ribosomal RNA and associated proteins (including enzymes). The assembly of protein involves three steps, initiation, elongation and termination. Initiation starts with the binding of a specific transfer RNA (tRNA) to initiate or start translation. The tRNA contain triplet sequences opposite to the mRNA and carry the specific amino acids for assembly. Often the first sequence encodes for the amino acid methionine (AUG) (the "start" sequence) followed by the first amino acid of the protein being assembled. The ribosome interacts with both the initiating tRNA and the mRNA and encloses the mRNA. The specific binding of tRNAs that are specific to the next codon sequence occurs and each subsequent amino acid is attached to the protein chain, thus the stage of elongation. Enzymes on the ribosome create the peptide bonds between amino acids.

In the cytoplasm, mRNA gets rapidly degraded and does not linger in the cytoplasm for a long time. Protein synthesis is activated by specific cellular pathways that help regulate the amount and timing of protein synthesis. In cells that are actively producing lots of proteins, the nucleus also contains a prominent structure called the nucleolus. The nucleolus is the site of ribosomal RNA synthesis and assembly. The ribosomes are created in the nucleus and transported out into the cytoplasm for protein synthesis.

After the single amino acid sequence, or polypeptide chain is formed, the protein can undergo changes to create the final product. Some areas can be cleaved off, like the initial methionine which started the sequence. The protein can be bent and folded, and carbohydrate and lipid moieties can be added. This occurs inside the RER. Multiple smaller polypeptides or subunits can also be combined to form larger proteins. Small vesicles containing newly formed proteins bud off the RER near the Golgi apparatus and fuse with the Golgi.

Lipid production

Smooth ER (SER) is continuous with the RER and is devoid of ribosomes (See Figure 2.3). The SER is involved with lipid synthesis and usually not a prominent feature in most cells. The SER is prominent in liver cells which are cells important in lipid metabolism. The SER also stores high concentrations of calcium ions which are used for activating specific intracellular pathways. This is a prominent feature of muscle cells which use the calcium storage to regulate muscle contraction (see Chapter 5 and 6).

Cellular secretion

The Golgi apparatus appears as an oval-shaped structure which contains a collection of flattened tubules which give rise to secretory vesicles at the edges (See Figure 2.5, on the next page). The Golgi apparatus is the site of further protein modification and packaging of proteins into vesicles for transport. The proteins can be free in the lumen of the vesicle or can be embedded in the wall of the vesicle for transport to the plasma membrane. Vesicles that are released from the Golgi apparatus can then be transported to other cellular organelles or released from the cell via exocytosis. There are multiple types of vesicles found in cells, however, secretory vesicles are specific vesicles that release substances to the outside of the cell.

Another structure that is involved with vesicle formation is the endosome. Endosomes are tubular structures that lie in close proximity to the plasma membrane and often sit between the plasma membrane and the Golgi apparatus. Certain vesicles that form at the plasma membrane by endocytosis fuse with the endosome for recycling. The endosome can then form vesicles and return them to the Golgi or in some cells, like neurons, return the vesicles to the plasma membrane for exocytosis. Both the Golgi and the endosome are used for sorting, modifying and directing vesicles within the cell.

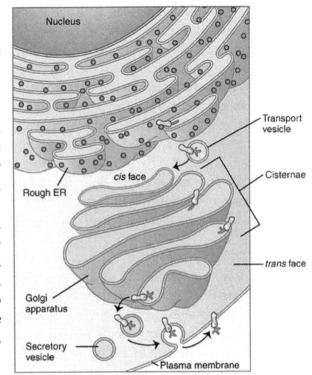

Figure 2.5

Energy production and storage

All metabolic functions within cells are dependent upon energy. Energy comes from several sources within the cell, but the majority of the energy is produced by the mitochondria. Mitochondria come in a variety of shapes and sizes, but the most common shape is an elongated oval structure (See Figure 2.6). Cells that are extremely active contain lots of mitochondria, such as the liver and skeletal muscle, and inactive cells, such as a fibrocyte, contain very few mitochondria. Energy production or ATP synthesis is derived from several processes in the cell.

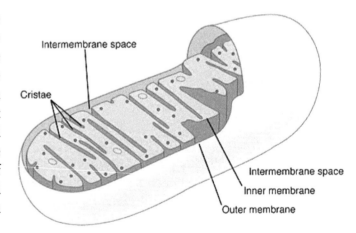

Figure 2.6

The breakdown of glucose, or glycolysis, occurs in the cytoplasm of cells and produces a small amount of ATP. Glycolysis in the absence of oxygen is termed anaerobic respiration. When oxygen is present, pyruvic acid diffuses inside the mitochondria to enter the Krebs cycle, also known as the citric acid cycle or the tricarboxylic acid (TCA) cycle where it is degraded into CO_2 and H_2O and gives off lots of ATP (up to 38) (See Figure 2.7).

Figure 2.7

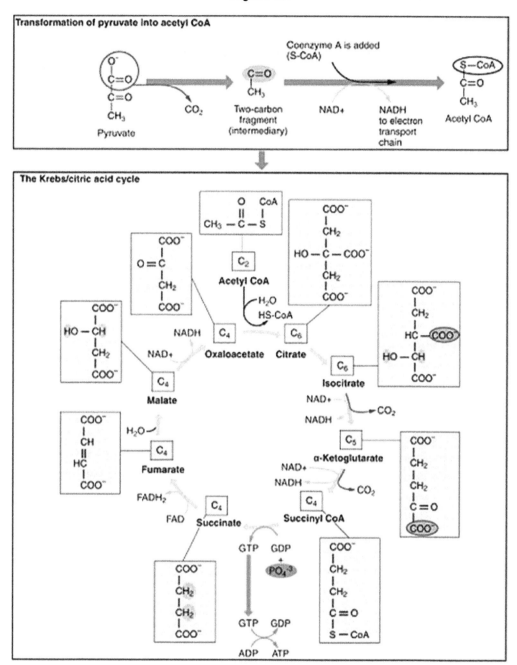

The mitochondria contains two membranes. The outer membrane is highly permeable contains several enzymes that are involved in the breakdown of lipids into substrates that can be utilized for metabolism. The inner membrane has many folds that invaginate into the center of the mitochondria and greatly increase the surface area of the inner membrane. The inner cavity contains the matrix and is the location for most of the enzymes that are responsible for the oxidation of fatty acids and the Krebs cycle. The molecules involved with the electron transport chain, the cytochromes, are located on the inner membrane and produce the final ATP product.

The mitochondria also contains a circular DNA molecule and ribosomes within the matrix that are similar in structure to bacteria. It is hypothesized that during evolution, parasitic bacteria invaded cells to develop a symbiotic relationship with the cells. Mitochondria can move or migrate within cells and they tend to aggregate in areas with the highest metabolic activity. Their shape tends to conform to the region of the cells that they reside and thus there are a wide variety of shapes and sizes of mitochondria among cells of animals.

Cytoskeleton and cell movement

All cells retain a certain structure or shape which is determined in part by the cytoskeleton, a fine network of structural components within the cell. The cytoskeleton contains three categories of structural elements, microfilaments, intermediate filaments, and microtubules, along with specific linking proteins that hold the framework or scaffold together. The cytoskeleton can also connect to the plasma membrane as well as organelles and appear to anchor certain structures in place. Cells, however, are not static structures and can bend and change shape fairly easily. Some cells like macrophages and white blood cells move around the body and throughout tissues by amoeboid movement; some cells like muscle cells are highly contractile and change shorten or elongate; and some cells contain cilia and flagella that wave in a lumen and create movement of fluid and mucus. All cellular movement of cells is aided by the structural elements of the cytoskeleton.

Microfilaments are the thinnest of the cytoskeletal elements and made up of a chain or a filament of globular actin proteins (G actin) connected together. Two strands of filamentous actin (F actin) wind together to form microfilaments. Microfilaments are found in many cells and are involved with the ability to change shape. Within muscle fibers, the actin microfilaments are highly organized and associated with another protein, myosin which creates the ability to shorten (see Chapter 5). Microfilaments are also found in microvilli and allow microvilli to lengthen or shorten as need arises. The length of microfilaments can be easily changed within the cell based on the needs of the cells and can aid in movement (however, this is not the molecular basis of muscle contraction).

Intermediate filaments are composed of various types of proteins which are specific to the types of cells in which they reside. Filamentous proteins combine to create a strong fibrous network of filaments of intermediate size. Intermediate filaments are structurally rigid and under normal conditions do not change shape regularly. These help to maintain a specific cellular structure. For example, the tall, simple columnar epithelial cells lining the lumen of the small intestine need to maintain their shape in order to create a barrier and help to regulate absorption of certain material while allowing the passage of other material.

Microtubules are the largest of the cytoskeletal elements. The microtubules can also easily change length and can be assembled or disassembled very easily. Microtubules are created by combining 13 tubulin globular proteins into the circumference of a circle. Tubulin molecules are then attached to each other to create a tube which can be lengthened or shortened as need arises. The microtubules arise from a cellular structure called the centrioles. The centrioles sit in the cell near the nucleus and are comprised of nine triplets of microtubules arranged in a circle. Microtubules also act as elevator shafts by which vesicles are transported within the cell. Protein linkers attach vesicles to the microtubules which then appear to "walk" along the microtubule to their destination. During cell division, microtubules also play a vital role in the function of the spindle formation and the movement of the chromosomes to each daughter cell.

A.   **B.**

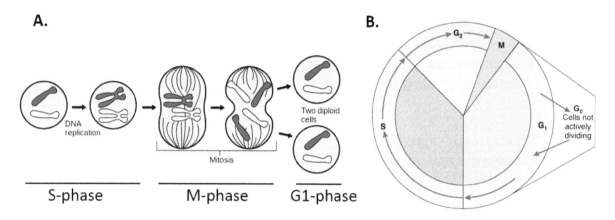

Figure 2.8

Cell cycle, replication and reproduction

The development of organisms and the ability to grow and age is dependent upon the ability of cells to divide or replicate. Cell division or replication is called mitosis (See Figure 2.8.). Mitotic cell division is the process by which a cell is able to replicate and produce two identical daughter cells. Remember that an individual organism begins with the fusion of two gametes (an oocyte and sperm, each containing 23 chromosomes) which combine to form a single cell with 46 chromosomes. The single cell then undergoes cellular division, or mitosis, to form more cells. As development progresses, cells undergo differentiation and become specialized for certain functions; early during development the formation of the primary tissues occurs. Many cells in the adult body maintain the ability to divide throughout life and this allows for continued growth and repair of tissues. Some cells, like most neurons and cardiac muscle cells, lose the ability to divide and if they become damaged or die, will not be replaced.

Just prior to cell division, the DNA, or the entire genome of the cell will undergo replication or synthesize the new DNA (S-phase). The DNA is not defined and appears as the tangled mass of DNA. The centrioles are already present as a duplicated pair. The cells may enter a small gap phase (G2) is which cells prepare for cell division. Cell division, or mitosis (M-phase) is a series of steps which form two identical cells and typically takes several hours to complete (Figure 2.8).

> ➤ *Prophase*: The first stage of mitosis is defined as the point at which individual chromosomes first appear visible in the light microscope. This is the time that the DNA is condensing and forms the chromosomal structure. Within cells, chromosomes function in pairs. A pair of homologous chromosomes are two

similar chromosomes that are genetically similar and are thus a similar shape and size. The cytoskeletal framework and nuclear membrane begins to breakdown and disassemble and the centrioles split and migrate to opposite poles of the cell. As the centrioles move across the cell, a spindle forms between the migrating centrioles and elongates as they continue to separate.

➢ *Metaphase*: The spindle begins to move across the middle of the cell and comes into contact with the choromosomes. Each chromosome is comprised of two chromatids (identical DNA structure) connected in the center by a centromere. The centromeres connect to the spindle at the kinetochore and the chromosomes line up in the center of the cell or the equator.

➢ *Anaphase*: The centromere splits and each chromatid of a single chromosome is drawn toward opposite poles. As this occurs the spindle changes shape thus drawing the genetic material toward each centriole and separating the DNA into two poles of the cell.

➢ *Telophase*: The final stage of mitosis is observed, when the nuclear envelope develops around the genetic material and the nucleoli form. The cell begins to separate by the formation of a central cleavage which effectively cuts the single cell into two cells of similar size. This is called cytokinesis.

After the M-phase, the two newly formed cells enter the growth stage (G_1 or G_0). Most cells enter the first gap phase (G_1) and most of the life of the cell takes place during this stage. The cells grow and perform their specialized functions. The G_0 phase is a slightly reduced state. Typically cells that enter G_0 do not enter the cell cycle again and cannot replicate.

Plasma membrane structure and components

The plasma membrane surrounds each cell creating a barrier between the external and internal environments. The plasma membrane is connected to the structures inside the cell such as the intracellular cytoskeleton as well as structures outside of the cell, such as fibers of the extracellular matrix. The plasma membrane is a selectively permeable membrane which regulates the movement of substances between the intracellular and extracellular compartments. The plasma membrane also contains surface molecular markers to aid in recognition of "self" to prevent destruction by its own immune defense system.

The plasma membrane is comprised of two layers of phospholipids (See Figure 2.9). There are four major phospholipids found in animals; phosphatidlycholine, phosphatidylethanolamine, phosphatidylserine and sphingomyelin. Each phospholipid contains a hydrophobic polar head and 2 hydrophobic tails of fatty acids. The phospholipids align together with one layer of the polar heads facing the aqueous solutions of the cytoplasm and one layer of the polar heads facing the extracellular fluid. The nonpolar tails from each layer face each other and form the inner portion of the membrane. The types of phospholipids that line the outer membrane are predominantly phosphatidlycholine and sphingomyelin, whereas the inner membrane is comprised primarily of phosphatidylethanolamine and phosphatidylserine.

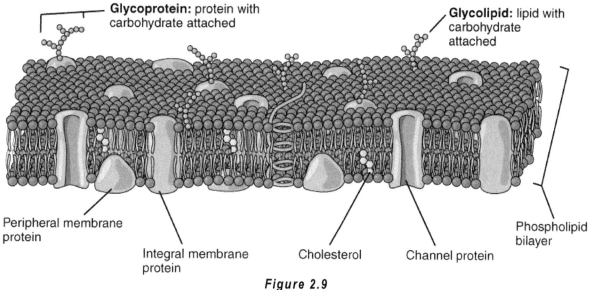

Glycoprotein: protein with carbohydrate attached

Glycolipid: lipid with carbohydrate attached

Peripheral membrane protein

Integral membrane protein

Cholesterol

Channel protein

Phospholipid bilayer

Figure 2.9

Another important phospholipid that is found in a common cellular signaling pathway is called phosphatidylinositol and is found in minor amounts in the inner layer of the plasma membrane. The plasma membrane is a dynamic structure and the phospholipids can move around in their plane freely (i.e., they cannot move from the outer to the inner membrane). Cholesterol is found in the lipid portion of the membrane and helps to reduce the fluidity of the membrane; it has a stabilizing effect on membrane fluidity. The structure of the plasma membrane effectively prevents water and solutes from penetrating the central region of the membrane. In order for most structures to pass the membrane and move from the intracellular compartment to the extracellular compartment or vice versa, they must have some sort of mechanism to get across the hydrophobic region of the membrane; unless of course the molecules are lipid soluble. Associated with the plasma membrane are numerous membrane proteins; approximately 50% of the cell surface is covered with proteins and 50% is covered with lipids (Figure 2.9). Some of proteins are embedded in the membrane and are called integral or intrinsic proteins. Most integral proteins span the entire plasma membrane and are involved in cell signaling pathways or transport mechanisms between the outside and the inside of the cell, however, some integral proteins are simply embedded into part of the plasma membrane. Integral proteins have certain residues that interact with the fatty acid core of the plasma membrane and act to anchor the protein in the membrane. Integral membrane can also be anchored to internal or external structures such as the cytoskeleton which situates certain proteins in specific locations on the cell surface. For example, epithelial cells often contain distinct membrane proteins on the apical surface and the basal surface which are involved in creating specific movement of substances across these cells.

Peripheral or extrinsic proteins are proteins that do not penetrate the plasma membrane. Peripheral proteins associate either directly or indirectly with integral proteins or with the polar heads of the plasma membrane. Some of the cytoskeletal proteins, such as the microfilament actin are peripheral proteins that associate with the plasma membranes. This connection between the cytoskeleton and the plasma membrane act to give cells their characteristic shapes. Membrane proteins play many important roles in cellular function such as functioning 1) as a marker molecule, 2) an attachment protein, 3) or transporting substances across the membrane, 4) a receptor protein and 5) enzymes.

Marker molecules

When examining cells through an electron microscope, cells appear to have a fuzzy surface coating the outside of the plasma membrane. This surface is made up of specific glycoproteins and polysaccharides attached to the outer surface of membrane proteins as well as carbohydrate moieties attached to glycolipids (see Figure 2.9). This collection of sugar moieties on the cellular surface is called the glycocalyx. The glycocalyx protects the cell surface and is involved in cell surface recognition processes. Cells of the immune system recognize foreign substances predominantly by cell to cell interactions. The glycocalyx contains specific markers which allow immune cells to pass by and not mount an immune response against cells of the body. These markers are unique to each individual.

Attachment proteins/membrane junctions

Cells of the body are surrounded by other cells and/or extracellular matrix (ECM). Although some cells of the body are able to migrate through tissues, like macrophages and other immune cells, many cells are anchored to other cells or to the extracellular matrix through specific protein interactions on the surface of the cell membranes. Cell adhesion molecules (CAMs) are specific membrane proteins that attach cells to other cells. Two major groups of CAMs are cadherins and the immunoglobulin (Ig) superfamily CAMs. Cells connect to one another through many individual cell to cell adhesion interactions, however specialized connections of dense clustering of CAMs create strong adhesive junctions. Two common junctions that contain cadherins are desmosomes and tight junctions (Figure 2.10).

A desmosome is a disk-shaped cluster of membrane surface proteins in one cell attached to linker proteins (the cadherins) which connect to an adjacent cell with the same structural components. Desmosomes contain especially adhesive glycoproteins on the outer cell surface and are attached intracellularly to the intermediate filaments of the cytoskeleton. Desmosomes are small, extremely tough connections which are found in high numbers in places that are under high mechanical stress such as the epithelium, or epidermis of skin.

Tight junctions hold some epithelial cells together and form a permeability barrier between the cells. This prevents substances from leaking between cells and prevents unwanted movement of substances from the lumen into the interstitial space of tissues. Tight junctions extend around the entire circumference of each cell and is comprised of two

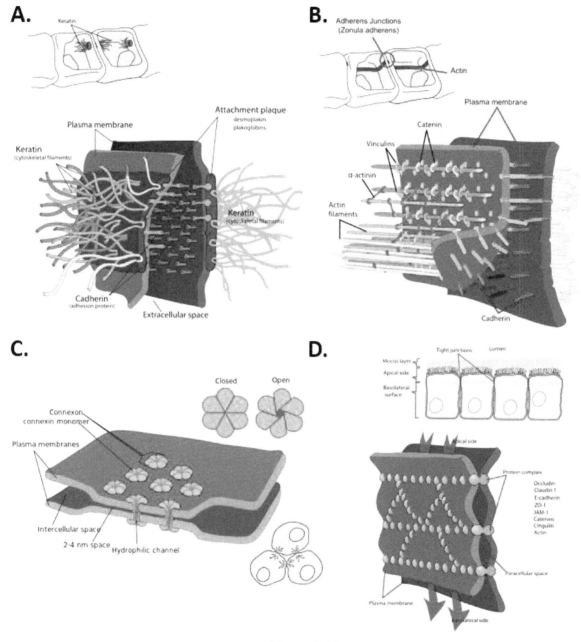

Figure 2.10

components, the zonula occludens and the zonula adherens. The zonula occludens creates the permeability barrier whereas the zonula adherens act to hold the cells together (a glue) and is made up of a band of cadherin molecules. Cells that contain tight junctions, often contain membrane proteins that are involved in the highly regulated movement of specific molecules across their surface. Some cells, like the endothelial cells lining the capillaries of the airways contain tight junctions that prevent movement of plasma or H_2O into the airways, but is thin enough to allow gas exchange across its surface.

Another type of cell to cell connection is a gap junction (Figure 2.10). The primary purpose of the gap junction is to provide a means of intracellular communication, however, since the cells are mechanically linked at the gap junction, they also provide a means of mechanical cellular linkage. A gap junction is a small round region of one plasma membrane containing numerous pores connected to pores in another cell and separated by a small space or "gap." Each membrane protein is comprised of 6 individual proteins called a connexin which combine to form a channel or a pore in one cell termed a connexon. A connexon from one cell connects directly with another cell's connexon forming a long channel through which ions and small molecules can pass through. Gap junctions are important in coordinating the function of smooth muscle, cardiac muscle and some epithelium. They are also found between cells as a means for transport of nutrients such as in bone.

Cells are also anchored to components of the ECM. Integrins are membrane proteins comprised of a heterodimer containing α and β subunits which bind to molecules of the ECM. Two types of junctions occur with integrins, hemidesmosomes and focal adhesions. The hemidesmosome is similar to the desmosome and contains a disk-shaped protein aggregate which is attached to the intermediate filaments of the intracellular compartment and to proteins of the ECM. Hemidesmosomes are predominantly found anchoring the basal surface of epithelial cells to the basement membrane. Recall that the ECM contains a mixture of proteins in the form of fibers and ground substance. Focal adhesions are collections of integrin proteins which attach the actin filaments of the cytoskeleton to the ECM. These are commonly found in fibroblasts of connective tissue but are found widespread throughout the body.

Transport proteins

Transport proteins are membrane proteins involved with the movement of substances across the plasma membrane. All transport proteins are also called transmembrane proteins because they span the entire plasma membrane. Transmembrane proteins, like all proteins, are synthesized in the RER by linking individual amino acids together. Each piece of the protein that spans the length of the membrane is ~20-25 amino acids in length and is created within the membrane of the RER. The proteins are transported to the Golgi apparatus and to the plasma membrane embedded within the membrane of vesicles. Transport proteins can be divided into three broad categories, channel proteins, carrier proteins and ATP powered pumps.

Channel proteins are transmembrane proteins that contain a center, cylindrical pore that is water soluble and allows substances to pass through from one side of the plasma membrane to the opposite side (Figure 2.11). Channel proteins are selectively permeable depending on the size of the diameter of the pore, the charge of the amino acid residues lining the pore, and the number of water molecules interacting with the central pore. The state of channels (open, closed or inactive) are regulated by various mechanisms. Some channels are always open and are referred to as non-gated or leak channels. Non-gated, leak channels allow substances to freely pass through the pore based on concentration and electrical gradients. Many leak channels are highly selective and only allow a specific ion to pass through them. Some channels are voltage-gated and open in response to a change in voltage, i.e., a specific voltage, usually on the intracellular side of the channel, opens or closes the channel. Voltage-gated channels are commonly found in neurons and muscle cells and help regulate cellular communication through the generation and propagation of action potentials along these cells. Channels can also be ligand-gated or regulated by specific molecules (ligands) which act like a key which opens the gate of the channel. These are also called receptor proteins because the channel is acting as a receptor for a specific ligand. Another type of channel found predominantly in sensory neurons is a mechanically-gated channel which open in response to stretch or mechanical stress.

A.

B.

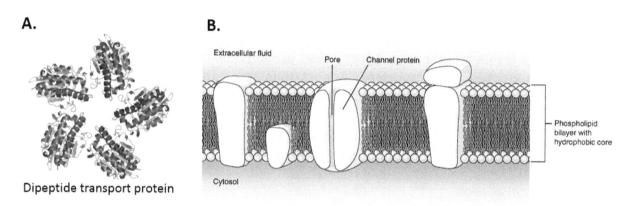

Dipeptide transport protein

Figure 2.11

Carrier proteins, also simply called transporters, transport specific molecules across a membrane. Unlike channels, these substances must bind to the transport protein to initiate a conformational change in the carrier protein which causes the movement of the substance from one side of the membrane to the opposite side. Carrier proteins exhibit several features including specificity, competition and saturation. Specificity refers to the ability of the substrate to bind to the site based on the specific shape or structure of the substrate and binding site. The affinity refers to how strong the substrate binds to the site. Binding sites on carrier proteins maintain a specific 3-dimensional structure with charged amino acids which influence the binding affinity of a substrate with the carrier protein. Competition occurs when two molecules of similar shape "compete" for the binding site. For example, many drugs are produced to compete with natural substances and often result in a decrease in the effectiveness of the natural compound (a type of inhibition). Carrier proteins can also become saturated meaning that the number of substances to be transported across a membrane may exceed the number of available carrier proteins. In other words, as the substance concentration increases, the rate of transport will also increase at a constant level until all available binding sites are filled. Once the available binding sites are filled, then the rate of transport will plateau or reach a maximal level of transport. For example, in the first portion of the kidney tubule, glucose is reabsorbed or carried across the apical side of the epithelium by a specific $Na+$/glucose transporter. Under normal conditions, all of the glucose that is filtered into the kidney tubule binds to transporters and is taken back up, such that no glucose is found in urine. During diabetes, the number of circulating glucose molecules increases. As the increased number of glucose molecules pass through the kidney tubule, the transporters become saturated and the amount of glucose transport is maximal. This is dependent on the set number of transporters present in the membrane. In this case, some of the glucose passes out of the body in urine causing an increase in the amount of urine, or diuresis.

The rate of transport of substances by carrier proteins is dependent upon the binding affinity of the substance for the carrier protein, the number of binding sites or transporters in the cell membrane and the rate of time that it takes for the carrier protein to undergo a conformational change to move the substance from one side of the membrane to the opposite side.

Carrier proteins or transporters that move a single molecule across a membrane in one direction is called a uniporter. Many carrier proteins can carry more than one molecule and these are called co-transporters. If more than one substance is carried across the membrane in the same direction, this is referred to as a symporter, whereas if two substances are moved in opposite directions, this is referred to as an antiporter.

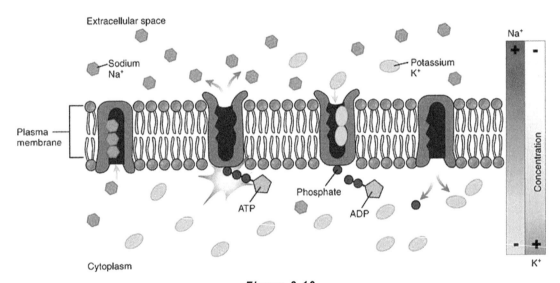

Figure 2.12

The third type of transport protein is the ATP-powered pumps (Figure 2.12). In the examples above, channels and carrier proteins, the substances tend to move in the direction of a concentration gradient and move from high concentrations to areas of low concentrations. There are many conditions in which cells and organelles need to move substances into an area of high concentration, however. For example, if you need to store calcium in the endoplasmic reticulum, you need to pump calcium from the cytosol (an area of low concentration) into the endoplasmic reticulum (an area of high concentration). Many of these transport proteins use ATP as an energy source to move things against their concentration gradient. The most common ATP pump in the body is called the Na^+/K^+ ATP pump, or the Na^+/K^+ ATPase. The Na^+/K^+ pump is found in the plasma membrane of most every cell and is highly conserved. The pump uses 1 ATP molecule to move 3 Na^+ ions to the extracellular compartment and 2 K^+ ions to the intracellular compartment both against their concentration gradients. The Na^+/K^+ pump functions by the binding of 3 Na^+ ions and a molecule of ATP on the intracellular side of the protein. ATP is hydrolyzed by an enzyme located on the pump, ATPase, which phosphorylates the pump releasing ADP. This causes a conformational change in the protein and moves the Na^+ ions to the extracellular space. This exposes 2 K^+ binding sites on the extracellular surface of the protein. K^+ binds to the sites causing another conformational change releasing the phosphate ion and transferring the 2 K^+ ions to the intracellular compartment. Once the K^+ is released, the protein is returned to its original conformation. The Na^+/K^+ pump is energetically costly and for most cells uses up to 1/5 of the total energy use by the cell; in neurons the cost of running the Na^+/K^+ pump is up to 2/3 of the total energy cost of the cells.

There are a variety of other types of ATP-powered pumps used by cells to pump ions against their concentration gradients. Some examples include calcium and hydrogen pumps which use ATP to pump calcium or hydrogen into areas of high concentration. Calcium pumps are commonly used in muscle cells to store high levels of calcium in the endoplasmic reticulum for use in muscle contraction. Hydrogen pumps are used by lysosomes to pump H^+ ions from the cytosol into the lysosome to lower the pH. Hydrogen pumps are also used in the stomach to pump H^+ ions into the lumen of the stomach (with chloride ions) to produce a highly acidic lumen to aid in digestion.

Secondary active transport mechanisms combine ATP powered pumps to aid in the activity of a co-transporter. For example, in the lumen of the small intestine, the Na^+/K^+ pump actively moves Na^+ ions into the lumen of the small intestine to generate a high concentration of Na^+ in the lumen and a very low intracellular Na^+ concentration. This creates a strong driving force for Na^+ entry into the cell. Other transporters utilize this driving force to co-transport Na^+ with other substances, such as glucose and amino acids. This ensures that all available nutrients are absorbed across the intestinal lumen.

Receptor proteins

Receptor proteins that are found in the plasma membrane contain one or more highly specific binding sites to which a ligand can bind resulting in the activation of a cellular response. Ligands form non-covalent bonds (ionic bonds, hydrophilic/hydrophobic bonds) with receptors to initiate a conformational change in the receptor protein to initiate the cellular response. Receptor proteins are integral proteins that span the entire membrane and can be a channel, as described above, or a solid protein that is associated with specific intracellular proteins which recruit specific intracellular signaling cascades. In channel proteins, the specific ligand binds to a specific receptor site on the channel to initiate a conformational change which opens or closes the channel. For example, many excitatory neurons in the brain and spinal cord release the specific neurotransmitter, glutamate which acts as a ligand for the receptor protein, the AMPA channel. Glutamate binds to its receptor site on the AMPA channel and causes it to open, allowing the movement of Na^+ and K^+ through the pore of the channel. Some receptor proteins, however, are not channels, but are instead coupled to various intracellular proteins which get initiated upon activation of the receptor protein. For example, glutamate can also bind to another type of receptor called a metabotropic glutamate receptor which is coupled to a specific G-protein pathway (see Section 2 – Cell signaling transduction) causing the activation of a cellular response. In these types of examples, the receptor can lead to the opening of a channel nearby, or it can lead to additional cellular responses.

Like carrier proteins, receptors demonstrate chemical specificity, saturation, and competition. Receptor proteins have specific structural elements to which very specific ligands can bind. Many drugs are produced to be structurally similar to ligands and therefore can bind to various receptor proteins. An agonist is an exogenous compound, something produced outside of the body which mimics the effect of the endogenous compound, the ligand that is naturally produced in the body. For example, phenylephrine and pseudoephedrine which you can buy as a decongestant at any pharmacy works by mimicking the action of epinephrine on α-adrenergic receptors. In the nasal cavity this causes vasoconstriction and reduces the amount of mucus formed and secreted by the epithelium. On the other hand, an antagonist is an exogenous compound that blocks or inhibits the response of the endogenous compound. For example, some medicines that lower blood pressure work by inhibiting β-adrenergic receptors. Another example of an antagonist that are commonly available are antihistamines which block the effect of histamine on its specific receptors in mast cells to reduce allergic reactions in the body. Another histamine blocker is Tagamet which is used to target a different histamine receptor which results in a decreased secretion of acid in the stomach.

Membrane bound receptors can be regulated by cells by various signals (intracellular or extracellular). Increasing the number of receptors at the cell surface is called up-regulation. This can occur both naturally or by the action of certain drugs. Down-regulation is a decrease in the number of receptors at the cell surface. In some instances, if cells get stimulated too much, the cell responds by down-regulation of the number of receptors (another type of negative feedback mechanism).

Enzymes

All chemical reactions, in theory, are reversible and can be run in either the forward or reverse direction. Enzymes are proteins that can help reduce the activation energy of equations and speed up chemical reactions. Many enzymes act by binding a substrate and aiding in the separation of the substrate into two final products. In cells, enzymes are proteins that catalyze specific reactions. Enzymes can be found as membrane bound proteins, but they can also be found in many locations in the body, such as freely circulating (such as in the lumen of the gut), attached to proteins in cells, and in specific organelles within cells. Enzymes help many metabolic and catabolic reactions in cells. Enzymes also help regulate protein function, by increasing or decreasing the activity of proteins. For example, covalent modulation of proteins is a common method of changing the activity of proteins. An enzyme called a protein kinase uses ATP to add a phosphate group to the protein, a process called phosphorylation. Sometimes protein kinases are incorporated into or on the protein itself. Another enzyme, a phosphatase, is involved with the cleavage of the phosphate group from the protein or dephosphorylation.

Enzymes demonstrate the same characteristics as other receptors – chemical specificity, competition, and saturation. Enzymes increase the rate of reactions that would otherwise, occur spontaneously, except usually at extremely low rates. Co-factors are non-protein chemical compounds that are often used with enzymes to activate or enhance the enzyme's activity. Co-factors that cause an allosteric modulation or a conformational change in the enzyme are often minerals such as zinc, iron, and magnesium. Another type of cofactor is known as a coenzyme substrate. These coenzymes are typically vitamins and they involved in the transfer of chemical groups to the substrate to form the final end-products. The coenzyme typically changes structure during the reaction, however, it is not a net change; usually another reaction changes it back to its original state allowing it to be used again.

The rate of reactions, from the substrate to end-product, is dependent on 1) the amount of enzyme or its total concentration or 2) the amount of enzyme activity. Within cells, the amount of enzyme present in cells is determined by the amount of enzyme produced or degraded within cells. Likewise, enzyme activity can be regulated in cells via allosteric activation or allosteric inhibition. Inside cells, many reactions involve a series of enzymatic reactions or an enzyme cascade. In this situation, multiple steps are needed to form an end-product. In enzymatic cascades, there is usually a rate-limiting enzyme which is usually the slowest enzyme in the cascade which determines the speed of the entire cascade. In these cascades, often the end-product is an inhibitor of the rate-limiting enzyme; this is a form of negative feedback inhibition (refer back to Figure 1.7).

Membrane bound enzymes have the same characteristics of all enzymes, they are simply found on the surface of cells. For example, on apical surface of epithelial cells lining the small intestines, enzymes help to break down complex sugars, peptides, and lipids into simple molecules which can then be absorbed by the epithelial cells using specific transporters. In the blood, carbonic anhydrase is involved in the conversion of carbon dioxide into hydrogen and bicarbonate ions. And in neurons, enzymes are used to break down neurotransmitters and inactivate them. As you investigate each organ system, you will see that enzymes play critical roles in normal physiology.

Movement of molecules across the plasma membrane

Movement of molecules and H_2O throughout the body and across cell membranes occurs through a variety of mechanisms including diffusion, osmosis, facilitated diffusion, active transport, filtration, endocytosis and exocytosis. Some of these mechanisms employ membrane proteins to aid in the movement of molecules across the membrane, some of the mechanisms use pressure gradients to force movement from one extracellular space to another extracellular space and other mechanisms move substances by the formation and release of vesicles.

Diffusion

Molecules are in continuous motion. Molecular movement occurs in all states of matter (gas, liquid and solids). Within the body, molecules move by Brownian motion or the random movement of molecules in any liquid or colloid suspension. The rate of molecular movement is dependent upon several factors:

> ➢ Small molecules or low molecular weight particles move faster than larger molecules or high molecular weight particles.

> ➢ The larger the concentration gradient, the faster the rate of particle movement or alternatively, the smaller the concentration gradient, the slower the rate of movement.

> ➢ Heat energy increases the amount of kinetic energy and causes particles to move faster, and conditions where temperature is lowered or the kinetic energy decreases causes particles to move slower.

> ➢ More gaseous mediums allow easier particle movement and thus faster molecular movement. The more viscous or solid the medium becomes, the slower the molecular movement.

Figure 2.13

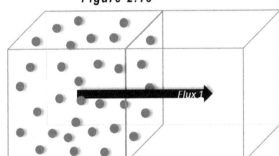

In physiology, diffusion is the term that is applied to the movement of solute particles in a solution from an area of high concentration to an area of low concentration. The movement of particles from a high concentration to a low concentration does not require external energy for molecular movement.

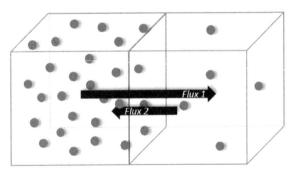

Movement of particles from one area to another area is called the net flux. In Figure 2.13, one compartment is filled with a high concentration of blue dye particles in water and is separated by a membrane that is permeable to the blue dye particles from another compartment which contains no particles, only water. Initially, as the blue dye particles are continually moving due to Brownian motion, they will begin to move from the compartment with blue dye to the compartment

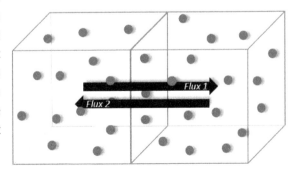

with no dye. Thus there is strong one-way flux (1) of particles from the first compartment to the second compartment as particles move down from a high concentration to a low concentration. But remember that molecules move randomly and so there will also be a one-way flux (2) of particles from the compartment with low concentration to the compartment with high concentration. The net flux movement of particles is equal to the one way flux 1 minus one way flux 2. Over time, an equilibrium will be reached and the same number of particles will be equally distributed across both compartments. Once this is achieved, particles continue to randomly move in both directions, but the net flux equals zero.

In cells, the net flux or movement of particles across cell membranes is dependent up the concentration gradient (c2-c1), but it is also dependent on the permeability (P) of the solute particle as well as the surface area (A) of the cell. In physiology, the equation for determining flux across a lipid plasma membrane can be defined as:

$$Flux = -PA\,(c2 - c1)$$

In the body, the nature of the phospholipid bilayer of cell membranes affects the permeability of substances and greatly reduces flux or diffusion of solutes and water across the membrane. Only non-polar, lipid soluble particles are able to move by simple diffusion across membranes and their rate of movement is determined by their lipid solubility (See Figure 2.14). Some steroid hormones are lipid soluble and act on receptors located within the cytosol or nucleus of cells. Molecules that are water soluble cannot diffuse through the lipid bilayer, therefore many of these substances cross membranes use facilitated diffusion or active transport mechanisms. Facilitated diffusion is simply the diffusion of particles that is aided by the use of a channel or transporter as described above.

Osmosis

Osmosis is the diffusion of water (or a solvent) across a semi-permeable membrane. In cells, large changes in cell volume due to large movements of water can easily disrupt normal cell function. The movement of water across cell membranes is affected by the number of solute particles or indirectly due to the concentration gradient of water. When solute particles are placed into a compartment of pure water, the solute particles will displace the water molecules and thus decrease the concentration of water, so one can think of the movement of water in terms of concentration gradient. However, students of physiology should learn to think about the movement of water in terms of osmotic pressure. The osmolarity of solutions is based on the total solute concentration. It does not depend on the types of solutes, but rather the total number of solute particles within a solution. The higher the osmolarity, the greater the number of

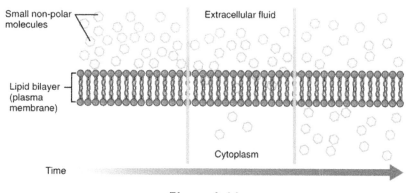

Figure 2.14

solute particles and the greater forces to attract water to that compartment. So the movement of water can be described as movement towards the high solute concentration.

Cells contain special water channels called aquaporins which allow water to freely flow in and out of cells, since water cannot pass through the lipid bilayer. Within the body, the osmotic pressure of the interstitial fluid and the osmotic pressure inside cells is the same (~0.3mOsmol). In other words, water movement in and out of cells is in equilibrium. In physiology or the study of medicine, we are highly concerned with the types of solutions that are injected into our bodies because the introduction of solutions with more or less solute particles can alter the osmotic pressure of the extracellular and the intracellular compartments and thus alter cell function. Solutions that have the same osmolarity of fluids (~0.3mOsmol) are said to be isosmotic. Solutions that have a higher number of solute particles (>0.3mOsmol) compared to tissues are hyperosmotic and solutions with a lower number of solute particles (<0.3mOsmol) are hyposmotic. The terms isosmotic, hyperosmotic and hyposmotic simply refer to the total osmolarity of the solutions, not the specific type of molecules found within the solutions. The effect of the solution on cells is termed the tonicity. If a solution has no effect on a cell size, then the solution is isotonic. If, however, the solution causes a cell to swell, it is called a hypotonic solution and if the solution causes a cell to shrink then it is called a hypertonic solution (See Figure 2.15).

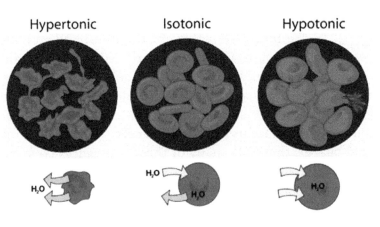

Figure 2.15

Endocytosis

Endocytosis is a method of transportation of substances from the outside of cells to the inside by pinching the cell membrane inward causing the formation of intracellular vesicles (See Figure 2.16). A common form of endocytosis that occurs in most every cell is called pinocytosis, from single celled organisms to complex humans. Pinocytosis forms small fluid filled vesicles and is non-specific. It is also called cell-drinking or fluid endocytosis. These vesicles fuse with lysosomes to break down particles and is a method for transfer of the extracellular fluid into the intracellular compartment. In vertebrates, pinocytosis is a very common phenomenon in endothelial cells, the epithelial cells that line the blood vessels, however, its exact role in endothelial cells is not entirely clear.

Figure 2.16

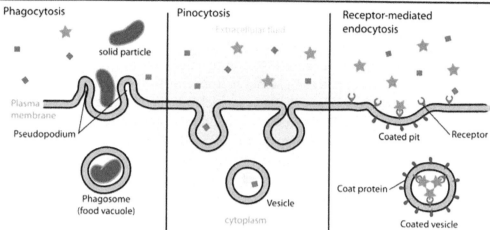

Endocytosis

Phagocytosis | Pinocytosis | Receptor-mediated endocytosis

solid particle

Plasma membrane

Pseudopodium

Phagosome (food vacuole)

Vesicle

Coated pit | Receptor

Coat protein

Coated vesicle

Another type of endocytosis is called receptor-mediated endocytosis. Specific receptors are expressed on the cell surface to which specific ligands can bind. When ligands bind to the receptor, an intracellular mechanism leads to the attachment of clathrin proteins which coat the forming vesicle. Once the vesicle internalizes, the clathrin coat begins to disintegrate and the vesicle fuses with an endosome. This mechanism is utilized to take in specific types of substances, often transporting molecules that are larger than those that can easily get through channels or transporters such as LDLs (or low density lipoproteins). Another form of receptor-mediated endocytosis is potocytosis. The invagination of the vesicle also starts with a ligand binding to a receptor, however, instead of clathrin proteins, caveolin proteins are used. Potocytosis forms intracellular vesicles in the cytosol which then fuse with endosomes.

Phagocytosis is another form of endocytosis that involves internalization of solid particles. In single celled organisms, phagocytosis is the mechanism by which nutrients are taken into cells. In more complex vertebrates, phagocytosis commonly occurs in cells of the immune system. Macrophages form large pseudopodia with specific receptors to gather large structures outside of the cells, bacteria or pieces of apoptotic cellular debris.

Exocytosis

Exocytosis is a method of releasing substances from the inside of the cell to the outside of the cell (See Figure 2.17).

Figure 2.17

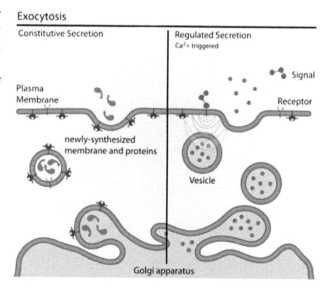

Exocytosis

Constitutive Secretion | Regulated Secretion
Ca²⁺ triggered

Signal

Plasma Membrane

Receptor

newly-synthesized membrane and proteins

Vesicle

Golgi apparatus

The cell produces various substances to be released in the ER and Golgi apparatus and puts them in vesicles which then fuse with the plasma membrane releasing the substances to the extracellular compartment. Two processes of exocytosis can be utilized by cells; 1) a highly regulated and Ca^{2+} dependent form of release or 2) a constitutive release that is not Ca^{2+} dependent. Most cells release substances by the constitutive method. All cells contain, membrane proteins which are inserted into the plasma membrane using the constitutive method. Cells also need to recycle the plasma membrane and initiate endocytosis. You can imagine that if you continually added new vesicles with new proteins to the plasma membrane, the surface area of cells would greatly enlarge. This type of membrane recycling occurs in all cells. Highly regulated exocytosis is a common mechanism found in many glandular cells and neurons. The process requires Ca^{2+} which binds to certain proteins associated with the fusing vesicle to promote fusion to the plasma membrane. This method of exocytosis will be covered in more detail in Chapter 3 – Neurophysiology.

CHAPTER 2, SECTION 1 – SUMMARY

➢ Cell physiology is a large encompassing field to which many entire textbooks are completely devoted.

➢ The nucleus of cells contain the DNA, or the entire genome. Protein synthesis starts in the nucleus with a process called transcription where the DNA is copied into mRNA. The mRNA moves to the ribosomes in the cytosol where translation occurs.

➢ The mRNA, ribosomes and tRNA work together to string amino acids together in correct sequences to synthesize proteins. Further protein modification occurs at the ribosome and within the Golgi-apparatus and the proteins are transported to their final destination using vesicles. Cells also produce lipids but this occurs in the smooth ER.

➢ Mitochondria are involved with the production of ATP, or the major energy source of cells.

➢ The cell structure and organelles are supported by an intracellular cytoskeleton made of microfilaments, intermediate filaments and microtubules.

➢ Cell replication or mitosis is a specific process with 4 phases; prophase, metaphase, anaphase and telophase. Prophase is preceded by DNA replication and starts as the DNA condenses into chromosomes. The chromosomes then line up in the center of the nucleus and attach to spindles during metaphase. During anaphase, each chromosome is split into two chromatids and each chromatid is drawn to opposite poles. The cell then creates a nuclear envelope around each nucleus and the cells split into two during the final stage, telophase.

➢ Cells are surrounded by a plasma membrane comprised of phospholipids and membrane proteins and separate the internal and external compartments.

Phospholipids contain a hydrophilic portion that faces the extracellular and the intracellular compartments. The phospholipids contain a hydrophobic region, two fatty acid tails that face the interior of the plasma membrane which effectively separate the two compartments.

➢ There are many different types of proteins that are embedded in the plasma membrane of cells. 1) Many proteins have specific carbohydrate and lipid moieties that are markers for cell identification. Immune cells recognize these marker proteins as "self" and therefore are not targeted for destruction. 2) Some proteins are involved with cell attachment and create specific attachment sites between cells such as the desmosome, a disk-shaped spot connection and tight junctions which form a permeability barrier between cells. Cells also attach to the extracellular matrix through integrins as well as hemidesmosomes which attach epithelial cells to the basement membrane. 4) Some proteins also regulate the passage of material from the outside of cells to the inside using specific membrane proteins such as channel proteins, transporters, receptor proteins and ATP-powered pumps. 5) Finally some membrane proteins act as enzymes and catalyze various chemical reactions.

➢ Movement across cells occurs via membrane proteins as well as endocytosis or the pinching of the membrane into a vesicle that forms on the inside of the cell and exocytosis or the fusion of an intracellular vesicle with the plasma membrane and the release of substances to the outside of cells.

➢ Inside the body, molecules move by Brownian motion. Movement of solute particles is influenced by the size of particles, the concentration gradient, the temperature and the thickness of the medium.

➢ Molecules move by diffusion gradients and move from an area of high concentration to an area of low concentration and requires no energy.

➢ The movement of water is termed osmosis and water moves from areas of low solute concentration to areas of high solute concentration.

Section 2 – Cell Signaling and Transduction

Many cells communicate through the actions of chemical messengers. Chemical messengers are released from cells and move through tissues to bind to specific receptors on target cells. Some of the most common chemical messengers are hormones and neurotransmitters. These chemical messengers or ligands bind to specific receptors to cause a signal transduction pathway. Many cells share common signal transduction pathways. In this section, we will discuss several signal transduction pathways that are common mechanisms used by many cells.

Intracellular receptors

Several hormones such as thyroid hormone, cortisol and aldosterone, are small hydrophobic molecules that travel through the blood bound to proteins. These molecules can diffuse through lipid membranes with varying permeability. Once released, the steroid hormones exit capillaries and enter cells by simple diffusion. Most receptors for lipid soluble molecules are found inside cells; there is no need for a membrane bound receptor if the

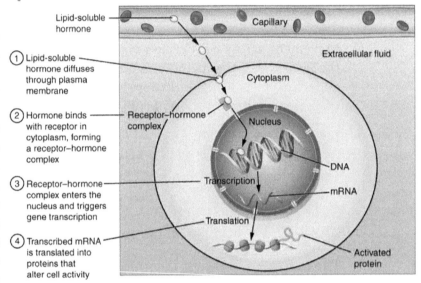

Figure 2.18

ligand can diffuse through membranes (See Figure 2.18). Depending on the cell, the receptors can be found located in the cytosol or more likely, in the nucleus. If the receptor is located in the cytosol, once the ligand binds to its receptor, the complex will translocate to the nucleus to affect gene transcription and the formation of new proteins. Nuclear receptors stay in the nucleus to directly affect gene transcription.

Intracellular receptors often form dimers which bind to specific regions of DNA called response elements and act as transcription factors. These receptor complexes can act on multiple genes and can result in the increase or decrease of gene transcription within cells. Many nuclear receptors are found already bound to the DNA, and the activation of the receptor by the ligand initiates gene transcription. For example, receptors for aldosterone are found in specific epithelial cells of the kidney tubule. Once the receptor is activated, gene transcription is initiated and mRNA is produced. The mRNA moves to the ribosomes and synthesizes new proteins that are involved in the transport of Na⁺.

Membrane bound receptors

Membrane bound receptors are more numerous than intracellular receptors due to the high number of water soluble substances produced and released from cells. The most common chemical messengers that act on membrane bound receptors are neurotransmitters and most hormones that are released from endocrine glands as well as hormones released from neuroendocrine cells that act paracellularly. In this section, we will review three major categories of membrane bound receptors and the common intracellular cell signaling paths.

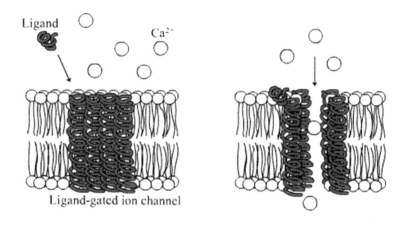

Figure 2.19

Ligand-gated channel receptors

As mentioned earlier, ligand gated channel receptors are specific receptors in which a ligand binds and causes a conformational change in the shape of the channel resulting in the opening or closing of the channel (See Figure 2.19). Many neurons that release neurotransmitters act on ligand-gated channels. The cellular response of activation of the ligand-gated channel is allow ions to flow through them causing a change in the voltage of the cell. This change in voltage is the primary mechanism for the generation or inhibition of action potentials. For example, if the ligand-gated channel is on a smooth muscle cell, the generation or inhibition of action potentials can result in the contraction or relaxation of the smooth muscle. Many ligand-gated channel receptors will be covered in more detail in Chapter 3.

Protein kinase receptors

The protein kinase receptors are a group of membrane bound proteins that have intrinsic enzyme activity. When a ligand binds to a protein kinase receptor, the receptor undergoes a conformational change and activate an enzyme located on its internal structure. Many of these enzymes are tyrosine kinases which use ATP to phosphorylate the tyrosine amino acid residues located on the membrane receptor itself, an example of auto-phosphorylation. This phosphorylated region of the protein then becomes a docking station for intracellular proteins. When an intracellular protein "docks" or binds to the receptor, it in turn gets phosphorylated. This can activate a chain of docking proteins to initiate a change in the cell metabolism such as cellular proliferation and differentiation. Insulin acts through a protein kinase receptor and enhances cellular metabolism and growth.

Another type of receptor that also has enzyme activity but is not a protein kinase is a group of guanylyl cyclase receptors. These types of receptors are less common than protein kinase receptors. Guanylyl cyclase receptor proteins have a receptor site and the enzyme guanylyl cyclase which converts guanosine-5'-triphosphate (GTP) to cyclic guanosine monophosphate (cGMP). cGMP is a common second messenger found in many cells (it can be created by guanylyl cyclases found in other locations). cGMP can initiate a variety of cellular responses depending on the specific cells; it can relax smooth muscle and lead to vasodilation, it can regulate ion channels, produce cellular glucose and initiate cellular apoptosis. Atrial natriuretic peptide (ANP) is a hormone that is released from the heart atria during conditions of increased pressure. The receptor for ANP is a guanylyl cyclase receptor. ANP act on receptors found in smooth muscles of blood vessels, activates the guanylyl cyclase activity and leads to increases in cGMP. The increased cGMP activates a cGMP-dependent protein kinase which leads to smooth muscle relaxation and vasodilation. This is turn decreases the blood returning to the heart and reduces blood pressure (another example of a negative feedback mechanism!).

G-protein coupled receptors

The g-protein coupled receptors (GPCRs) are the most common type of membrane bound receptors and can be found in all eukaryotic cells, from yeast to humans. In animals, GPCRs are located on many different cell types throughout the body and are therefore involved in many physiological roles. There are hundreds of distinct types of GPCRs however, in general, GPCRs can be grouped into three categories based on their general function.

1) GPCRs can stimulate adenylyl cyclase and activate the cAMP signaling pathway
2) GPCRs can inhibit adenylyl cyclase and inhibit the cAMP signaling pathway
3) GPCRs can stimulate phospholipase C and activate the phosphatidylinositol signaling pathway.

GPCRs are a group of transmembrane receptors that contain 7 membrane spanning regions of the protein. The internal region of the receptor is associated with an intracellular protein, the heteromeric G-protein which contains 3 subunits, α, β and a γ subunit. At rest, in its inactive form, the α-subunit has guanosine diphosphate (GDP) bound to its surface (Figure 2.20A). When a GPCR receptor is activated, a conformational change occurs in the receptor activating the α-subunit causing GDP to be displaced. In most cases, it appears as if the G-protein is loosely attached to the receptor before ligand binding, however, in some receptors the G-protein may attach after ligand binds. In either event, when the GDP is displaced, it opens a site on the α-subunit that has a high affinity for guanosine triphosphate (GTP). GTP is readily available in cells and quickly binds to its site (Figure 2.20B).

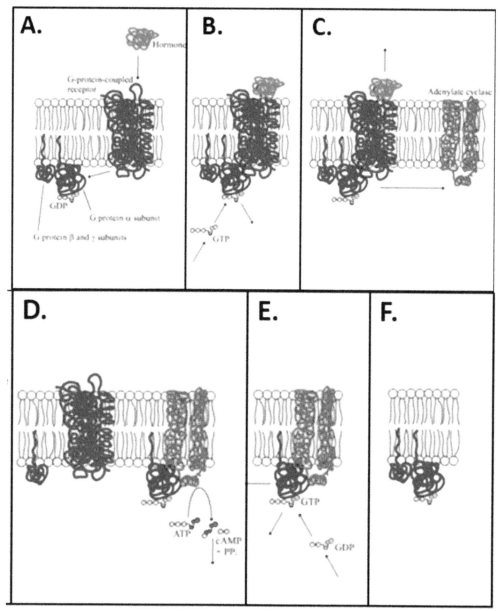

Figure 2.20

The binding of GTP initiates another conformational change in the G-protein causing the α-subunit to separate from the β/γ complex. The α-subunit and the β/γ complex are free to interact with other proteins, such as the interaction of the α-subunit with adenylyl cyclase (Figure 2.20C, D) and phospholipase C. The actions of β/γ complexes are not as well described and will not be covered. There are 4 main classes of heteromeric G-proteins (Table 2.1), G_s, G_i, G_q, and $G_{12,13}$. The actions of the α-subunits from the first three

G-protein, G_s, G_i, and G_q, are common among many cells and are well described. The interaction of the α-subunit with its target protein (adenylyl cyclase, phospholipase C or Rho kinase) causes the hydrolysis of GTP to GDP and the phosphate (P) is released (Figure 2.20E). The α-subunit detaches from the target protein and combines with the β/γ complex and is free to associate with the GPCR again (Figure 2.20F). If the ligand is still attached to the GPCR receptor or another ligand binds to the GPCR, the G-protein will be activated again.

Table 2.1. Common actions of the various alpha subunits of G-proteins.

α – subunit	Action
G_s	Stimulate adenylyl cyclase
G_i	Inhibit adenylyl cyclase
G_q	Activate phospholipase C
$G_{a12, a13}$	Enhance Rho kinase activity

Adenylyl cyclase

The "s" portion of the α-subunit G_s refers to its stimulatory action on adenylyl cyclase. When a ligand binds to the GPCR, a conformational change in the receptor activates the G-protein (See Figure 2.21). The α-subunit with attached GTP has a stimulatory effect on the enzyme adenylyl cyclase, a nearby membrane bound protein. Activation of adenylyl cyclase converts adenosine triphosphate (ATP) to cyclic adenosine monophosphate (cAMP). The most common action of cAMP is to activate cAMP-dependent protein kinases, typically protein kinase A. Remember that protein kinases are enzymes which phosphorylate proteins, specifically the serine and threonine amino acid residues on proteins. The specific proteins that get phosphorylated can vary from cell to cell; i.e., different cells have different proteins and thus this second messenger can have very different effects in different cells. Cells also contain a class of enzymes called phosphodiesterases which deactivate cAMP by degrading it to AMP. Phosphodiesterase activity is usually constitutively active meaning that the enzyme is always active and not highly regulated. Thus, the primary mechanism of regulating cAMP levels in cells is usually by increasing or decreasing the rate and amount of cAMP production.

The activation of adenylyl cyclase by G_s causes a secondary messenger cascade (described in the previous paragraph) which results in amplification of the initial signal. What this means is that a single ligand binding to a single GPCR can result in the phosphorylation of hundreds of intracellular proteins. Each stimulated GPCR can activate multiple G-proteins. Each G-protein can activate a single adenylyl cyclase producing a single cAMP which in turn, activates a single protein kinase. Each protein kinase phosphorylates multiple enzymes of which each enzyme can produce multiple end-products. This sequence of events leads to many end products formed from the activation of a single GPCR.

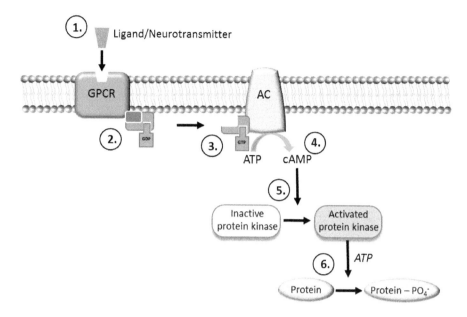

Figure 2.21

Another G-protein that has the opposite effect of G_s is G_i. The "i" portion of the α-subunit G_i refers to its inhibitory action on adenylyl cyclase. Activation of this G-protein by a stimulated GPCR inhibits adenylyl cyclase activity and reduces the amount of intracellular cAMP that is produced in the cell. This in turn will not activate protein kinase A and proteins will not be phosphorylated. Usually this turns off metabolic pathways. However, be careful, because the phosphorylation of a protein does not always indicate that a stimulatory effect occurs in the cell or in its metabolic path. Sometimes, phosphorylation of a protein may shut off a process and inhibit a pathway.

Phospholipase C

The third type of G-protein is called the Gq. When a ligand binds to a GPCR and causes a conformational change in the receptor, the associated G-protein is activated. The activation causes the displacement of GDP and allows GTP to bind and results in the disassembly of the G-protein. In this situation, the α-subunit activates a different target protein called phospholipase C (See Figure 2.22, on the next page). Phospholipase C is an enzyme that acts on a particular membrane phospholipid called phosphatidylinositol 4,5-bisphosphate (PIP$_2$). The enzyme cleaves PIP$_2$ into diacylglycerol (DAG) and inositol 1,4,5-trisphosphate (IP$_3$). Each of these two end-products have effects in cells. DAG can activate protein kinase C which phosphorylates the serine and threonine residues of proteins. IP$_3$ binds to IP$_3$ receptors on smooth endoplasmic reticulum. The IP$_3$ receptor is a calcium channel and activation opens the channel allowing calcium to flow out of the ER and into the cytosol. Calcium is another type of 2nd messenger which plays many important roles in cellular physiology. In cells, calcium can bind to a protein called calmodulin, which activates calcium-calmodulin dependent proteins which in turn can phosphorylate enzymes. For example, in smooth muscle, calcium binds to calmodulin which activates an enzyme called myosin kinase. Myosin kinase directly phosphorylates a myosin head causing contraction of smooth muscle.

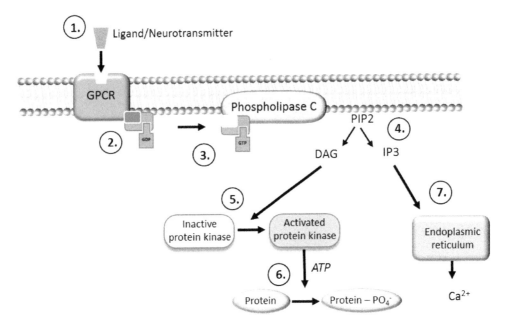

Figure 2.22

Regulation of G-protein activity

The activity of G-proteins in cells is regulated by the activation of the GPCR. Regulation of GPCR activity may involve the number of available ligands, the number of available receptors or the affinity of the binding sites on the GPCR. When endogenous ligands bind to GPCRs, they do not bind permanently. Remember that ligands only form non-covalent bonds (ionic bonds, hydrophilic/hydrophobic bonds) with receptors which are easy to break and therefore the ligand does not stay attached to the receptor for long periods of time. When the ligand (or the 1st messenger) is free, it moves by simple diffusion and can diffuse away from receptor sites. For example, in neuronal synapses, the amount of ligand or neurotransmitter in the free extracellular space is highly regulated. Released neurotransmitters are quickly degraded or taken up by nearby cells and the amount of ligand quickly decreases. The number of GPCRs located in the plasma membrane can also be down-regulated or up-regulated based on the needs of the individual cell. Finally, individual GPCR activity can be modified by phosphorylation or modification which may cause a decrease in affinity for 1st messengers or may prevent G-protein interactions with the GPCR. These mechanisms which regulate the GPCR indirectly regulate the downstream G-protein signaling cascade.

CHAPTER 2, SECTION 2 – SUMMARY

➤ Communication between cells can occur by the release of chemical messengers which bind to specific receptor which can initiate receptor-mediated pathways.

➤ Chemical messengers can be steroid hormones which can readily diffuse through cell membranes to activate intracellular receptors which often result in either an increase or a decrease in protein transcription and translation.

➤ Most chemical messengers are water soluble and activate membrane bound receptors.

➤ Ligand-gated channels are receptor proteins that are also a channel protein. Activation of the ligand-gated channel can either open or close the channel.

➤ Protein kinase receptors are receptors that initiate enzymatic activity when activated. Many of these result in autophosphorylation which causes downstream signaling cascades.

➤ The most common type of membrane bound receptor is the G-protein coupled receptors (GPCRs). These receptors are coupled to a G-protein which initiate a variety of intracellular signaling pathways and cause the amplification of the initial signal to create large cellular responses. GPCRs can 1) stimulate adenylyl cyclase, 2) inhibit adenylyl cyclase or 3) activate phospholipase C.

➤ The activity of the receptor, the number of receptors, and the amount of chemical messengers are regulated by various cellular mechanisms to influence cellular transduction.

References and Suggested Readings

Katritch V, Cherezov V, Stevens RC. 2013. Structure-function of the G-protein coupled receptor superfamily. Annual Review of Pharmacological Toxicology. 53:531-556.

Shen L, Weber CR, Raleigh DR, Yu D, Turner JR. 2011. Tight junction pore and leak pathways: a dynamic duo. Annual Reviews of Physiology 73:283-309.

Van Itallie CM, Anderson JM. 2006. Claudins and epithelial paracellular transport. Annual Reviews of Physiology 68:403-429.

Chapter 3: Neurophysiology

The nervous system controls all behavior, thought, emotion, movement and regulation of internal structures and organs. Information from the environment (external and internal) is sensed by specific sensory receptors, transferred to integrative centers within the brain and spinal cord which initiates an appropriate motor response. The entire nervous system functions by cell-to-cell communication though highly organized pathways in order to control behavior and maintain and regulate homeostasis and normal organ function. The nervous system is extremely fast and can initiate quick responses to stimuli.

Cell signaling via the release of specific cell signaling molecules and their effect on other cells is found in nearly all types of life forms. Neural systems, however, evolved with increasing size of animals and the need to sense external environments. As animals began to enlarge, simple diffusion mechanisms were unable to meet the metabolic demands of the tissues. For example, organisms needed to be able respond to external stimuli such as sensing a possible food source and moving the body toward that food source. Thus, the sensors, neurons and the structures responsible for movement, myoepithelial and muscle cells, appear to originate together phylogenetically. The neural networks that appear first phylogenetically are found in Cnidaria (*Hydra* spp.). Cnidaria and ctenophores (combjellies) have established networks that control body movement through a simple neuromuscular system. These networks contain the necessary components of a neural network; sensory neurons, interneurons and motor neurons, and the cells communicate via direct cell-to-cell contact. In higher evolved species such as the vertebrates, the neural systems are highly complex, although the basic plan of a neural network still exists, a sensory neuron to sense stimuli, interneurons to communicate that sensory information to various locations within the nervous system and a motor neuron to initiate an efferent response.

In vertebrates, the nervous system is traditionally divided into two divisions. The central nervous system (CNS) is encased in the cranial cavity and the vertebral column and contains the brain and spinal cord. The peripheral nervous system (PNS) is everything outside of these regions such as the nerves of the body and the structures associated with nerves, plexuses and ganglia. Individual neurons communicate to other neurons or their target cells via electrical and chemical signals.

Section 1 – Introduction to Nervous Tissue

Cells of the Nervous System

The nervous system is made up of billions of cells! The nervous tissue contains primarily cells and very little extracellular substance. There are two broad categories of cells within the nervous system; neurons and glia. Neurons are cells that communicate (send and receive information) with other cells and carry out the functions of the nervous system (activate motor responses). Glia are supporting cells of the nervous system and help to maintain the appropriate environment for the neurons to function properly and survive. Glia also play specialized roles, such as the ependymal cell which secretes the cerebral spinal fluid which bathes the brain and spinal cord, cushioning and protecting the brain tissue from its hard, bony case. Glia also provide nutrients to neurons and play an important immune functions in the brain and spinal cord.

Neurons

Neurons are the cells of the nervous system that send and receive information. They are the cells that sense external stimuli, sensory neurons. They are the cells that are responsible for integration and they pass information from cell to cell throughout various regions of the brain and spinal cord. They are also the cells that send signals to glands and muscles in order to initiate some sort of motor response. There are many different types of neurons, but the general structure of all of these neurons is essentially the same. Neurons contain three main regions: a cell body, dendrites and an axon (See Figure 3.1). The cell body is also called the cell soma or perikaryon and is the location of the nucleus as well as most of the cell's machinery for metabolic processing; rough endoplasmic reticulum (RER), Golgi, mitochondria, etc...

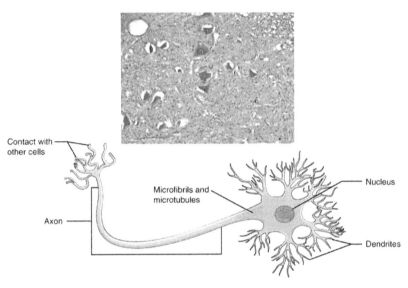

Figure 3.1

The nucleus is centrally located and contains a prominent nucleolus, the site of ribosomal RNA synthesis, indicating that the cell is active in the production of proteins. The cell body of neurons also contains many mitochondria to support the high energy demands of the cell, numerous RER with many ribosomes and an extensive Golgi apparatus to help with protein synthesis and normal cell function. The RER is so distinct and prominent that it appears in histological examination and is called Nissl bodies or Nissl substance. The cell body has many processes that project outward. Most of the processes are dendrites which carry information toward the cell body and one single axon that extends away from the cell body and carries information to its target cell.

In many neurons, there is an extensive branching of the dendrites which receive signals from other neurons at specialized cell-to-cell contacts, called synapses. Many of the synapses occur at structures called dendritic spines. Dendritic spines are small buds protruding from the dendritic tree that form a specialized synapse with the axon of another neuron. Dendrites contain microtubules and a specialized type of intermediate filament, the neurofilament, which is only found in neurons. At the point of attachment to the cell body, the dendrites become thicker and other organelles can be found such as mitochondria, endoplasmic reticulum, polyribosomes and free ribosomes.

The axon also originates from the cell body. At the junction between the cell body and the axon, there is a thickening called the axon hillock. This region contains an absence of Nissl substance and thus appears pale in comparison to the surrounding cytoplasm of the cell soma. The initial segment is term that is applied to the region of the axon where the action potential begins and is found between the axon hillock and the start of the first myelin sheath (in myelinated axons). In the initial segment, electron micrographs show a dark, dense granular layer under the plasma membrane, which is also observed in the Nodes of Ranvier (the segments found between myelin sheaths). These regions are now known to contain a high density of voltage gated Na^+ channels and are involved in the generation of the action potential at the initial segment and regeneration of the action potential at the nodes of Ranvier. The term axon hillock and initial segment are often used interchangeably or loosely because of the overlap of the regions. Technically the action potential starts at the initial segment or within a region of the axon hillock.

The axon itself contains primarily microtubules and neurofilaments and can be distinguished from the dendrites by the absence of ribosomes. Axons can be short (<mm) or extremely long (up to several meters) in length. The neuron uses the microtubules as a vehicle to transport vesicles up and down the axon. Anterograde transport moves vesicles from the cell body down the axon toward its end-terminal. This type of transport use specific proteins that attach to microtubules and use ATP to move two categories of vesicles toward the ends of axons. Some vesicles carry neurotransmitters down to the end of axon terminals. Kinesin proteins are involved with the relatively fast transport of vesicles (up to 400mm/day) carrying neurotransmitters. Some vesicles carry basic metabolic machinery, such as membrane bound proteins and proteins used to lengthen or change the end of axons. The transport of these vesicles utilize a slow mechanism of anterograde transport that is not fully understood. Retrograde transport carries vesicles from the axon terminal up to the cell body using a different type of transport protein, dynein. Dynein proteins also use ATP to move along the microtubules but in the opposite direction as the kinesin proteins. Anterograde transport is used for recycling mechanisms as well as carrying signaling products from the axon terminal up to the cell body. In general, a single axon extends away from a cell body but will branch toward the end terminal and send axon collaterals to synapse with various target cells. At the end-terminals or synaptic boutons, the axon contains stored vesicles filled with neurotransmitter and many mitochondria for energy production.

Neurons can be described based on their function, anatomical structure, the types of neurotransmitters that they carry, or their location in specific regions of the nervous system. In general, neuronal function includes sensation, integration and motor response. Sensory neurons are neurons that sense various stimuli and transmit that information to the central nervous system. Afferent is a directional term that means toward a specific region. Therefore, a sensory neuron or an afferent neuron is the neuron that projects from the PNS toward the CNS carrying information regarding the senses into the brain and spinal cord. Efferent is the directional term that means away from a specific region. This term is often used to describe the motor neurons that project away from the CNS to their target tissues, the effectors, located in the PNS to cause a motor response. Interneurons are neurons within the central nervous system that connect neurons together, e.g., a simple reflex can connect a sensory neuron and a motor neuron using an interneuron.

Figure 3.2

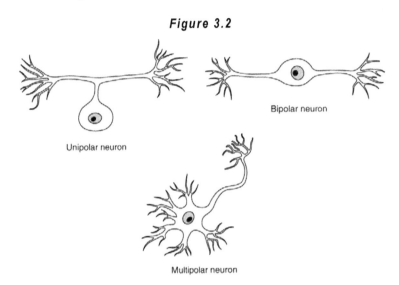

Neurons can also be described based on their anatomical shape (Figure 3.2). Bipolar neurons have two primary processes extending from the cell body, one axon and a single dendrite. They are not very common neurons but can be found in a couple areas such as the retina. During development, a large population of bipolar neurons become pseudounipolar neurons. The two extensions (axon and dendrite) develop into a single, long axon that extends from the periphery and projects to the spinal cord; the cell body sits off a short extension from the axon in a ganglia which is a collection of cell bodies of neurons. In vertebrates, sensory neurons are psuedounipolar neurons which extend from the periphery to the CNS and their cell bodies are located in dorsal root ganglia or specific ganglia associated with cranial nerves. Multipolar neurons are the most common type of neuron in the nervous system. The cell body can take on multiple shapes such as stellate-shaped, triangular, fusiform, or polygonal. Multipolar neurons contain many dendrites that extend off the cell body giving them their particular shape and a single axon that projects away from the cell body.

Neurons can also be described based on the types of neurotransmitters that they produce. For example, neurons that produce and secrete acetylcholine (ACh) are called cholinergic neurons and neurons that produce and secrete dopamine are called dopaminergic neurons. Finally, neurons can also be labeled based on their location or where they project in the brain and spinal cord. For example neurons that reside in the cortex are called cortical neurons and neurons in the raphe nuclei are called raphe neurons. Commissural neurons are neurons that cross the brain and connect the left and right hemispheres. And finally, projection neurons are neurons that project from one region of the brain to another area over relatively long distances.

Within the nervous system, the anatomical regions of neurons are grouped together in the body in a highly organized system. For example all of the cell bodies group together and all of the axons group together. In the PNS, the cell bodies of neurons are grouped together and form a structure called a ganglia. As mentioned above, the sensory neuron cell bodies are found in the dorsal root ganglia just outside of the spinal cord and in several ganglia associated with specific cranial nerves. The motor neurons of part of the autonomic nervous system are found clustered into ganglia as well and are specific to various divisions of the autonomic nervous system (see Section 3). In the PNS, the axons of neurons run together and form the nerves that are found in the PNS. For example, when you hit your elbow on a table, sometimes it triggers a sensation of pain and tingling which lasts a short period of time. This is due to hitting a nerve in the arm which carries sensory information from the arm to the brain for sensory processing. Within the CNS, the cell bodies of neurons are clustered together in specific groups based on function and are called nuclei or columns. For example, the cell bodies of the raphe neurons are clustered into groups called the raphe nuclei and can be found in the brainstem. In the CNS, the axons of neurons also run together and are called tracts, columns, or funiculi.

Neuroglia

The primary function of glial cells is to provide structural support for neurons and to control the environment surrounding neurons; for example they shuttle nutrition from blood vessels to neurons, remove waste products, maintain electrochemical environments, and remove foreign debris. Glia are also critical to proper early development of the CNS and they guide neurons to their correct locations. Glial cells do NOT propagate action potentials and therefore do not send or receive information. There are different types of glial cells found within the CNS and the PNS. Within the CNS, there are 5 types of glial cells; astrocytes, oligodendrocytes, ependymal cells and microglia (Figure 3.3). Whereas in the PNS, there are only 2 types of glial cells; Schwann cells and satellite cells.

Astrocytes or astroglia can be found in all areas of the brain and spinal cord. They are highly branched cells which play important roles in numerous functions within the CNS. The cells contain long processes that make contact with most free surfaces of the neurons and can be found associated with the dendrites, cell bodies and axons. Some astrocytic

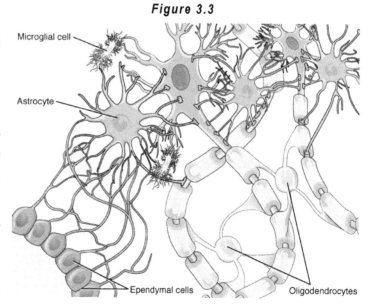

Figure 3.3

Microglial cell

Astrocyte

Ependymal cells

Oligodendrocytes

processes have a specialized ending called "end feet" which line the entire interface between the CNS and other tissues, such as the connective tissue lining the outside of the brain and spinal cord as well as all of the blood vessels that course through the CNS. Astrocytes come in multiple shapes such as the star-shaped astrocytes and specialized elongated astrocytes, such as the Müller cells of the retina. Star-shaped astrocytes that are associated with the axon portion of neurons which run through tracts, columns and funiculi (called the white matter) are called fibrous astrocytes. Other star-shaped astrocytes which are found in the nuclei associated with the cell bodies and dendrites (the gray matter) are called protoplasmic astrocytes. All astrocytes are involved with buffering the pH and controlling the microenvironment of the extracellular space surrounding neurons. The astrocytes that are found along dendrites and cell bodies surround synapses and are involved with removal of excess neurotransmitter, astrocytes buffer K^+ concentrations along axons and astrocytes are involved with providing neurons with their nutrients, growth hormones and removing waste products.

Astrocytes also help to form what is known as the blood brain barrier (BBB). The BBB is actually formed by tight junctions between endothelial cells lining the capillaries in the brain. These tight junctions prevent fluid from leaking out of blood vessels into the CNS tissue. However, astrocyte end-feet surround all blood vessels and help regulate what substances enter and leave the CNS. They also play an important role in the response to injury. Whenever the BBB is broken, astrocytes will undergo cell division (cell proliferation) and create a new barrier; often at the expense of neuronal integrity. For example, in conditions of stroke or spinal cord injury, broken blood vessels expose the CNS tissue to the blood. Astrocytes create a "wall" surrounding this breach, not caring if they damage functional neurons in the process. Controlling astrocyte proliferation after injury helps to retain some neural function. Finally, astrocytes are components of the CNS used for structural support and are involved with development; they create scaffolds along which neurons grow and migrate.

Oligodendrocytes are glial cells of the CNS that myelinate axons. The oligodendrocyte wraps its plasma membrane around the axon, repeatedly causing the cytoplasm of the oligodendrocyte to be extruded leaving behind layers and layers of lipid membrane. This creates a tight barrier on the axon and prevents exchange of material between the axon and the extracellular environment and is called myelin (See Figure 3.4). Special protein interactions between the axon and the oligodendrocyte delineate certain axons for myelination during development. A single oligodendrocyte can myelinate multiple axons. The myelination is not continuous along the length of the axon. Individual myelin sheaths will be separated by bare segments on the axon called nodes of Ranvier. The nodes of Ranvier are in contact with astrocytes and is the site of action potential propagation and ionic exchange. Myelination greatly increases the speed of the propagation of the action potential. Oligodendrocytes are also associated with non-myelinated axons. In this case, the oligodendrocyte simply covers the axon but does not wrap multiple times around the plasma membrane of the axon. The exact role of the oligodendrocyte on non-myelinated axons is not clear.

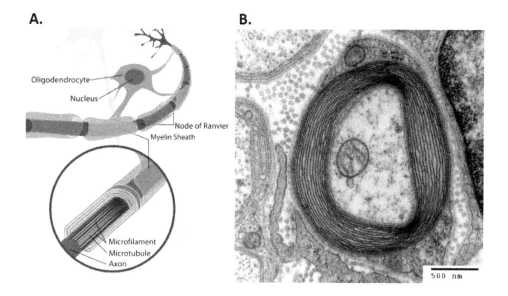

A.

Oligodendrocyte
Nucleus
Node of Ranvier
Myelin Sheath
Microfilament
Microtubule
Axon

B.

500 nm

Figure 3.4

Microglia are considered the immune cells of the CNS. Microglia phagocytose foreign debris at the site of injuries and function like a macrophage. During injury such as stroke or trauma, they release various cytokines and induce an inflammatory response.

Ependymal cells are the last type of glial cells found in the CNS. Ependymal cells line all of the ventricles and spaces found within the brain and spinal cord. Within the ventricles, 4 large open spaces in the brain, a specialized structure called the choroid plexus forms and secretes cerebral spinal fluid (CSF) which bathes the brain and spinal cord. The choroid plexus is formed by specialized ependymal cells and a capillary bed. The ependymal cells use fluid from plasma to produce and secrete the CSF. A separate choroid plexus can be found in each of the ventricles.

The PNS contains two types of glial cells; Schwann cells and satellite cells. Schwann cells are comparable to oligodendrocytes and are the glial cell responsible for myelination of axons found in the PNS. Unlike oligodendrocytes, Schwann cells can only form a single myelin sheath around a single axon. Schwann cell myelin sheaths also contain small pockets of cytoplasm at the edges of the myelin sheath, close to the Node of Ranvier called Schmidt-Lanterman clefts. The roles of these structure is not clear.

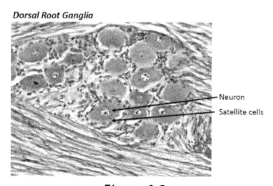

Dorsal Root Ganglia

Neuron
Satellite cells

Figure 3.5

Schwann cells also associate with non-myelinated axons and simply surround the axon with its cell. When Schwann cells interact with non-myelinated axons they can interact with multiple axons. Schwann cells also secrete a basal lamina over the outside surface of neurons which is thought to act as a barrier and protects the neurons from the extracellular environment.

Satellite cells are the only other type of glial cell found in the PNS. The satellite cells are analogous to the astrocyte and protect PNS neuron cell bodies found in ganglia (See Figure 3.5). The surround the cell bodies and dendrites and provide a barrier to the extracellular environment.

Structure of a peripheral nerve

Nerves are found in the PNS and are comprised of the axons of sensory neurons that project to the CNS as well as axons of motor neurons that project from the CNS to the PNS. Most nerves are considered mixed nerves because they contain both sensory and motor axons. A few exceptions can be found in the cranial nerves which may be either completely sensory, like the optic nerve or completely motor like the hypoglossal nerve. Around the outside of the axons in a nerve, the Schwann cell secretes a thin basal lamina which is covered by a small amount of thin connective tissue called the endoneurium. Within the nerve, axons that travel to similar locations are bundled together into fascicles which are surrounded by a tough connective sheath called the perineurium. The perineurium contains specialized fibroblasts that are also covered with a basal lamina. The fibroblasts of the perineurium form tight junctions with each other creating another barrier similar to the BBB. The fascicles are then grouped into the final peripheral nerve and surrounded by a tough collagen sheath called the epineurium. These connective tissue sheaths provide a structural and protective layer surrounding the neurons of the PNS.

Electrical properties of neurons

The nervous system plays a role in many activities throughout the body. For example, neurons are involved in 1) sensory reception and transduction, 2) controlling muscles and glands, 3) maintaining homeostasis 4) influencing organ functions, 5) controlling all mental activity, including emotion, thinking, learning, memory and 6) consciousness. In order to accomplish these wide range of diverse activities, the neurons in all locations use the same basic neural mechanism, neural transmission.

Specific changes in membrane potential can be elicited in the laboratory by injecting current into neurons. If the current makes the cell more negative, this is called a hyperpolarizing current. You can make a neuron more and more negative and nothing of significance will happen to the neuron. If you inject current and make the neuron more positive then it is called a depolarizing current. At some point, the threshold potential will be reached and an action potential will be elicited. The action potential is a very quick (~1 msec) rise in membrane potential which then returns back to rest. Even if you inject more positive current above the threshold current, the same action potential of the same magnitude will be triggered. Thus, action potentials are said to be "all-or-none," showing the same full action potential each time or none at all. Neurons produce action potentials only in their axons and the information is transferred to other neurons or target tissues across a synapse. On the receiving end, the tissues or neurons respond with a change in membrane potential which influences each target cell in a specific manner. The electrical properties of neurons are the direct result of differences in ionic concentrations across the cell membrane as well as the permeability of the membrane to the various ions.

Resting membrane potential

All cells in the body have a slightly negative resting membrane potential compared to the interstitial space. This is primarily due to the action of the Na^+/K^+ pump which can be found in virtually all cells and pumps 3 Na^+ ions out of the cell for every 2 K^+ ions that enter. This is considered an electrogenic pump because more positive ions leave the cell compared to those that enter the cell creating an electrical imbalance. This difference in voltage can be measured by placing an electrode directly inside a cell and comparing that voltage to an electrode placed outside of a cell; by convention the voltage outside of the cell is set to zero. The difference in voltage (or potential) is considered the membrane potential or the voltage of the membrane (V_m). Some tissues such as neurons and muscle are electrically excitable and they achieve this excitability, in part, by increasing the amount of charge difference across the cell membrane; i.e., having a very negative interior. This section will limit the discussion to neuron excitability, however, many of the same principles can be applied to muscles and will be covered in more detail in Chapter 5 and 6.

Figure 3.6

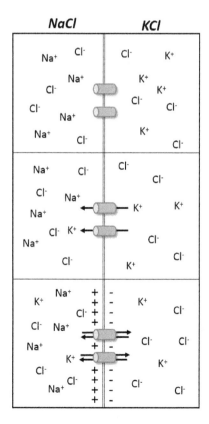

In neurons, the concentration of K^+, proteins and phosphates (PO_4^-) is relatively high in the intracellular compartment compared to the extracellular compartment, whereas the extracellular compartment is high in Na^+, Ca^{2+} and chloride (Cl^-) concentrations (See Table 3.1, on page 61). The cell achieves these gradients by having a cell membrane that is semi-permeable to various ions and proteins. Figure 3.6 demonstrates how a negative resting membrane potential can be achieved by simply making a membrane leaky to K^+. For example, if two chambers are separated by a semi-permeable membrane and chamber 1 (analogous to the outside of the cell) is filled with NaCl and chamber 2 (analogous to the inside of the cell) is filled with KCl and the membrane is permeable to only K^+, then K^+ will move down its concentration gradient toward the side filled with NaCl. As K^+ moves from compartment 2 to compartment 1, an electrical gradient begins to develop due to the removal of positive charge from compartment 2 leaving behind a negative charge. Thus, compartment 2 becomes more negative compared to compartment 1 which is becoming more positive due to the influx of positive ions. Eventually, the negative charge of compartment 2 will begin to attract positive charge and K^+ ions can flow through the leak channel toward compartment 2. This electrical gradient also influences the amount of K⁺ movement. Thus, it is easy to recognize that K⁺ movement is influenced by not only a concentration gradient, but also an electrical gradient. A similar situation occurs across the membranes of neurons and the membrane is selectively permeable to various ions which help to establish an electrical difference between the intracellular and extracellular compartments.

Neurons have a relatively negative interior compared to the extracellular compartment. This is achieved primarily due to the selective permeability of the membrane. The plasma membrane of neurons contains many leak channels for K⁺. As K⁺ leaks out of the cell down its strong concentration gradient, it leaves behind an interior filled with many proteins and with PO_4^- which create a negative interior. The membrane also contains the electrogenic Na⁺/K⁺ pump which leaves the interior slightly negative. Together these create a negative interior of neurons.

In neurons, each type of ion is influenced by both the concentration and electrical gradients that are established across a membrane. The electrical and chemical equilibrium for each ion across a cell membrane can be described using the Nernst equilibrium potential. The Nernst equilibrium potential for any particular permeable ion (X) is dependent on several factors including the gas constant (R), the absolute temperature (T), the Faraday constant (F), the valence of the particular ion (z), and the ratio of the ion (X) concentration gradient between the outside (out) and inside (in) of the membrane.

$$E_X = \frac{RT}{Fz} \ln \frac{[X]out}{[X]in}$$

Simplification of the equation can be achieved by changing the absolute temperature to room temperature 21°C and converting natural log to base ten log. The equation can be rewritten as:

$$E_X = \frac{58}{z} \log \frac{[X]out}{[X]in}$$

This simplified equation can be used to determine the driving forces for each individual ion related to neuronal function, being careful to include the valence of the ion. For example, in order to determine the Nernst equilibrium potential for K⁺ in a cell that has an internal K⁺ concentration of 400mM and an external K⁺ concentration of 20mM you would calculate:

$$E_{K+} = 58 \log \frac{[20]}{[400]}$$

Thus, the Nernst equilibrium potential for K⁺ is -75mV (the valence is +1 and therefore not an issue). Under these conditions, when the cell is permeable to K⁺, the K⁺ ions move down their electrical and chemical gradients (either in or out of cells) to achieve an internal membrane potential of -75mV. So at rest, if the cell has a measured V_m at -

70mV and a K⁺ channel opens, K⁺ will leave the cell and make the cell more negative (toward -75mV). The equilibrium potential is also known as the reversal potential, because if the cell was at resting at -80mV, if a K⁺ channel opened up, K⁺ would enter the cell to make the cell more positive (toward -75mV). This is because the electrochemical gradients for K⁺ are going to equilibrate at -75mV. In most neurons, cell membranes are relatively leaky for K⁺ due to the presence of special K⁺ leak channels, therefore the resting membrane potential of neurons is relatively negative (or close to the equilibrium potential for K⁺). The resting membrane potential of the cell does not equal the Nernst equilibrium potential for K⁺ because several other factors influence the resting membrane potential such as other ions and pumps like the Na⁺/K⁺ pump. The Nernst equilibrium potential for each ion can be calculated based on values obtained from Table 3.1. Values are presented for both mammals as well as the giant squid axon since the original experiments were performed using the giant squid axon and will be explained later (see *Action Potentials*). Be sure to consider the valance of the ion when making your calculations.

Table 3.1. The intracellular and extracellular concentrations (mM) of the major ions in the squid and mammalian systems.

ION	Intracellular	Extracellular
SQUID		
Potassium (K⁺)	400	20
Sodium (Na⁺)	50	440
Chloride (Cl⁻)	40-150	560
Calcium (Ca⁺⁺)	0.0001	10
MAMMAL		
Potassium (K⁺)	140	5
Sodium (Na⁺)	5-15	145
Chloride (Cl⁻)	4-30	110
Calcium (Ca⁺⁺)	0.0001	1-2

In neurons, the ions that have the most influence on resting membrane potential are Na⁺, K⁺ and Cl⁻. The combined effect of the various ion equilibrium potentials combined with their permeabilities can be described using the Goldman-Hodgkin-Katz equation. This equation describes the V_m at rest and considers the electrochemical equilibrium for each ion and it's permeability at rest.

$$V_m = 58 \log \frac{P_K[K^+]out + P_{Na+}[Na^+]out + P_{Cl}[Cl^-]in}{P_K[K^+]in + P_{Na+}[Na^+]in + P_{Cl}[Cl^-]_{in}}$$

The Goldman-Hodgkin-Katz equation takes into account the permeability of all the major ions that influence the membrane potential. Ca2⁺ is not included because it is virtually impermeable to the membrane. The permeability ratio of each ion is shown below.

$$P_{K^+} : P_{Na^+} : P_{Cl^-} = 1 : 0.04 : 0.45$$

Thus the resting V_m is primarily dependent upon the permeability to K^+. The influence of Cl^- is present but its equilibrium potential is negative and close to resting V_m and there is less permeability, therefore not a large influence. The Goldman-Hodgkin-Katz equation only describes the resting membrane potential of a neuron at steady state, i.e., not changing. Changes in the voltage (V) of the membrane potential are accomplished by the movement of ions (current, I) across the membrane through channels which have a certain resistance (R). This relationship is describe by Ohm's Law.

$$V = IR$$

Therefore, when an ion channel opens, ions flow through the channels which maintain a certain resistance and generate a current which will change the membrane voltage. Another way to think of the resistance of the channel is to think about how many ions travel through the channel i.e., its conductance (G). Resistance of the channel is equal to the inverse of the conductance (G) of the channel.

$$R = \frac{1}{G}$$

So when a membrane get stimulated, membrane channels open (or close) and result in a change in the ionic movement across the membrane. For any given ion (X), the amount and direction of ion flow (I) through a membrane is equal to its driving force (the membrane potential minus the equilibrium potential for that ion) times its conductance (G).

$$I_x = (V_m - V_x) \, x \, G_x$$

Thus, current will increase as the driving force or the conductance of an ion increases and vice versa.

Cable properties of neurons

Current flow across cell membranes and throughout the cytoplasm of neurons are due to passive properties that are intrinsic to all areas of the neuron; the dendrite, cell body and the axon. Recall that the cell membrane is composed of a lipid bilayer and is extremely thin. At rest, when the cell's interior is relatively negative compared to the positive exterior, there is a charge gradient that builds up and is stored across the membrane. In this regard, the membrane acts as a capacitor and stores energy. Any change in charge or current flow across the membrane utilizes this stored energy. If current is injected into a neuron, two different currents occur. The ionic current is the physical movement of the ions across the membrane from inside to outside and the capacitive current is the movement of the ions at the interior and exterior surface of the lipid membrane. Together, the time that it takes the ionic current and the capacitive current to occur is called the time constant (τ or tau). Tau is defined as the time it takes the signal to decay1/e (e equals the base of the natural logarithm 2.718...) or 37% of its starting value. The time constant is influenced by the resistance (R) and the capacitance (C).

$$\tau = RC$$

Thus, in large neurons which tend to have a lower resistance and a large capacitance the time constant tends to be shorter. And in smaller neurons with a higher resistance and a smaller capacitance, the time constant tends to be longer. In general, normal values for tau are in the range of 1 to 20 msec; i.e., each individual neuron has a different time constant. The shorter the time constant the quicker the change in current flow across the membrane.

Current also flows through the cytoplasm of neurons along their length. As current flows down the length of a dendrite, cell body, or an axon, it loses charge by passively diffusing away from its original site. Remember that diffusion carries particles in all directions. Thus, axons, cell bodies, or dendrites with a short length constant (λ or lambda) do not carry a charge a long distance before leaking out. Lambda or the length constant is dependent upon the resistance of the membrane (r_m) and the resistance of the intracellular cytoplasm (r_i) as well as the resistance of the extracellular interstitial fluid (r_o).

$$\lambda = \sqrt{\frac{r_m}{r_o + r_i}}$$

Therefore, to increase the flow of ions down the length of an axon or dendrite, the resistance of the membrane should be as high as possible which will decrease ionic loss across the membrane, and the resistance of the cytoplasm and the interstitial should be as low as possible. Myelinated axons are typically of large diameter such that the myelin sheath increases the membrane resistance and the large diameter decreases the cytoplasm resistance and therefore greatly increases the speed of conduction.

The time constant and length constant are passive features of all neurons and influence the spread of ions across the membrane and through the cytosol. These passive properties influence the speed of graded potentials, receptor potentials and some of the underlying properties of action potentials.

Changes in membrane potential

At rest, neurons have a negative resting membrane potential. In order to elicit cellular communication, the membrane potential of neurons is changed in order to cause specific cellular responses. The membrane potential can change in response to changing the permeability of K^+, Na^+, Cl^- or even Ca^{2+}. The permeability to each ion can either increase or decrease and the cell responds by becoming more positive or more negative. In general, if the cell becomes more positive, this is referred to as cellular depolarization, whereas if the cell becomes more negative, this is referred to as hyperpolarization. These terms are applied to describe when the cell is actively changing voltage in either direction. Sometimes more specialized terms can be used for describing the phases of an action potential.

Changes in resting membrane potential can occur by altering the K^+ concentration gradient or by changing K^+ permeability. Since the resting membrane potential is greatly influenced by the presence of K^+ leak channels, any change in the K^+ concentration gradient will alter the resting membrane potential. For example, if the extracellular concentration of K^+ increases (in other words, there is less gradient between the inside and outside) then less K^+ will leave the cell and the cell will depolarize or become more positive. The opposite happens when the K^+ extracellular concentration decreases; more K^+ will leave the cell through leak channels causing the cell to hyperpolarize or become more negative. Similarly, any increased permeability to K^+ will alter the membrane potential. Opening a ligand-gated K^+ channel or even a voltage-gated K^+ channel will hyperpolarize the membrane (more K^+ leaves the cell). Or closing a K^+ channel will result in cellular depolarization (more K^+ stays inside the cell).

Changes in membrane permeability to Na^+ will also alter the membrane potential. Opening a Na^+ channel will result in the influx of Na^+ into the cell and result in cellular depolarization. This is because there is a strong driving force for Na^+ to enter the cell; a strong concentration gradient and a strong electrical gradient. The equilibrium potential for Na^+ is ~+55-+65mV. Closing a Na^+ channel will decrease the influx and result in hyperpolarization. Unlike K^+ however, changing the extracellular concentration of Na^+ will not alter the resting membrane potential. This is because the cell is relatively impermeable to Na^+ at rest, therefore altering its values have no effect on resting membrane potential.

Changes in the permeability to Cl^- can also change the resting membrane potential. However, in the case of Cl^- the equilibrium potential is negative and so opening the Cl^- channel can result in a slight depolarization or a hyperpolarization, but the membrane potential remains at a negative value.

Changing the permeability to Ca^{2+} also results in cellular depolarization. Ca^{2+} concentration and electrical gradients favor the movement of Ca^{2+} into the cell. In regards to membrane potential, Ca^{2+} depolarizes cells. However, Ca^{2+} is an important cell signaling molecule and influences cells in many other ways, such as promoting exocytosis or initiating muscle contraction.

Graded potentials

A graded potential is simply a small change in potential (voltage) that is typically initiated at a synapse which decays over distance. The amount of voltage change is dependent on how many channels open and how long they remain open allowing ions to enter or leave the neuron. For example, if you open a ligand-gated Na^+ channel, a small amount of Na^+ would enter the cell causing the cell to become more positive. The ligand-gated channel does not stay open for long and so you only get a certain quantity of positive charge entering the cell. If you open 20 channels, more Na^+ will enter the cell and the cell will become more positive and so on. Thus, the size of the potential varies in size or in other words is graded. Graded potentials vary in amplitude, they are localized change in charge and they decay over distance – they can occur in all regions of the neuron; the dendrites, cell body or the axon. Graded potentials can be positive as was just explained or they can be inhibitory. For example, if a K^+ channel opened, K^+ would leave the cell and the cell would become more negative. Graded potentials are also called synaptic potentials because they occur at synapses. (see *Synapses*).

Receptor potentials

A receptor potential is also a small change in potential that decays over time, however, receptor potentials are triggered by a specific stimulus and are found on one end of a long axon of sensory neurons. Our senses are detected by various types of stimuli that directly open a channel (not at a synapse). For example, mechanosensory receptors in the skin may open by directly stretching a receptor and causing Na^+ channels to open, or a chemoreceptor on the tongue might act by a molecule binding to a receptor and causing a channel to open. Once a channel opens and positive charge enters the cell, this may initiate an action potential directly on the axon. These receptor potentials are found in sensory neurons (see Chapter 4).

Action potentials

Neurons communicate with other neurons or cells via the action potential. The cellular mechanisms underlying the action potential was described by Alan Hodgkin and Andrew Huxley. Hodgkin and Huxley started their experiments in the 1930's but were interrupted by World War II and didn't finish and publish their work until the 1950's. Hodgkin was first introduced to the squid giant axon during a Fellowship to Woods Hole, MA USA. Hodgkin and Huxley to advantage of the giant axon of the squid as a model to study neuronal function. Because of its extremely large size, intracellular recordings could be accomplished with relative ease. They were able to finish their studies after the war in Cambridge, England.

Hodgkin and Huxley (1952) originally used a technique called the voltage clamp technique to explore the membrane properties of the giant squid axon when they changed the membrane potential. This technique allowed the researchers to inject current into the neuron and "clamp" the cell membrane at a certain voltage. When this was done, the researchers could measure what happened to the membrane potential. Hodgkin and Huxley found that when they depolarized the squid axon, two types of currents were activated, i.e., they were voltage-dependent. If the channel was a ligand-gated channel, nothing should happen to the membrane if you changed the membrane voltage. Figure 3.7 (on the next page) shows a graph similar to what Hodgkin and Huxley recorded. As the membrane was depolarized to increasing values, they saw a rapid increase in the Na^+ conductance that always turned off even though the voltage was still being applied. We now know that a voltage-gated Na^+ channel opens quickly during depolarization and it will stop functioning, or inactivate, a short time after opening. When the membrane was clamped at a depolarized state, the permeability to potassium increased. We now know that this is due to the opening of voltage-gated K⁺ channels. These channels tend to open slower than the voltage-gated Na⁺ and did not shut off during the depolarization state.

Action potentials are specific changes in membrane potential that originate in the axon of neurons due to the presence of voltage-gated channels. Voltage-gated channels are only found in the axon and therefore action potentials ONLY occur in axons and NOT the dendrites or cell bodies of neurons. The action potential has several characteristic phases as was shown by

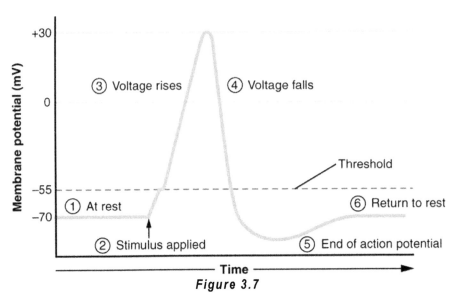

Figure 3.7

Hodgkin and Huxley's original work using the giant squid axon. At rest, the resting membrane potential is negative due to K⁺ leak channels, some permeability to leak Cl⁻ channels, and the Na⁺/K⁺ pump (Figure 3.7-1). At rest, the membrane potential can be calculated using the Goldman-Hodgkin-Katz equation. A small positive current inside the cell (graded potential or receptor potential) can activate voltage-gated Na⁺ channels causing them to open (Figure 3.7-2). There are a large concentration of voltage-gated Na⁺ channels located at the initial segment within the axon hillock. If enough positive charge (~-60mV) reaches the axon hillock to open a significant number of voltage-gated Na⁺ channels, Na⁺ will move down its concentration gradient into the cell causing the cell to quickly become more positive (Figure 3.7-3). This will activate and open more voltage-gated Na⁺ channels. The Na⁺ channels are fast and open quickly causing rapid cell depolarization and the upstroke of the action potential. The voltage-gated Na⁺ channels also quickly inactivate resulting in repolarization of the membrane back toward resting membrane potential. Inactivation of the Na⁺ channel is due to an intracellular globular portion of the channel that swings and blocks the intracellular side of the pore and Na⁺ movement ceases (Figure 3.8).

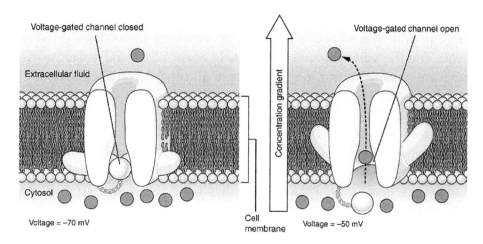

Figure 3.8

In the giant squid axon (an unmyelinated axon), there are also voltage-gated K⁺ channels which open slowly. The K⁺ channel also activates during depolarization (around -30mV), but the opening is slow and K⁺ will leave the cell down its concentration gradient. Once the voltage-gated Na⁺ channel is inactivated and the K⁺ channel is open, the cell will begin to repolarize (See Figure 3.7-4). The K⁺ channels are slow to close and therefore the membrane potential will approach the Nernst equilibrium potential for K⁺ and the cell will become more negative relative to resting membrane potential (See Figure 3.7-5). This phase is often called the afterpotential. The Na⁺ channels will begin to return to their original closed state as the cell becomes more negative; the gate closes and the inactivation gate opens. The K⁺ channels slowly close and resting membrane will be reestablished (See Figure 3.7-6).

If a small stimulus or a subthreshold stimulus is applied to an axon and not enough positive charge is given to open a sufficient number of voltage-gated Na⁺ channels, a graded potential will occur and the signal simply decays over time. If a larger stimulus (another graded potential) is given and a sufficient number of voltage-gated Na⁺ channels open, an action potential will be elicited. The average threshold value is approximately -60mV. If a larger stimulus is applied to the neuron, a suprathreshold stimulus, an action potential will fire, but the size of the action potential will be the same as initiated by a simple threshold stimulus. This is because during an action potential, all available voltage-gated channels are activated and contribute to the overall shape of the action potential. The action potential is said to be "all-or-none" phenomenon. That is, there will either be a complete action potential that gets initiated at the initial segment or no action potential at all.

Once an action potential is generated it gets propagated down the entire axon. This occurs due to the placement and function of voltage-gated channels along the length of the axon. A voltage-gated Na⁺ channel opens due to influx of positive charge which results in the influx of Na⁺ (more positive charge), which opens more channels and results in more influx of positive charge, etc... Once the action potential starts, a domino effect of opening more channels is created due to the positive feedback mechanism of voltage-gated Na⁺ channels.

During the time that an action potential is occurring, the voltage-gated Na^+ channels open, inactivate and the voltage-gated K^+ channels open. When these events occur, there is no way to activate another action potential since all of the available channels are in use. This period of time is called the absolute refractory period. After this time period, when the voltage-gated K^+ channels are still open, but some of the Na^+ channels have returned to their original state, it is possible to activate another action potential, but the strength of the stimulus must be greater. This is because the membrane is still permeable to K^+ which drives the membrane potential towards the Nernst equilibrium potential for K^+ and the cell is harder to depolarize. It is also because there may not be as many Na^+ channels that have returned to their closed state. The presence of refractory periods ensures the each action potential is a separate entity and is separated by a pause.

In invertebrates like the giant squid axon, evolutionary pressures caused the size of neurons to enlarge in order to speed up the transmission of action potentials. The larger the diameter of the axon, the lower the resistance, thus, the greater the speed of the action potential. Myelination or the wrapping of a membrane around an axon also evolved to decrease membrane resistance. Myelination appears to have evolved independently in multiple groups; Annelida, Arthropoda, and in Chordates. The myelin that forms in each of these groups comes from different types of cells and show different levels of function. In vertebrates, myelin sheaths are produced by oligodendrocytes in the CNS and Schwann cells in the PNS and function by increasing the speed of transmission of action potentials while allowing neurons to remain relatively small. Myelination increases the resistance of the membrane and prevents charge leakage across the cell membrane thus increasing the length constant.

In vertebrates, each myelin sheath covers a distance of approximately 1 mm along the axon and is separated from another myelin sheath at the node of Ranvier. Each node of Ranvier contains a high concentration of voltage-gated Na^+ channels (~1000-2000 channels/μm^2 at the node of Ranvier versus ~2-200 channels/μm^2 in non-myelinated axons) which is important in recharging the membrane at each node. In axons, the ionic current or local current (the movement of Na^+ through the cytosol) can only extend a maximum of 2-3 mm in length before dissipating and losing its strength. The length of myelin sheaths (~1 mm) is sufficient to allow enough positive current to reach the next node of Ranvier and activate enough fast, voltage-gated Na^+ channels to recharge the cell membrane by creating another influx of Na^+ which propagates the action potential.

The profile of the action potential in myelinated axons of vertebrates is slightly different than that of action potentials of non-myelinated axons. This is due to the specialized arrangement of voltage-gated channels. Voltage-gated Na^+ channels are densely located within the nodes of Ranvier. On each side of the node of Ranvier, there is an area called the paranodal region in which the individual ends of the myelin sheath make contact with the axon. There are very few channels in the paranodal region. Just past the paranodal region, under the myelin sheath, is a region that is rich with voltage-gated K^+ channels, the juxtaparanodal region. The middle region of the myelin sheath is simply called the internodal region. In myelinated axons, the voltage-gated K^+ channels do not play a role in action potential generation and propagation, and only the voltage-gated Na+ channels are involved. Therefore, the depolarization phase of the action potential is due to the rapid opening of the voltage-gated Na^+ channels and then the inactivation of the Na^+ channel results in the repolarization phase and the return to resting membrane potential. In demyelinating or dysmyelinating diseases such as multiple sclerosis, the paranodal regions become leaky and expose the juxtaparanodal regions and the voltage-gated K^+ channels resulting in hyperpolarization. This creates problems with action potential propagation and often results in neuronal dysfunction.

In vertebrates, axons are characterized based on their size and degree of myelination. Type A fibers are the fastest and they have the largest diameters and are heavily myelinated. Type A fibers are commonly found in somatic motor neurons and most sensory neurons and conduct action potentials at rates of 15-120 m/sec. Type B fibers are medium-diameter sized axons which are lightly myelinated. They are commonly found in part of the autonomic nervous system and conduct action potentials at rates of 3-15 m/sec. Finally, the smallest sized axons are called Type C fibers and they are unmyelinated. They are also commonly found in different parts of the autonomic nervous system and conduct action potentials the slowest; 2 m/sec or less.

Synapses

Synapses are specialized cellular connections that can be found between

> - neuron and another neuron
> - a neuron and a muscle cell
> - a neuron and a gland cell
> - a muscle cell and another muscle cell.

In the late 1800s, there was great controversy and debate surrounding the question of how nerves and muscles (skeletal or located in various organs) interacted. Two conflicting theories arose regarding neuronal function; the Neuron Doctrine stated that neurons are individual entities which influence other tissues and the Reticular Theory suggested that the brain and nerves acted as a single network that directly connected to nerves and tissues much like the electrical wiring in a house performs. In 1906, the Nobel Prize was awarded to Camillo Golgi and Santiago Ramón y Cajal for their "work on the structure of the nervous system" despite the fact that Golgi believed in the Reticular Theory and Ramón y Cajal believed in the Neuron Doctrine. Since that early debate, we know now that neurons are individual entities and that they can communicate with other cells via two routes; across a chemical synapse in which two cells interact via chemical mediators as well as directly through an electrical coupling between two cells.

Electrical Synapses

An electrical synapse is a direct connection between two cells and allows ions to freely flow from one cell to another cell. These connections are called gap junctions (Figure 3.9). Essentially, a gap junction is a large pore found on each cell and joined such that a large gap occurs between the two cells. On each cell, the pore or channel is formed by 6 individual proteins called connexins. The 6 connexins form the channel protein called a connexon. In most

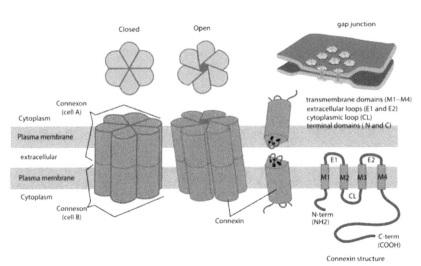

Figure 3.9

cases, the purpose of having a large gap is to allow ions to freely flow from one cell to the next which will ensure that if an action potential occurs in one cell, an action potential will also occur in all cells that are connected to it. In tissues like the heart or the smooth muscle of a blood vessel, it is easy to imagine that if one cell fires an action potential and causes contraction of the muscle, you would want all of the cells to contract and work together. Gap junctions ensure that this will happen and all of the muscle cells will contract as a single unit. Gap junctions are also found in the CNS where large collections of neurons work together synchronously to perform functions. Electrical synapses function bi-directionally, that is, information can be transferred in either direction.

Chemical Synapses

The chemical synapse is a specialized 'connection' between a neuron and another cell (neuron, muscle or gland cell). In a chemical synapse one cell releases chemical messengers, neurotransmitters, to influence another cell and cause a very specific response (Figure 3.10). The presynaptic side of the synapse contains neurotransmitters which are produced, stored in vesicles and released into a synaptic cleft. The neurotransmitters diffuse across the synaptic cleft and bind to receptors located on the postsynaptic to generate a postsynaptic response of the receiving cell. In general, the actions at a chemical synapse occur in a series of steps.

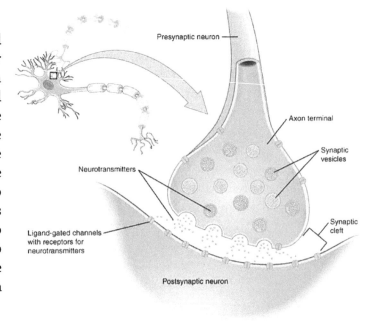

Figure 3.10

4) As the action potential moves down the axon to the end terminal, the influx of positive charge from Na^+ inside the cell will cause voltage-gated Ca^{2+} channels to open at the end terminal of the axon.

5) Ca^{2+} moves down its concentration gradient and rapidly enters the presynaptic end-terminal.

6) In the end-terminals of neurons, Ca^{2+} interacts with synaptic vesicles to promote exocytosis.

7) Neurotransmitters are released into the synaptic cleft and diffuse across the synaptic cleft.

8) Neurotransmitters bind to specific receptors located on the post-synaptic membrane to initiate a cellular response.

Transmission across a synapse is only in one direction, from the presynaptic cell to the postsynaptic cell. Transmission at a synapse requires 5 essential steps. The pre-synaptic neuron must 1) synthesize neurotransmitter, 2) neurotransmitters must be concentrated and packaged into vesicles. The neuron must 3) release the neurotransmitter which 4) bind to receptors and trigger some response in the post-synaptic neuron. Finally, 5) the action of the neurotransmitter must be terminated.

Synthesis of neurotransmitters can occur in two locations within neurons, either in the cell body or in the end-terminal. Large poly-peptides such as opioids, substance P, and

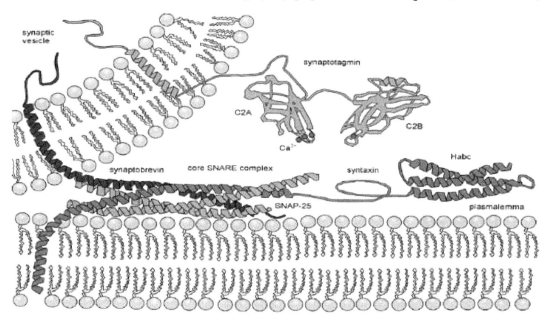

Figure 3.11

neuropeptide Y are produced by the process of normal protein synthesis which occurs in the nucleus, the ribosomes and the Golgi apparatus and are located in the cell body. Neuropeptides are packaged into vesicles and transported down the axon using retrograde transport mechanisms. Small molecules, like acetylcholine, glutamate, GABA, and serotonin are produced and packaged into vesicles from endosomes in the end terminal. Some neurons produce multiple types of neurotransmitters and are stored into different vesicles.

The vesicles that store peptides are large and in electron microscopy appear dark and therefore are called large dense core vesicles. The vesicles that carry smaller molecules tend to be small, clear vesicles. Vesicles cycle through various stages before exocytosis can occur. Vesicles are docked and primed before fusing with the plasma membrane through a series of steps that are only partially understood.

Exocytosis is the fusion of an intracellular vesicle with a cell membrane causing the contents of the vesicle to be released to the outside of the cell (See Figure 3.11). In all cells, exocytosis requires Ca^{2+}. In neurons as the action potential moves down the axon, the influx of Na^+ cause voltage-gated Ca^{2+} to open at the end terminal. Many of these voltage-gated Ca^{2+} channels are found in tight association with the docked vesicles. Ca^{2+} moves into the cell and interacts with synaptotagmin, a protein found on the vesicular membrane. Once this happens helical proteins found on the vesicle membrane, such as syntaptobrevin, can interact with helical proteins on the plasma membrane such as syntaxin and SNAP-25. The helical proteins on the vesicle intertwine with the proteins on the plasma membrane pulling the vesicular membrane close to the plasma membrane and induce fusion. Fusion of the membranes releases the neurotransmitters into the synaptic cleft.

Neurotransmitters move by simple diffusion and are free to interact with specific receptors on the post-synaptic membrane. A receptor that is also a channel is called a ligand-gated ion channel or an ionotropic receptor (See Figure 3.12). Alternatively, a neurotransmitter may bind to a receptor that activates a particular metabolic pathway to ultimately cause a post-synaptic response or a change in membrane permeability. These receptors are called metabotropic receptors and most utilize G-proteins as an intermediary step that leads to an ion channel opening or closing (Figure 3.11). These are called the G-protein coupled receptors (GPCRs) which were reviewed in Chapter 2.

The ultimate effect of a neurotransmitter at a chemical synapse is to open or close an ion channel and cause a change in the postsynaptic membrane potential, or in other words to produce a postsynaptic potential (PSP). If the PSP is excitatory and results

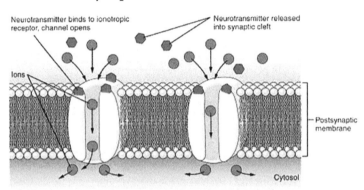

(a) Direct activation brings about immediate response

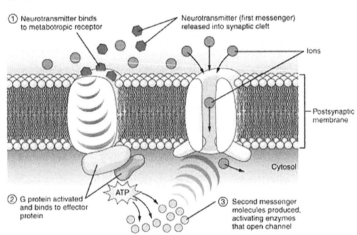

(b) Indirect activation involves a prolonged response, amplified over time

Figure 3.12

in cellular depolarization of the postsynaptic membrane and drives the membrane toward threshold, this is called an excitatory postsynaptic potential or EPSP. If the PSP is inhibitory or hyperpolarizes the postsynaptic membrane or keeps the membrane away from threshold, this is called an inhibitory postsynaptic potential or IPSP. The sum of all of the EPSPs and the IPSPs on a neuron will increase or decrease the likelihood that an action potential will be produced in the axon of the postsynaptic neuron.

Consider a situation in which a neurotransmitter leads to the opening of a Na^+ channel on the post-synaptic membrane. Na^+ will rush inside the postsynaptic cell causing depolarization. This graded response is called an EPSP and will decay with certain time and length constant for a given neuron. At a different synapse, a neurotransmitter might cause a K^+ channel to open and K^+ will go down its concentration gradient and will leave the cell resulting in an IPSP. In most synapses which result in the opening of a Cl^- channel, an IPSP will occur independent of the direction that Cl^- flows. For example, if the $E_{Cl^-} \sim -65mv$ and the resting membrane potential is -70mV, then opening a Cl^- channel will cause chloride ions to leave the cell and the membrane potential will become more positive or depolarize. How can this be inhibitory? Remember that the cell will depolarize only to -65mV which will maintain the cell at a negative value. The cell will NOT depolarize past threshold and is therefore not excitatory. During certain conditions however, Cl- can be excitatory if the opening of the Cl- results in cellular depolarization leading to threshold and the development of action potentials.

Neurotransmitters left in the synaptic cleft will continue to activate receptors whenever they come into contact. Therefore the action of the neurotransmitter must be terminated quickly. There are multiple mechanisms by which neurotransmitters are removed from the synaptic cleft. In some synapses, enzymes are present in the synaptic cleft which quickly breakdown neurotransmitters. In many synapses, transporters are present, usually on the presynaptic terminal, to transport the neurotransmitter back into the end-terminal for reuse or enzymatic digestion. In the CNS, astrocytes are located on the edges of synapses and also transport and enzymatically breakdown neurotransmitters. Each specific synapse and neurotransmitter has specific mechanisms in place for neurotransmitter removal and termination (see *Neurotransmitters and Receptors*).

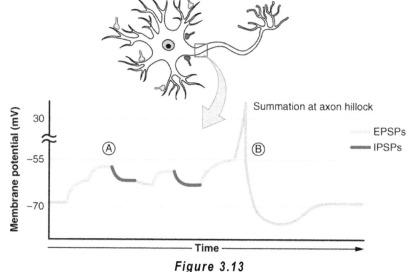

Figure 3.13

Thousands or hundreds of thousands of inputs make contact with a single neuron and influence whether an action potential will be initiated or not. When one neuron projects its end terminal toward another neuron, it can make a synapse at the dendrite (axodendritic connections) or at the cell soma (axosomatic connection) or at the end-terminal of the other neuron (axoaxonic connection). All of the EPSPs and IPSPs from the axodendritic and axosomatic synapses are integrated at the axon hillock and if the membrane potential is above threshold, the voltage-gated Na^+ channels in the initial segment will open and an action potential will fire. The graded potentials, the EPSPs and IPSPs, can add together or summate (Figure 3.13). For example, if a presynaptic neuron fires a single action potential and causes a single EPSP, a small graded potential occurs. If the presynaptic neuron fires several action potentials in rapid succession, the amount of neurotransmitter that is released into the synaptic cleft increases. This allows neurotransmitter to bind to receptors for longer periods of times before the neurotransmitter is removed and the size of the EPSP enlarges. This addition of multiple EPSPs arising from a single source is called temporal summation. Spatial summation is another form of combining graded potentials. If two neurons (A and B) make excitatory contacts onto another neuron C and both A and B fire action potentials simultaneously, then neuron C will receive two graded potentials in two different locations or spaces on its neuron. If the neurons A and B are spatially near each other on neuron C and the length constants long enough then the two EPSPs or the current from the two EPSPs will summate. The idea of summation occurs with IPSPs as well. For example, if two neurons fire action potentials and elicits an EPSP and an IPSP, the two will add and can negate each other.

Each individual neuron receives information from many, many different inputs arising from different locations. This is a form of convergence. For example, neurons that control blood pressure receive information from many different areas of the body and these inputs converge and are integrated to determine an appropriate motor response. Divergence also occurs in the nervous system and one neuron can influence many different neurons. For example a pain sensory neuron makes projections to reflex pathways to withdraw a limb away from the pain as well as project to cortical areas involved in conscious awareness of pain.

Action potentials and graded potentials are both changes in membrane potential, however, there are distinct differences in their specific characteristics (See Table 3.2, on the next page). The amplitude and duration of the action potential remains the same every time an action potential fires, whereas graded potentials vary in height and length depending on the number of ligand-gated channels getting activated. The action potential is propagated the entire length of the axon whereas, graded potentials fade over distance and can be found in any area on the neurons (dendrite, cell soma, or axon). The action potential is always depolarizing and the graded potentials can be depolarizing or hyperpolarizing. Finally the action potential is an all-or-none phenomenon whereas the graded potentials can undergo spatial and temporal summation and change shape as they travel across the neuron.

Table 3.2. Differences between graded potentials and action potentials

Property	Graded Potential	Action Potential
Amplitude	Varies in height	Constant
Duration	Variable 1ms to >1sec	~1msec
Propagation	Fades with distance	All or none
Polarity	Depolarizing or hyperpolarizing	Depolarizing
Interactions	Spatial and temporal summation	Single, unitary (no interaction)
Location on neuron	Dendrite, cell body and axon	Axon

CHAPTER 3, SECTION 1 – SUMMARY

➤ The nervous system controls all thoughts, emotions, behavior, movement and regulation of internal structures and organs.

➤ Nervous systems first originated in the invertebrates and can be found in Cnidaria. The first neural systems were simple and many consist of simple reflex arcs with a sensory neuron, interneurons and a motor neuron.

➤ In vertebrates the nervous system is divided into two major categories, the central nervous system (CNS) which is found in the brain and spinal cord and the peripheral nervous system (PNS) which is all neural tissue that is found outside of the CNS.

➤ Neurons are the cells that send and receive information. They sense external and internal stimuli, they integrate information stored in neuronal networks and they initiate motor responses.

➤ Neurons are highly structured cells with a cell body with dendrites that receive information and an axon which communicates to other cells. Neurons can be classified based on their shapes (psueudounipolar, bipolar and multipolar), the type of neurotransmitters that they synthesize (e.g., dopaminergic or catecholaminergic, based on their function (sensory afferents or motor efferents) or based on the locations of their projections (commissural neurons connect left and right sides of the cerebral hemispheres).

➤ There are four types of glial cells in the CNS. The astrocytes are involved with forming the blood-brain-barrier, they buffer the pH and control the microenvironment surrounding neurons, and they play important roles in immune responses within the CNS. Oligodendrocytes myelinate axons in the CNS which helps to increase the speed of action potentials. Microglia are also glial cells of the CNS and they are primarily involved with cleaning cellular debris and initiating immune responses in the CNS. The last type of glial cell in the CNS is the ependymal cells which line ventricles and produce the cerebral spinal fluid which bathes the entire brain and spinal cord and provides cushion and support for the tissues.

➤ In the PNS, there are two types of glial cells. The Schwann cells myelinate axons in the PNS and the satellite cells surround the cell bodies of neurons in ganglia and play a protective role.

➤ The resting membrane is established by creating specific ionic gradients across the plasma membrane of neurons. Neurons contain large quantities of intracellular proteins with negative charge and a high concentration of K^+. Na^+ and Cl^- are found in high concentration outside cells.

➤ The Nernst equilibrium describes the electrical and chemical equilibrium that is established across the plasma membrane for each ion.

➤ The Goldman-Hodgkin-Katz equation describes the resting membrane potential; it takes into account the Nernst equilibrium potential for multiple ions as well as their relative permeability.

➤ Passive current flow in neurons can be described in terms of a time constant (tau, τ), the time it takes the ionic current and the capacitive current to change, as well as a length constant (lambda, λ), the time it takes current to flow down the length of the dendrite, cell body or axon.

➤ Graded potentials are small changes in membrane potential that decay over distance. They change with a specific time and length constant and occur on all regions of the neuron, the dendrites, cell bodies and axons.

➤ Receptor potentials are a type of graded potential that is found in the special endings of sensory neurons. They influence the frequency of action potentials of the sensory neuron.

➤ Action potentials are only generated in axons and are all-or-none phenomenon. They occur only if a threshold depolarization is reached. The action potential has a depolarization phase, a repolarization phase and an after-hyperpolarization phase. An action potential leads to the release of neurotransmitters at the end-terminal.

➤ Synapses are connections between a neuron and another neuron, or muscle cell, or gland cell, or between muscles cells.

➤ An electrical synapse is also known as a gap junction. The channel allows ions to flow freely from one cell to another cell and action potentials can spread in either direction.

➢ A chemical synapse is the Ca^{2+} dependent release of neurotransmitters from the post-synaptic membrane which acts on receptors located on the post-synaptic membrane.

➢ An EPSP is a slight depolarizing graded potential on the post-synaptic membrane in response to release of neurotransmitters.

➢ An IPSP is a slight hyperpolarizing graded potential on the post-synaptic membrane in response to the release of neurotransmitters.

➢ Summation of all graded potentials from many inputs determine whether an action potential will be initiated in the post-synaptic membrane.

Section 2 - Neurotransmitters and Receptors

There are hundreds of different types of neurotransmitters in the body. The main classes for known neurotransmitters are acetylcholine (ACh), biogenic amines, amino acids, neuropeptides, gases, and purines. Most neurotransmitters have multiple types of receptors that are specifically localized at each synapse (Table 3.3). The interaction between the neurotransmitter and the receptor at a given synapse determines the specific response of the target tissue. This section will review some of the more common types of neurotransmitters and their receptors found in the CNS and the PNS.

Table 3.3. Some common neurotransmitters and their receptors. Notice that some neurotransmitters have both ionotropic and metabotropic receptors whereas others only have one type of receptor.

Neurotransmitter	Ionotropic Receptor	Metabotropic receptor
Acetylcholine (ACh)	Nicotinic AChR	Muscarinic AChR
Glutamate	AMPA, NMDA, kainate	mGluR
GABA	$GABA_A$ $GABA_C$	$GABA_B$
Glycine	Glycine R	—
Serotonin (5-HT)	5-HT3	5-HT1,2,4-7
Norepinephrine (NE)	—	α adrenergic, β adrenergic
Epinephrine (Epi)	—	α adrenergic, β adrenergic
Dopamine	—	D1 – D5
Histamine	—	H1 – H4
Purines	P_2X	P_2Y, adenosine

Acetylcholine

Neurons that produce ACh can be found in both the PNS and the CNS. In the PNS, ACh is the most common neurotransmitter and can be found at all neuromuscular junctions (between α-motor neuron and a skeletal muscle cell), between the pre and post ganglionic neurons of the autonomic nervous system, and in the post-ganglionic neurons of the parasympathetic division of the autonomic nervous system. In the CNS, cholinergic neurons can be found in multiple locations including brainstem reticular neurons that project to the thalamus and multiple locations. In the spinal cord, the pre-ganglionic cell bodies of the autonomic nervous system arise from the intermediolateral cell column found in the thoracic, lumbar and sacral regions.

In 1920, Otto Loewi designed the experiment that first demonstrated that synaptic transmission occurs by the release of a chemical mediator across a synapse. Loewi set up an experimental protocol that used two separate chambers through which fluid could flow from one chamber to the next. The first chamber contained a frog heart which was innervated with an intact vagus nerve. The chamber contained a second frog heart with its nerves cut or denervated. The frog heart can be removed from the body and it will continue to spontaneously beat due to the presence of pacemaker cells which are able to spontaneously depolarize and cause the heart to contract. When Loewi stimulated the vagus nerve in chamber 1, the heart rate began to slow down. After a short delay, the solution from chamber 1 began to bathe the heart in chamber 2 and that heart also began to slow down. This demonstrated that something was being released from the vagus nerve in chamber 1 to influence the heart in chamber 2. This definitively showed that there was a chemical released from a neuron to influence its target tissue. In this case, the neurotransmitter was Acetylcholine (ACh). Since then ACh was found to be released at neuromuscular junctions onto skeletal muscle and most of the pioneering work on ACh and its mechanisms of action were performed using the neuromuscular junction.

Cholinergic neurons produce ACh from acetyl coenzyme A and choline using a specific enzyme, choline acetyltransferase. Acetyl-CoA and choline are found in all cells in the body, but only some neurons contain choline acetyltransferase which is necessary for the production of ACh. These neurons also contain a large number of Na^+-dependent choline co-transporters that transport large amounts of choline into the end terminals of cholinergic neurons. ACh is synthesized in the cytoplasm and transported into vesicles using a vesicular ACh transporter. Vesicles are produced with a highly acidic interior from endosomes located in the end terminal. The transporter exchanges H^+ for ACh and thus concentrates ACh in vesicles.

ACh is released from presynaptic membranes by exocytosis and crosses the synaptic cleft to interact with specific receptors located on the post-synaptic membrane. There are two main classes of ACh receptors, nicotinic ACh receptors and muscarinic ACh receptors. The nicotinic ACh receptors are ionotropic receptors that require two molecules of ACh for activation and the muscarinic ACh receptors are metabotropic receptors and require one molecule of ACh for activation.

Figure 3.14

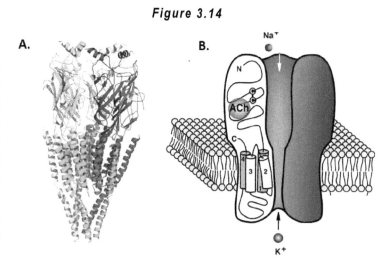

In skeletal muscle, the nicotinic ACh receptor is comprised of 5 subunits creating a central pore (Figure 3.14). The receptor contains two α-subunits which are required for ACh binding sites and a β, γ and δ subunit. Upon activation, the nicotinic ACh receptor is permeable to and K^+ and each of these ions move down their concentration and electrical gradients (Na^+ enters the cell and K^+ leaves the cell). The equilibrium potential for this combined current is close to 0mV which is a depolarizing current and results in an EPSP or in the context of skeletal muscle, a miniature end-plate potential (MEPP). In a neuromuscular junction, there are sites near the synapse which contain a high density of voltage-gated Na^+ channels. These quickly become activated and leads to the development of an action potential on the plasma membrane of the muscle cell and subsequent contraction (see Chapter 5).

In neurons, the nicotinic ACh receptor is also comprised of 5 subunits, however, there are only 2 types of subunits, the α- and β-subunit and each of these has multiple isoforms; the α-subunit contains 7 isoforms and the β-subunit contains 3 isoforms. The subtle differences in subunit isoforms allows for differences in affinity, opening and closing probabilities and times, etc... The neuronal form of the nicotinic receptor also requires two molecules of ACh binding to the α-subunit for activation and is permeable to both Na^+ and K^+.

The muscarinic ACh receptors are metabotropic receptors and there are five subtypes (M1-M5). Each receptor requires one molecule of ACh for activation and all act through G-coupled receptors to affect their target tissue. M1, M3 and M5 act through Gq pathway and the activation of the PLC signaling pathway, whereas M2 and M4 are coupled through Gi and the inhibition of the cAMP signaling pathway. These results can have different cellular responses depending on the downstream signaling pathways that get activated or inhibited. For example, ACh released from the vagus nerve acts on the heart through the M2 receptor which results in a decrease in K^+ permeability and a decrease in Ca^{2+} permeability causing a slowed heart rate.

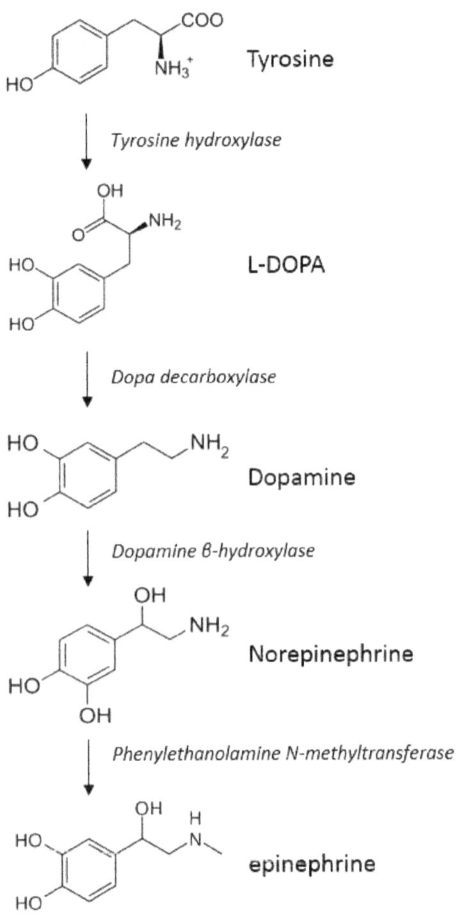

Biogenic Amines

The class of biogenic amines includes the catecholamines (dopamine, norepinephrine and epinephrine), serotonin and histamine. All of the biogenic amines are synthesized and packaged into vesicles in the end-terminals of neurons. As their name implies, they all contain an amine group, however, the

Figure 3.15

Tyrosine

Tyrosine hydroxylase

L-DOPA

Dopa decarboxylase

Dopamine

Dopamine β-hydroxylase

Norepinephrine

Phenylethanolamine N-methyltransferase

epinephrine

catecholamines also contain a catechol structure (a benzene ring with two adjacent hydroxyl groups).

Catecholamines

Catecholamines are all derived from the common amino acid precursor, L-tyrosine (Figure 3.15). L-tyrosine is converted to L-dihydroxyphenylalanine (L-DOPA) by the enzyme, tyrosine hydroxylase (TH) located in the cytoplasm of the end terminals of catecholaminergic neurons. The enzymatic reaction of TH is the rate-limiting step in the production of the catecholamines and is under strict regulatory control mechanisms. Another enzyme, DOPA decarboxylase converts L-DOPA to dopamine in the cytoplasm. Dopamine is then transported into vesicles by the vesicular monoamine transporter (VMAT) using a proton antiporter. This common sequence of steps occur in all of the catecholaminergic neurons.

Dopamine

Dopamine is a neurotransmitter produced and localized to distinct nuclei within the brain. Dopaminergic neurons are found in areas involved with emotion and reward pathways, and many of these neurons are also found in the basal nuclei and play an important role in the modulation of somatic motor control. In neurons, dopamine is stored in vesicles for release. Once dopamine is released into the synaptic cleft, dopamine can interact with receptors on the post-synaptic membrane. All of the five dopamine receptors (D1-D5) are G-protein coupled metabotropic receptors. D1 and D5 receptors are linked to Gs and activate the cAMP signaling pathway. D2, D3, and D4 are linked to Gi and inhibit the cAMP signaling pathway.

Dopamine is cleared from the synaptic cleft using a couple of mechanisms. Dopamine can be metabolized by two enzymes, monoamine oxidase (MAO) and catechol O-methyltransferase (COMT) located in the synaptic cleft. Or dopamine can be taken back into the pre-synaptic terminal by a Na^+-dependent dopamine co-transporter (DAT) located on the presynaptic membrane or located on astrocytes. Once dopamine is transported into the cytoplasm, dopamine can be reused by the neurons or metabolized by MAO or COMT located in the cytoplasm of the neuron or the astrocyte. If dopamine is released in high amounts, dopamine can spill out of the synapse. Autoreceptors for dopamine can be found on the edges of the synapse on the presynaptic terminal and act in a negative feedback manner to help regulate dopamine biosynthesis and release. Autoreceptors initiate a decrease in the synthesis and the packaging of neurotransmitters into vesicles. Each subsequent action potential in the pre-synaptic terminal will then release less neurotransmitter. Finally, dopamine can also be

Norepinephrine

In the CNS, noradrenergic neurons are found in brainstem nuclei such as the locus coeruleus and the axons project widely to forebrain structures as well as the spinal cord. In the PNS, post-ganglionic neurons of the sympathetic nervous system are also noradrenergic and innervate most organs of the body. Norepinephrine (or noradrenalin) is synthesized in neurons from dopamine. In noradrenergic neurons, TH is also the rate-limiting step and TH converts L-tyrosine to L-DOPA. Dopamine is produced in the cytosol and transported into vesicles using DAT. Once inside vesicles, an enzyme, dopamine-β-hydroxylase, converts the dopamine to norepinephrine. Action potentials in the pre-synaptic neuron cause the release of vesicles containing norepinephrine from the pre-synaptic terminals. Norepinephrine diffuses across the synaptic cleft to bind to receptors located on the post-synaptic membrane.

The adrenergic receptors are all G-protein coupled metabotropic receptors. There are five different types of possible adrenergic receptors; α1-adrenergic receptor, α2-adrenergic receptor, β1-adrenergic receptor, β2-adrenergic receptor and β3-adrenergic receptor. The α1 receptor is linked to G_q which activates the PLC pathway and in the PNS results in the increase of intracellular Ca^{2+} and the contraction of smooth muscle. This receptor is found in multiple areas including many blood vessels which results in vasoconstriction. The α2 adrenergic receptor is linked to G_i which inhibits adenylyl cyclase and decreases cAMP synthesis. The α2 adrenergic receptor is an autoreceptor in neuronal synapse of the CNS and can be found located on pre-synaptic terminals. Recall that an autoreceptor inhibits the amount of neurotransmitter synthesized and released during stimulation. The α2 adrenergic receptor can also be found on the post-synaptic membrane in a few areas of the body including the cells of the pancreatic islets of Langerhans and inhibit the release of insulin and promote the release of glucagon. The β-adrenergic receptors are all linked to G_s although the G_i subunit has also been shown to associate with the β2-receptor. The β1-adrenergic receptor is found only in the heart and results in the increase of heart rate and stroke volume. Activation of the β1-receptor activates G_s which stimulates adenylyl cyclase and increases the production of cAMP. cAMP activates protein kinases which open Ca^{2+} channels located on the plasma membrane and ER causing an increase in heart rate and the force of contraction. The β2-adrenergic receptors are found in multiple locations including the smooth muscle of the digestive tract and causes muscle relaxation. The β3-adrenergic receptor is localized to adipose cells and is involved in lipolysis and thermogenesis. Adrenergic receptors are also found on CNS neurons and initiate intracellular signaling cascades which lead to the formation of post-synaptic potentials (EPSP or an IPSP).

Norepinephrine is removed from the synaptic cleft by the enzymes MAO and COMT which can be found in the synaptic cleft and in the cytosol of the presynaptic terminal. Norepinephrine can be transported into the pre-synaptic terminal due to a high affinity carrier protein.

Epinephrine

Epinephrine containing neurons are also called adrenergic neurons. Norepinephrine is another catecholamine that is derived from tyrosine. Again the rate-limiting step in the conversion of tyrosine to its final end-product is TH. Dopamine is produced in the cytoplasm of end-terminals, transported into vesicles using DAT and subsequently converted to norepinephrine and finally to epinephrine by the enzyme, phenylethanolamine-N-methyltransferase (PMNT). Adrenergic neurons are found in a few locations in the brainstem and project to areas of the brain and spinal cord. Adrenergic neurons also act on the same G-protein coupled adrenergic receptors as norepinephrine. The majority of the epinephrine in the body, however, comes from the adrenal medulla and is secreted as a neurohormone in response to sympathetic stimulation; both epinephrine (80%) and norepinephrine (20%) are released from adrenal medullary cells. In neurons, epinephrine is released from the pre-synaptic terminal and binds to receptors located on the post-synaptic membrane. Epinephrine is quickly degraded in synapses by the enzymes MAO and COMT.

Serotonin

Serotonergic neurons are found in nuclei scattered throughout the brainstem, primarily in a group of nuclei called the raphe nuclei and project to widespread areas of the brain and spinal cord. In the brain, serotonin is involved with modulation of sleep/wake states, emotion, mood, and learning. Altered serotonin function is implicated in many clinical conditions related to sleep, mood and emotion, such as anxiety disorders, eating disorders, obsessive compulsive disorder, post-traumatic stress syndrome, schizophrenia, sleep disorders, substance abuse and more. Despite the widespread effects of serotonin in the brain and spinal cord, most of the serotonin in the body is not stored in neurons but it is found in neuroendocrine cells of the digestive tract and involved in digestion. It is also found in platelets and is involved in platelet clotting.

In neurons, serotonin is produced in the cytoplasm of the presynaptic end-terminals. Oxidation of tryptophan is catalyzed by the enzyme tryptophan-5-hydroxylase which produces the end-product 5-hydroxytryptophan (Figure 3.16). The enzyme aromatic-L-amino acid decarboxylase converts 5-hydroxytryptophan to 5-hydroxytryptamine (5-HT or serotonin). Serotonin is packaged into vesicles for storage and release. Serotonin is released from the presynaptic terminals in response to action potential stimulation.

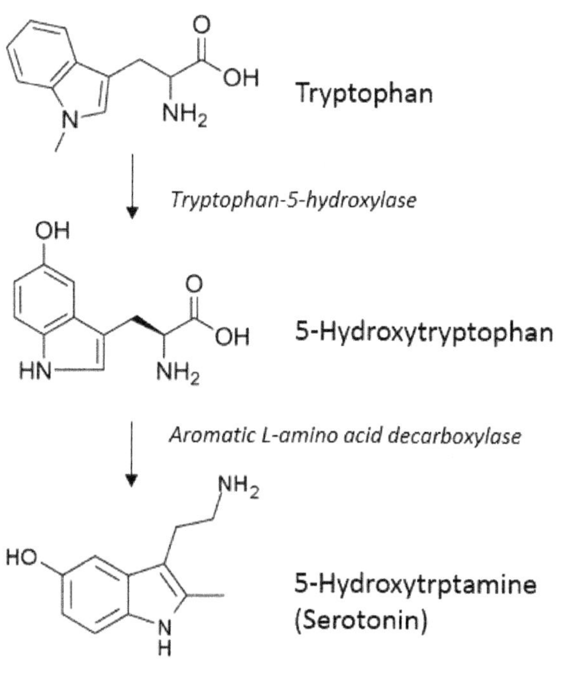

There is one serotonin receptor that is a ligand-gated or ionotropic receptor (5-HT3) and the rest of the serotonin receptors are G-protein coupled metabotropic receptors. There are 7 types of 5-HT receptors that are numbered sequentially from 1-7. There are multiple subtypes of the several of the receptors. The serotonin receptors associated with G_i and inhibit the cAMP pathway are the 5-HT1 and 5-HT5 receptors, the serotonin receptors associated with G_s and stimulation of the cAMP pathway are 5-HT4, 5-HT6 and 5-HT7

Figure 3.16

Tryptophan

Tryptophan-5-hydroxylase

5-Hydroxytryptophan

Aromatic L-amino acid decarboxylase

5-Hydroxytrptamine (Serotonin)

receptors. And the 5-HT2 receptor is associated with G_q and activation of the PLC pathway.

The 5-HT5A and 5-HT7 are also found localized to the presynaptic membrane and function as an autoreceptors involved in negative feedback. Serotonin is quickly taken back by the pre-synaptic terminal using serotonin transporters (SERT). Serotonin can then be metabolized by MAO or recycled and repackaged into vesicles for release.

Amino Acids

The primary excitatory and inhibitory neurotransmitters of the CNS are amino acids. Most excitatory synapses within the brain and spinal cord utilize glutamate as their neurotransmitter and comprise more than 50% of all synapses in the brain alone. The most common inhibitory neurotransmitters of the CNS are γ-aminobutyric acid (GABA) and glycine. GABA is more widespread than glycine and can be found in most local interneurons as well as the Purkinje cells of the cerebellum, a type of projection neuron. Glycine is more localized and comprises ~50% of the inhibitory neurons in the spinal cord; while GABA is found in rest.

Glutamate

Glutamate, a nonessential amino acid, is the primary excitatory neurotransmitter of the brain and spinal cord. Glutamate does not cross the blood brain barrier, therefore it must be synthesized within the CNS. In the cytosol of axon end terminals, glutamine is converted to glutamate by the enzyme glutaminase and glutamate is packaged into vesicles using specific vesicular glutamate transporters (VGLUT). Cytosolic glutamate also comes from excitatory amino acid transporters (EAATs) located at the pre-synaptic terminal. EAATs are involved in recycling glutamate from the synaptic cleft and are a type of Na^+-dependent co-transporter which uses the strong driving force of Na^+ to quickly move glutamate out of the synaptic cleft. Glutamate can also be synthesized in neurons using simple glycolysis and the Krebs cycle. However, the majority of the glutamate in these excitatory neurons is derived from the glutamate-glutamine cycle.

The glutamate-glutamine cycle involves a coordination of events that occur between astrocytes and neurons. Recall that astrocytes are localized to synapses and are involved in the uptake of neurotransmitters that spill away from the synaptic cleft. At glutamatergic synapses, astrocytes contain EAATs on their plasma membrane which transport glutamate out of the synaptic cleft into the astrocyte cytosol. In astrocytes, the enzyme glutamine synthetase, converts glutamate to glutamine which is then released to the extracellular space by the system-N transporter 1 (SN1). System-A transporter 2 (SAT2) localized to glutamatergic neurons are involved with the uptake of glutamine. This glutamate-glutamine cycle between astrocytes and neurons is an important component regulating glutamate within the CNS. At high doses, extracellular glutamate is neurotoxic and can severely damage and kill neurons. The glutamate-glutamine cycle ensures that low levels of glutamate are in the extracellular space; glutamine which is not toxic to cells can be released to the extracellular space with no consequence.

When glutamatergic neurons fire action potentials, a certain number of vesicles fuse with the pre-synaptic membrane and glutamate is released into the synaptic space. Glutamate crosses the synaptic cleft and binds to receptors located on the post-synaptic membrane to initiate a cellular response. There are multiple types of glutamate receptors including both ionotropic and metabotropic receptors. The ionotropic glutamate receptors are named for the specific chemicals that have been found to activate them and are called the α-amino-3-hydroxyl-5-methyl-4-isoxazole-proprionate (AMPA) receptors, the N-methyl-D-aspartate (NMDA) receptors and the kainate receptors. In the brain, AMPA and NMDA receptors are often found co-localized on the post-synaptic membranes of the same synapse. AMPA receptors are ligand-gated receptors which are permeable to both Na^+ and K^+. Activation of the AMPA receptor depolarizes the cell toward 0mV which results in an EPSP. The NMDA receptor is also a cationic channel, however, when glutamate initially binds to the receptor cations cannot flow through the channel due to a Mg^{2+} plug. In order to open the NMDA channel, the post-synaptic membrane must be depolarized to a much greater degree (~20-30mv of depolarizing current). When a strong stimulus is applied, the Mg^{2+} is expelled from the pore to the extracellular space (down its concentration gradient) and Na^+, K^+ and Ca^{2+} can flow through the channel down their respective concentration gradients (Na^+ and Ca^{2+} flow into the cell and K^+ flows out of the cell). This also results in cellular depolarization, but remember that Ca^{2+} is also a second messenger and can activate other processes in cells. In neurons, the NMDA channel is involved in the process of long term changes in the cell. Interestingly, the NMDA channel also needs glycine to bind to the receptor to activate the channel. Although glycine is one of the major inhibitory neurotransmitters in the spinal cord, it is also an amino acid that can be found in the extracellular fluid of the cerebral spinal fluid (CSF). The coordinated activity between the pre and post-synaptic membranes and the activation of AMPA and NMDA receptors underlie one mechanism of long term synaptic plasticity.

Synaptic plasticity refers to the ability of neurons to change a synapse. Changes is synapses can occur in either the pre or post synaptic membrane which result in an altered post-synaptic response. Different types of changes can be initiated that can lead to short-term changes that occur over a short time period (milliseconds to minutes) and are called short-term plasticity and changes that are initiated occur over a longer period of time (minutes, to days, to years) are called long-term synaptic plasticity. A classic example of long-term synaptic plasticity was discovered in the sea slug, *Aplysia californica*, by Eric Kandel who shared the Nobel Prize in Physiology or Medicine in 2000 with Arvid Carlsson and Paul Greengard "for their discoveries concerning signal transduction in the nervous system." It was later revealed that similar mechanisms of long-term synaptic plasticity occur in the mammalian hippocampus and is involved with the formation of memories; long-term potentiation.

A single action potential from a pre-synaptic glutamatergic neuron releases a certain quantity (or quanta) of neurotransmitter which activates AMPA receptors on the post-synaptic membrane causing an EPSP of a certain voltage. A high frequency of action potentials in the pre-synaptic neuron will release quanta of neurotransmitter at a high frequency and results in high levels of glutamate in the synaptic cleft. The glutamate continues to activate AMPA receptors on the post-synaptic membrane over a long time period resulting in the summation of EPSPs and the subsequent depolarization of the post-synaptic membrane. If the depolarization is sufficient to activate NMDA receptors then intracellular Ca^{2+} rises in the post-synaptic cytosol. Intracellular Ca^{2+} can lead to the upregulation of AMPA receptors on the post-synaptic membrane. If this occurs, a single action potential and a single quanta of neurotransmitter from the pre-synaptic neuron will now initiate an EPSP of a larger size because the glutamate can activate a larger number of receptors on the post-synaptic membrane. This enhanced EPSP is referred to as long term potentiation (See Figure 3.17). This is one mechanism underlying long-term plasticity.

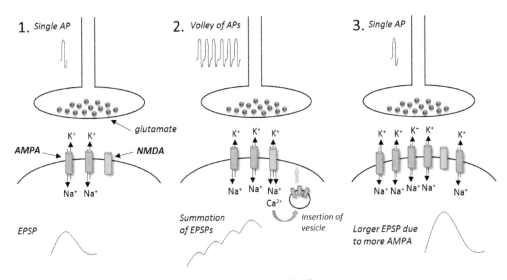

Figure 3.17

Another class of glutamate receptors are the metabotropic glutamate receptors (mGluR1-8). The majority of mGluRs connect to intracellular G-proteins and activate intracellular signaling cascades leading to excitation. mGluR1 and mGluR5 are coupled to G_q whereas the rest are associated with G_i and many of these appear to be involved in pre-synaptic inhibition (autoreceptors) There are exceptions however, most notably in the retina of the eye where activation of mGluR leads to an inhibition (see Chapter 4).

Another form of synaptic plasticity is long-term depression. An example of long-term depression occurs in the cerebellum and involves mGluR receptors (See Figure 3.18). Cerebellar Purkinje cells are found in the cerebellum and are the largest neurons in the body and contain GABA. Purkinje cells receive inputs from multiple types of cells including the parallel fibers originating from granule cells as well as climbing fibers. Both of these synapses are excitatory synapses. The parallel fiber releases glutamate which binds to AMPA receptors causing

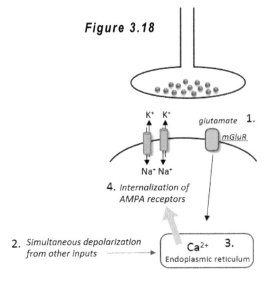

depolarization of the membrane. There are also mGluR present which get activated, but do not play a major role when only parallel fibers are active. The mGluR is associated with G_q which leads to the activation of PLC and the formation of DAG and IP3. DAG activates PKC and IP3 leads to the release of intracellular Ca^{2+} stores. Under these simple conditions, the activation of the mGluR does not have much effect. However, if there is simultaneous stimulation of climbing fibers along with parallel fibers then long-term depression occurs. When the climbing fiber and the parallel fibers are stimulated, the Purkinje cell becomes even more depolarized. This depolarization leads to the opening of Ca^{2+} channels and an influx of more Ca^{2+}. The activation of PKC plus extra high intracellular Ca^{2+} leads to the up-regulation or endocytosis of AMPA receptors at the synapse. A reduction in the number of AMPA receptors at the synapse between parallel fibers and the Purkinje cell leads to a decreased EPSP or long-term depression.

GABA (gamma amino-butyric acid)

GABA is an inhibitory neurotransmitter that is found in neurons located in widespread areas of the brain and spinal cord. The synthesis of GABA results from the enzyme glutamic acid decarboxylase (GAD) which is only found in GABAergic neurons. Normal cellular metabolism via the TCA cycle produces glutamate which can be converted to GABA by the presence of GAD in the cytosol of GABAergic neurons. GAD is only present in GABAergic neurons producing GABA in the cytosol of the end-terminals of neurons. GABA is packaged into vesicles using a vesicular inhibitory amino acid transporter (VIATT). Action potentials in GABAergic neurons cause the release of a quanta of GABA from the pre-synaptic terminal into the synaptic cleft. There are three types of GABA receptors found on post-synaptic membranes. $GABA_A$ and $GABA_C$ receptors are both iontropic. Activation of the $GABA_A$ or $GABA_C$ receptor results in an influx of Cl^- through a Cl^- channel and a subsequent IPSP on the post-synaptic membrane. The $GABA_B$ receptor is a metabotropic receptor that is also a G-protein coupled receptor that is associated with Gi. Inhibition of adenylyl cyclase leads to the activation of K^+ channels and results in cellular hyperpolarization and an IPSP on the post-synaptic membrane. GABA is removed from the synaptic cleft by a Na^+-dependent co-transporter for GABA located on the presynaptic neuron and nearby astrocytes.

Glycine

Glycine is also an inhibitory neurotransmitter of the CNS, but it is found more localized to the spinal cord. Glycine is produced by normal cell metabolism in the cytosol of glycinergic neurons and packaged into vesicles using the same VIATT that is found in GABAergic neurons. Glycine is released from the pre-synaptic terminals by action potentials, glycine crosses the synaptic cleft and binds to glycine receptors found on the post-synaptic neurons. Glycine receptors are ionotropic receptors which open a Cl^- channel. They are very similar in function to the $GABA_A$ or $GABA_C$ receptor. Glycine is cleared from the synaptic cleft by Na^+-dependent glycine co-transporters located pre-synaptically and on astrocytes.

Purines and ATP

Some ATP is found co-localized with all classical neurotransmitters in vesicles. Receptors for purines, ATP and adenosine are found in widespread areas of the brain and spinal cord. Receptors for ATP include the ionotropic P2X receptor which is a non-selective cationic channel and is therefore excitatory. The P2Y receptors and the adenosine receptors are metabotropic G-protein coupled receptors.

Neuropeptides

Peptides are a short string of amino acids (small proteins) that often are released from glands in the form of hormones. Many of these peptides are also synthesized and released from neurons as neurotransmitters. Within the CNS, there are several groups of neuropeptide neurotransmitters, the brain-gut peptides, the opioid peptides, the pituitary peptides, the hypothalamic releasing peptides and other miscellaneous peptides. Neuropeptides are synthesized in neurons in the same manner that other proteins are synthesized. The mRNA produced in the nucleus is translocated to the ER where large pre-propeptides are produced and transferred to the Golgi apparatus. Cleavage of proteins into smaller active peptides along with protein modification occurs in the Golgi or in the vesicles that bud off the Golgi. Vesicles with peptides are transported in the anterograde direction for storage and release from the end terminals of axons. Neuropeptides are often co-transported with other small molecule neurotransmitters. For example, vesicles containing substance P (SP) can be co-released with vesicles containing glutamate by sensory neurons that detect pain, the nociceptors. SP acts on neurokinin receptors, another group of G-protein coupled receptors.

The brain-gut peptides are a class of peptides that are found in regions of the gut as well as the neurons of the brain. Some of the more common peptides are SP, cholecystokinin (CCK), and vasoactive intestinal peptide (VIP). In the spinal cord, SP can be inhibited by opioids, another group of peptide neurotransmitters. Endogenous opioids, beta endorphin, dynorphins and enkephalins are neurotransmitters that are involved in axo-axonic synapses. The endogenous opioids also act on a group of G-protein coupled receptors, the delta (δ), kappa (κ), and mu (μ) receptors.

Other Neurotransmitters

Other types of neurotransmitters involve molecules that do not fit easily into a typical class of neurotransmitter. These neurotransmitters are not packaged into vesicles and released by exocytosis, but rather they are released in response to regulated Ca^{2+} levels and therefore still fit the profile of neurotransmission. Two of the more well-known neurotransmitters include nitric oxide, a gas, and the endocannabinoids.

Nitric oxide (NO) is a gas which can be released at synapses to influence cells nearby. In neurons, nitric oxide is produced from arginine using the enzyme neuronal nitric oxide synthase (nNOS). nNOS is found in neurons and is regulated by intracellular Ca^{2+} levels.

The gas, NO acts on various intracellular mechanisms such as the activation of guanylyl cyclase which increases cGMP levels in cells and induces intracellular signaling paths.

The endocannabinoids are hydrophobic molecules that are released by the post-synaptic membrane in response to elevated Ca^{2+} levels. In some inhibitory synapses of the hippocampus and cerebellum, GABA is released from the presynaptic membrane and causes an IPSP on the post-synaptic membrane. Increases in Ca^{2+} levels in the post-synaptic membrane cause the release of endocannabinoids which act in a retrograde fashion to inhibit the release of neurotransmitters from the pre-synaptic terminal. Endocannabinoids bind to two types of cannabinoid receptors (CB1 and CB2) which are also G-protein coupled metabotropic neurons. The endocannabinoids and their receptors can be found scattered throughout the CNS and PNS.

CHAPTER 3, SECTION 2 – SUMMARY

- ➢ Neurons that produce ACh are found in both the CNS and the PNS.

- ➢ ACh can bind to the ionotropic, nicotinic ACh receptors located on neurons or skeletal muscle cells and cause depolarization. Or ACh can bind to metabotropic, muscarinic ACh receptors located on smooth muscle, cardiac muscle or glands and cause either stimulation or inhibition of the tissue.

- ➢ The catecholamines are derived from a common precursor molecule and produce dopamine, norepinephrine and epinephrine.

- ➢ Dopamine has 5 possible metabotropic G-protein coupled receptors that it could bind to. D1 and D5 are coupled to G_s and activate the cAMP signaling pathway whereas D2, D3, and D4 are linked to G_i and inhibit the cAMP signaling pathway.

- ➢ Norepinephrine and epinephrine bind to 5 possible adrenergic receptors. The adrenergic receptors include the α1, α2, β1, β2, and β3 adrenergic receptors. The α1 receptor activates G_q signaling cascade and in the PNS results in the vasoconstriction of blood vessels. The α2 receptor is an autoreceptor and is coupled to G_i and inhibits the release of neurotransmitter from the pre-synaptic terminal. The β-receptors are all coupled to a G_s signaling cascade. The β1 is found only in the heart and stimulates heart rate and the force of contraction. The β2 receptor is found in multiple places and causes relaxation of smooth muscle and the β3 receptor is found on adipose tissue and causes lipolysis and helps in the regulation of body temperature.

- ➢ Serotonin is derived from the amino acid tryptophan and is involved in neural networks related to mood, emotion, and sleep/wake cycles. There are many ionotropic and metabotropic receptors that serotonin can bind to (5-HT 1-7).

➢ Glutamate is the primary excitatory neurotransmitter of the CNS. It is involved virtually every region of the brain. Glutamate can bind to ionotropic (AMPA, NMDA, and kainate) and metabotropic receptors (mGluR1-8). Glutamate is involved in synaptic plasticity and can be shown to activate long term potentiation (a form of memory) and long term depression depending on the type of receptor activation.

➢ GABA and glycine are the primary inhibitory neurotransmitters of the CNS. GABA is found in widespread regions of the brain and spinal cord, whereas glycine is more localized to the spinal cord. Many of the receptors for both neurotransmitters are Cl^- ionotropic receptors that lead to cellular hyperpolarization.

➢ Other neurotransmitters include ATP and its derivatives, various neuropeptides as well as the opioids and nitric oxide. Each neurotransmitter has specific receptors that they bind to and cause specific intracellular changes.

Section 3 – Autonomic Nervous System

Classically, the peripheral nervous system can be broadly divided into two functional divisions; the sensory (or afferent) division and the motor (or efferent) division. Inputs that arise from the skin and muscles are called somatic sensory afferents, inputs that arise from the organs are called visceral sensory afferents, and inputs that contain special information about vision, olfaction, gustation, hearing and balance are called special sensory afferents. Motor efferents are typically divided into the somatic motor division which controls the skeletal muscles and the autonomic motor division which controls smooth muscle, cardiac muscle and glandular tissue throughout the body. The autonomic nervous system (ANS) can further be divided into the sympathetic (Figure 3.19) and parasympathetic divisions (See Figure 3.20).

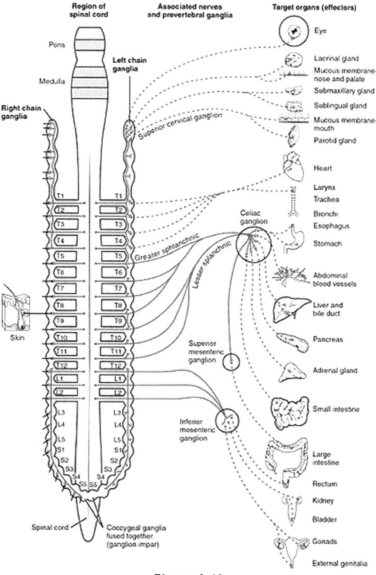

Figure 3.19

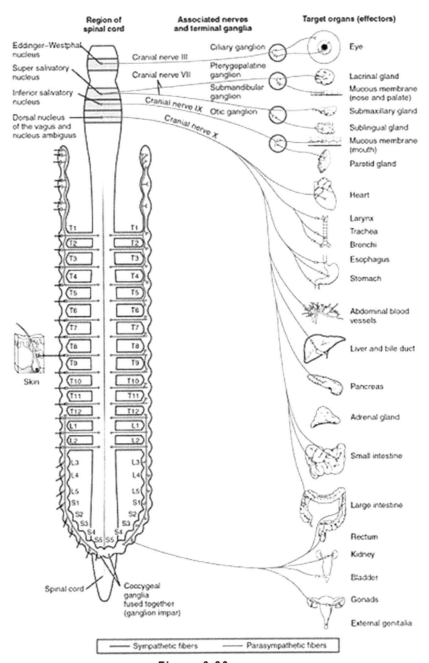

Figure 3.20

Alternatively, scientists can divide the PNS into two systems based on location; the somatic nervous system and ANS. In this manner, the somatic division contains the sensory inputs and motor outputs controlling skeletal muscles and skin. The autonomic division contains the sensory and motor outputs controlling the viscera. In this manner, the visceral sensory afferents are referred to as autonomic sensory afferents. In general, the ANS controls involuntary functions, visceral functions and internal reflexes which helps to maintain an optimal internal environment and homeostasis. Whereas the somatic division controls actions of a voluntary nature; voluntary action of skeletal muscles and the reflexes that utilize sensory afferents to control skeletal muscle. To simplify and make things less confusing, this textbook will describe the ANS using the classical terminology and will be confined to only the motor divisions of the sympathetic and parasympathetic systems. The enteric nervous system is also sometimes considered part of the ANS. These neurons innervate the gut and will be covered separately in the digestive system (Chapter 9).

The ANS differs from the somatic motor system in multiple ways (See Figure 3.21, on the next page). The somatic motor division uses one cholinergic neuron to control skeletal muscle function. The cell body of the somatic motor neuron is located in the ventral horn of the spinal cord and its axon leaves through the ventral root to join a spinal nerve to target skeletal muscles. Somatic motor neurons release ACh at the neuromuscular synapse which diffuses across the synaptic cleft to bind to nicotinic ACh receptors located on skeletal muscles. An EPSP is initiated in the plasma membrane quickly followed by an action potential (Chapter 5). The ANS uses two neurons to innervate its target tissue (a smooth muscle or gland cell). One neuron projects from the lateral horn of the spinal cord to a ganglia in the PNS and is called the pre-ganglionic neuron. The pre-ganglionic neuron synapses with a second neuron in the ganglia which then projects to the target tissue and is therefore called the post-ganglionic neuron. Pre-ganglionic neurons are cholinergic and release ACh which bind to a neuronal type of nicotinic ACh receptor on post-ganglionic neurons within ganglia. The second neuron, the post-ganglionic neuron is either cholinergic or adrenergic depending on whether the neuron is from the parasympathetic or the sympathetic divisions, respectively. The second, post-ganglionic neuron innervates smooth muscle, cardiac muscle, or glandular tissue to initiate an excitatory or an inhibitory response. The receptors on the target tissue are either muscarinic ACh receptors or adrenergic receptors depending on the type of neuron innervating the tissue. Finally, the somatic nervous system functions in the control of voluntary movements using skeletal muscles, whereas the ANS controls unconscious mechanisms regulating visceral functions.

Most tissues that are innervated by the ANS receive inputs from both the sympathetic and the parasympathetic divisions. Usually the inputs will exert opposite effects on a specific organ. For example, the heart is innervated by sympathetic neurons which excite the tissue and increase the heart rate and the force of contraction; whereas, the parasympathetic neurons inhibit or slow down the heart rate. Autonomic neurons are always in some sort of "on" state and are involved in regulation of visceral function while the organism is alive. The amount of signal coming from one division alternates with the amount of signal coming from the opposite division and these can change under different situations. For example, during exercise, the amount of activity from the sympathetic nervous system increases while the activity from the parasympathetic activity decreases. When an organism is quietly resting, parasympathetic activity is enhanced and sympathetic activity is decreased. This allows for fine tuning and regulation of the organs and organ systems based on needs of the whole body.

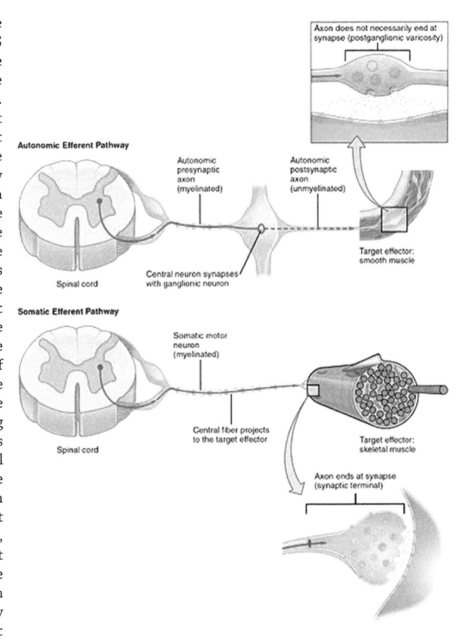

Figure 3.21

Sympathetic nervous system

The sympathetic nervous system helps regulate mechanisms involved in the "fight or flight" response and helps regulate the body's response to various stressors and physical activity. In doing such activities, the sympathetic nervous system activates many systems simultaneously. The sympathetic division of the ANS arises from a column of cells located in the lateral horn of the spinal column (the intermediolateral cell column) from T1 to L2. The pre-ganglionic axon extends out of the spinal cord through the ventral root and projects to the post-ganglionic neuron located in a peripheral ganglia, either a chain ganglia or collateral ganglia. The cholinergic pre-ganglionic neuron releases ACh and excites the post-ganglionic neuron by binding to a nicotinic ACh receptor. Many of the axons of the pre-ganglionic neurons terminate in the chain ganglia

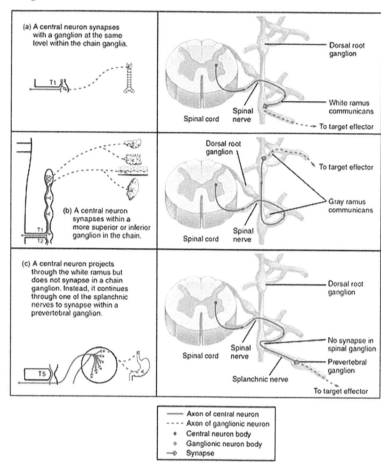

Figure 3.22

which reside just outside of the vertebral column. Therefore, in general, the length of the pre-ganglionic neuron tends to be short. Most post-ganglionic neurons then extend to the target tissue and therefore tend to be long. The post-ganglionic neurons are primarily adrenergic and release norepinephrine onto their target tissue. Depending on the tissue, either α- or β-adrenergic, G-protein coupled metabotropic receptors can be found and depending on the intracellular pathway that is activated, the response can be either excitatory or inhibitory. For example, sympathetic activation excites heart tissue but inhibits gastric functions.

Sympathetic neurons travel through three major pathways to reach their target tissue, spinal nerves, sympathetic nerves and splanchnic nerves, with one exception (innervation of the adrenal gland) (Figure 3.22). As sympathetic pre-ganglionic neurons arise from the spinal cord (T1-L2), all of them start by exiting through the ventral root and entering a spinal nerve. As the nerve exits the intervertebral foramina (small hole between vertebra), the sympathetic axons leave the spinal nerve to go into a small branch, the white ramus communicans, and enters the chain ganglia. The chain ganglia is a collection of ganglia sitting along the vertebral column. Some sympathetic neurons travel though spinal nerves to reach their target tissue, such as neurons that control of sweat glands, arrector pili muscles and blood vessels of skin. These neurons enter the chain ganglia and the pre-ganglionic neurons will synapse with a post-ganglionic neuron in the chain ganglia. The post-ganglionic sympathetic neuron will exit the chain ganglia through a small branch called the gray ramus communicans to re-enter the spinal nerve to reach its target tissue.

Sympathetic axons that travel through sympathetic nerves to reach their target also start in the spinal nerve coming off of the spinal cord and enter the chain ganglia via the white ramus communicans. These axons also make a synapse within the chain ganglia. All axons that enter the chain ganglia, enter the ganglia at the same level of the spinal cord from which they arise. Once an axon enters the chain ganglia, it may make a synapse at the same level from which it entered, or it may go up or down a segment or two before making a synapse. Sympathetic nerves exit the chain ganglia as a separate nerve to target organs in the thoracic cavity.

The last type of nerve that a sympathetic axon may travel through to reach its target tissue is a splanchnic nerve. These axons arise from the spinal cord and exit the ventral root with all other motor fibers. The axons will enter the chain ganglia via the white ramus communicans like all sympathetic axons, however, they do NOT make a synapse in the chain ganglia. They pass through the chain ganglia and enter a splanchnic nerve in the abdominal cavity. The splanchnic nerves project to collateral ganglia where pre-ganglionic sympathetic neurons make a synapse with post-ganglionic neurons in the collateral ganglia before projecting to its target tissue.

One exception or special situation is the innervation of the adrenal gland. Sympathetic neurons that target the adrenal gland arise from T10 – L1 and the pre-ganglionic neuron enters the white ramus communicans into the chain ganglia and pass into splanchnic nerves without making a synapse. They travel to the collateral ganglia but again do not make a synapse. The pre-ganglionic neuron makes a synapse directly onto the chromaffin cells of the adrenal medulla. The chromaffin cells of the adrenal medulla are modified post-ganglionic neurons. Pre-ganglionic sympathetic neurons release ACh which activate nicotinic ACh receptors on chromaffin cells. Chromaffin cells release epinephrine (80%) and norepinephrine (20%) into the interstitial space and they enter blood vessels to affect target tissues acting as a type of neurohormone.

Most sympathetic neurons release norepinephrine at their target tissues. There are 5 types of adrenergic receptors which may be located on the target tissue, the $\alpha1$ and $\alpha2$ receptors, and the $\beta1$, $\beta2$ and $\beta3$ receptors. All of the adrenergic receptors are metabotropic G-protein coupled receptors which can lead to excitation or inhibition of muscle contraction or glandular secretion. The $\alpha1$ adrenergic receptors are found on smooth muscle of blood vessels and other tissues such as the urinary sphincter. Activation of $\alpha1$ receptors activates G_q which in turn activates PLC producing IP3 and DAG. This causes an increase in concentration of intracellular Ca^{2+} which leads to the opening of Ca^{2+} channels resulting in smooth muscle contraction (see Chapter 5). The $\alpha2$ adrenergic receptors are autoreceptors found on the presynaptic terminals. Activation of the α2 receptor stimulates G_i which leads to an intracellular signaling cascade and opens K^+ channels leading to hyperpolarization of the pre-synaptic terminal. This can reduce or block synaptic transmission. The β1 adrenergic receptor is predominantly found on cardiac muscle. Stimulation of the β1 receptor leads to activation of G_s and adenylyl cyclase leading to increased intracellular cAMP. cAMP activates protein kinases which leads to increases in intracellular Ca^{2+} and increases the speed and force of contraction of the heart muscle (see Chapter 6). The β2 adrenergic receptors are involved in the relaxation of smooth muscle and can be found in digestive organs, the airways, and the urogenital system. Many of the β2 receptors are coupled to G_s but some are also coupled to G_i. In general the downstream effects lead to reduced intracellular Ca^{2+} and smooth muscle relaxation. The last adrenergic receptor, the β3 receptor is primarily involved in the regulation of lipolysis and thermogenesis. The β3 receptor is also coupled to G_s and activation of adenylyl cyclase leading to breakdown of lipids and release of energy stores during sympathetic stimulation.

Parasympathetic nervous system

The parasympathetic nervous system is activated during times of whole body relaxation. The parasympathetic nervous system helps regulate feeding behaviors and basic homeostatic functions. Neurons of the parasympathetic division of the autonomic nervous system arise from four cranial nerves, the oculomotor nerve (III), the facial nerve (VII), the glossopharyngeal nerve (IX), and the vagus nerve (X), as well as from a column of cells found in the sacral region of the spinal cord (S2-S4). The cholinergic pre-ganglionic neurons project to autonomic ganglia which are located near or on the visceral organs that they innervate and release ACh. The neurotransmitter binds to nicotinic ACh receptors and excites the post-ganglionic neuron. Post-ganglionic neurons are also cholinergic and release ACh on its target tissue where muscarinic ACh receptors reside. The response of the target tissue can be either excitatory or inhibitory depending on the type of muscarinic receptor and the subsequent intracellular pathways that are initiated. There are 5 types of muscarinic receptors (M1-M5). Again, some receptors (M1, M3 and M5) are coupled to G_q and activate the PLC signaling pathway, whereas the other receptors (M2 and M4) are associated with G_i which inhibits the cAMP signaling pathway. Depending on the intracellular path that gets activated, the response can be either excitatory or inhibitory.

CHAPTER 3, SECTION 3 – SUMMARY

➢ The autonomic nervous system innervates the smooth muscle, cardiac muscle and glandular tissue which constitute the involuntary motor control system.

> The sympathetic nervous system arises from T1-L2, has a myelinated pre-ganglionic axon which releases ACh, the post-ganglionic neuron has a nicotinic ACh receptor on the cell body and is unmyelinated. The post-ganglionic neuron releases norepinephrine onto its target tissue which can activate any the specific adrenergic receptor located on the post-synaptic terminal ($\alpha1$, $\alpha2$, $\beta1$, $\beta2$, and $\beta3$).

> Sympathetic neurons can travel along spinal nerves, sympathetic nerves, and splanchnic nerves to reach their target tissue. The adrenal medulla consists of modified post-ganglionic neurons which release the neurohormones, epinephrine and norepinephrine into the plasma.

> Parasympathetic neurons originate from 4 cranial nerves (III, VII, IX, and X) and from S2-S4. The unmyelinated, pre-ganglionic neuron is myelinated and they tend to be long and innervate autonomic ganglia which are located in or near the target tissue. The myelinated, catecholaminergic, pre-ganglionic neuron releases ACh which binds to a nicotinic ACh receptor located on the post-ganglionic neuron. The unmyelinated post-ganglionic neuron is also catecholaminergic and releases ACH onto the target tissue. The target tissue contains a muscarinic ACh receptor which are coupled to a G-protein signaling cascade.

Section 4 – The Central Nervous System

Sensory information arises from the PNS and enters the CNS through the spinal cord to travel up to the brain. Motor information flows primarily down from the brain and out through the spinal nerves that exit the spinal cord. There are also 12 pairs of cranial nerves which attach to the brain directly and carry sensory and motor information to and from the CNS. The brain and spinal cord are highly organized and information flows through these regions in very specific patterns.

During early development, the brain and spinal cord start as a small patch of ectoderm that becomes the neuroectoderm which invaginates and forms a neural tube. The most rostral region of the tube will become the brain and the lower region becomes most of the spinal cord. The rostral region develops three primary bulges which form during early development; the prosencephalon, the mesencephalon and the rhombencephalon. The prosencephalon forms two lateral cavities which extend and form into the lobes of the cerebral hemispheres. The floor of the lateral cavities will become the diencephalon. The brainstem is formed by the mesencephalon and part of the rhombencephalon. The mesencephalon is the region that becomes the midbrain and is most rostral portion of the brainstem. A portion of the rhombencephalon becomes the rhombic lip which extends over the brainstem and forms the cerebellum. The lower regions of the rhombencephalon become the pons and medulla. The medulla is continuous with the spinal cord.

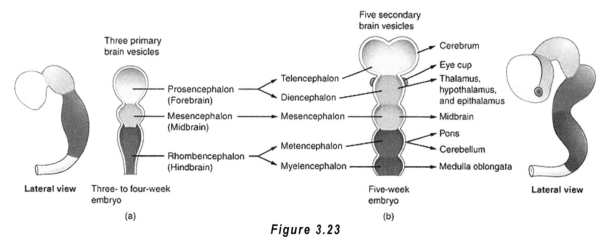

Figure 3.23

The neural tube is a cavity that is lined with ependymal cells. During development, the tube narrows in regions and enlarges in other areas (Figure 3.23). In the adult mammalian brain, 4 open spaces called ventricles remain, each with a choroid plexus, a specialized region of ependymal cells and blood vessels which produce and secrete the cerebral spinal fluid (CSF). The first two lateral ventricles are found in the right and left cerebral hemispheres. They drain via interventricular foramen into the 3rd ventricle which can be found in the center of the diencephalon separating the right and left thalamus and hypothalamus. The 3rd ventricle is drained by a narrow tube, the cerebral aqueduct which traverses the midbrain and enters the 4th ventricle. The 4th ventricle is situated between the cerebellum and the brainstem. The CSF circulates within the ventricles via a pressure gradient. The highest pressure is at the site of production in the ventricles and CSF flows from the ventricles to exit out of the 4th ventricle through three small holes, two lateral apertures and one medial aperture. CSF flows into a space surrounding the brain and spinal cord, called the subarachnoid space. The CSF circulates through the subarachnoid space covering the outer surface of the brain and spinal cord providing protection and cushion for the neural tissue. The CSF drains into the venous circulation by exiting through small structures called arachnoid granulations into a large vein called the superior sagittal sinus which is situated in the longitudinal fissure.

The entire brain and spinal cord are encased in three protective connective tissue sheaths or layers (Figure 3.24). Adhering to the neural tissue by a type of glial basement membrane is a 1-3 layer of cells of special fibroblasts called the pia mater. It is connected via a fine trabecular network of fibroblasts to another layer of specialized fibroblasts, the arachnoid mater. Between the arachnoid and pia mater and traversing between the trabecular network is the subarachnoid space filled with CSF. The outermost edge of the connective tissue is the dura mater. Surrounding the brain, the dura mater is continuous with the periosteum of bone and is tightly connected to the bony surfaces. Surrounding the spinal cord, there is a small space between the dura mater and the vertebral bones called the epidural space. This space is filled with areolar connective tissue and adipose cells.

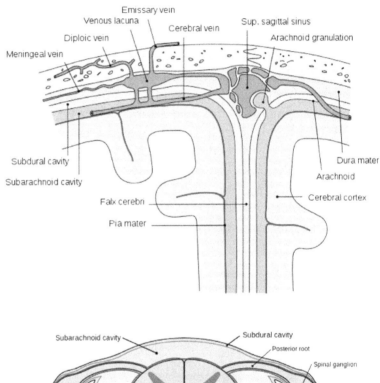

Figure 3.24

The spinal cord

Like all structures in the body, the spinal cord is highly organized. Along the longitudinal axis, the spinal cord starts at the brainstem and is divided into several regions as it projects down the body. The spinal cord in separated into 5 regions; the cervical, thoracic, lumbar, sacral and coccygeal regions. The back of the head, neck, shoulders and portions of the arms are supplied by neurons of the first portion of the spinal cord, the cervical region. The cervical spinal cord is divided into 8 cervical segments with 8 pairs of spinal nerves attached to each segment. The area of the chest and some of the arm and shoulder is supplied by neurons from the thoracic region of the spinal cord. The thoracic spinal cord contains 12 segments along with 12 pairs of spinal nerves. The abdominal region and legs are supplied with the 5 pairs of lumbar nerves which originate from the 5 lumbar segments of the spinal cord. The sacral region of the spinal cord also contains 5 segments of the spinal cord with 5 pairs of nerves. Finally a single pair of coccygeal nerves arise from the coccygeal segment of the spinal cord. The sacral and coccygeal nerves serve the pelvic region of the body.

All spinal nerves contain both sensory and motor information and are therefore considered mixed nerves, with one exception, the first cervical spinal nerve contains only motor information. The cervical and lumbar regions of the spinal cord are slightly enlarged due to the greater number of nerves entering and leaving this region of the spinal cord due to the arms and legs.

When the spinal cord is viewed in cross section, the central region appears as a gray colored butterfly-shape and is therefore called the gray matter (See Figure 3.25). The central butterfly shape is due to the specific pattern of neurons localized within the spinal cord. The cell bodies of neurons along with dendrites and synapses are found in the center of the spinal cord and form a butterfly shape. The gray matter has two enlargement on the dorsal side called the dorsal horns and is the site of entrance of all sensory information entering the spinal cord. The ventral gray matter, forms the dorsal horns and contains the cell bodies of the somatic motor system and is the site of all outgoing motor information. In the center region of the spinal cord primarily in the thoracic cord is another small lateral horn which contains the intermediolateral cell column (the cell bodies of the sympathetic nervous system). The axons of sympathetic neurons project out through the ventral horn with all motor fibers.

The gray matter is surrounded by an outer white-colored region, called the white matter. The white matter of the spinal cord contains the axons of nerves projecting up and down the spinal cord and are predominantly myelinated, thus giving the tissue a white appearance. The white matter is separated into regions based on their location, the dorsal columns or dorsal funiculi, the lateral column or lateral funiculi, and the ventral column or funiculi.

Figure 3.25

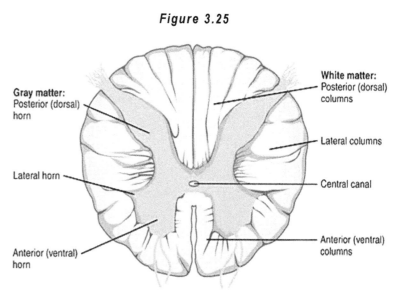

The brain

The brain consists of the neural tissue that is encased in the skull. The brain contains the brainstem, cerebellum, diencephalon and telencephalon. Each region is specialized for carrying out specific functions. The brain is a highly complex organ of which we understand some basic components. Many complex features we do fully not understand. For example, some simple basic neural mechanisms of "memory formation" we understand, like how a synapse is strengthened, but we don't understand where the "memory is stored or how it is stored or how we retrieve the stored data from our neural networks. The brain contains many trillions of neurons which function independently and together to carry out the functions of our body. Here we will briefly overview some of the major structures in the brain and what their major functions are.

Brainstem

The most inferior portion of the brain is called the brainstem (See Figure 3.26). The brainstem is found throughout all vertebrates and controls basic vital functions which are necessary for life. Control of the respiratory system, the cardiovascular system, and swallowing are regulated by centers located in brainstem regions. In addition, the brainstem controls some important reflexes related to vision and hearing which allow animals to quickly respond to potential threats in their environment. The brainstem contains the medulla oblongata, the pons and the midbrain. The medulla contains many collections of neuronal cell bodies or nuclei that control these basic autonomic functions and reflexes. The pons sits just superior to the medulla also contains some nuclei related to autonomic function as well as major nuclei which connect the descending somatic motor projections to the cerebellum and is involved in fine-tuning motor control. The midbrain is the smallest portion of the brainstem and contains centers involved with reflex activity such as coordinating visual, hearing and tactile reflexes. These are basic reflexes which help organisms avoid predators or ensure safety.

Figure 3.26

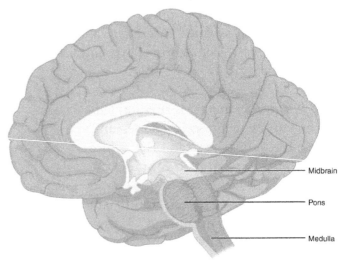

Midbrain

Pons

Medulla

The medulla, the pons and the midbrain also contain a group of neurons called the reticular formation which are involved in the coordination of the respiratory and cardiovascular systems with sleep and wake states. The brainstem also contains all of the ascending sensory tracts and all of the descending motor tracts that connect the spinal cord to the cortical regions of the brain (and vice versa) as well as nuclei for most of the cranial nerves (III through XII) (Figure 3.27).

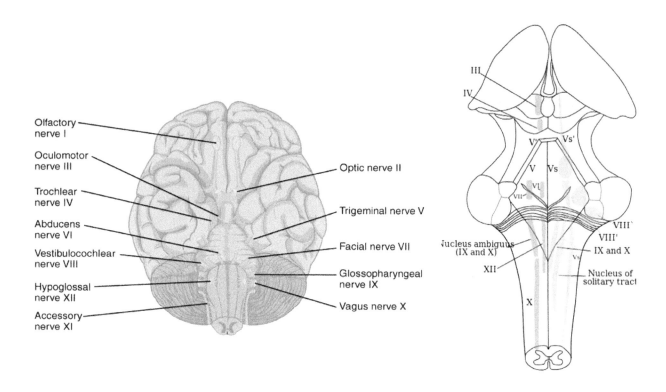

Olfactory nerve I

Oculomotor nerve III

Trochlear nerve IV

Abducens nerve VI

Vestibulocochlear nerve VIII

Hypoglossal nerve XII

Accessory nerve XI

Optic nerve II

Trigeminal nerve V

Facial nerve VII

Glossopharyngeal nerve IX

Vagus nerve X

III

IV

V' Vs'

V Vs

VI

VII'

VIII'
VIII'

Nucleus ambiguus (IX and X)

XII

Vs

IX and X

Nucleus of solitary tract

X

Figure 3.27

Cerebellum

The cerebellum is attached to the dorsal surface of the brainstem and connects physically and functionally to all regions of the brainstem. The cerebellum uses peripheral sensory information regarding proprioception to help modify the activity of motor neurons, and influence and fine tune basic motor movements of the body. The cerebellum helps to control nearly every aspect of skeletal motor function such as balance, posture, coordination of eye movements and the coordination of all limb movement in the body. The cerebellum uses sensory information from muscles and joint receptors to detect motor errors between an intended movement and the actual movement and responds by correcting any errors in that movement. This occurs very quickly, such that the "error" is not visible. Many of these "corrections" about motor movement are stored as motor memories. For example, in order to perform a complex motor movement such as skiing or snowboarding or riding a bike the first time, you have to think about what your body is doing and make alterations to your movements trying various movements to see what works best. Eventually with practice, these movements become easy and sometimes it is even hard to describe what muscles you are even activating to perform a specific motion.

The cerebellar peduncles (superior, middle and inferior) are specific structures that carry the neurons that connect the cerebellum to the brainstem. The descending motor axons from the cerebral cortex send collaterals to connect to nuclei in the pons. These pontine nuclei project information through the middle cerebellar peduncle to the cerebellum. Information from sensory afferents is projected into the cerebellum through the inferior cerebellar peduncle and the middle cerebellar peduncle. Outgoing information from the cerebellum is primarily projected out the superior cerebellar peduncle through the midbrain to the motor cortex. The intended movement can therefore correct errors in movements as they are being made. The inferior peduncle is primarily involved in reflex movement related to balance and cerebellar neurons project to vestibular nuclei in the brainstem.

Even though the cerebellum is relatively small, the cerebellum contains more neurons than the cerebral cortex. One of the neurons is called the Purkinje cell which is the largest neuron in the brain. The Purkinje cell is an inhibitory cell that releases GABA and is intricately involved in the inhibition of errors detected in movements.

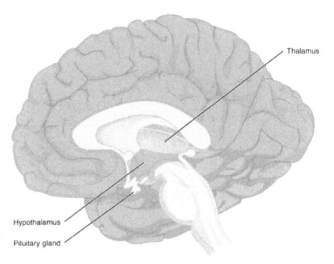

Figure 3.28

Diencephalon

The diencephalon is a region of highly specialized nuclei and tracts running between the brainstem and the cerebral cortex (Figure 3.28). The diencephalon contains 4 distinct regions called the dorsal thalamus, hypothalamus, epithalamus, and subthalamus. On each side of the brain, the dorsal thalamus or simply the thalamus is the largest of the structures. The thalamus is an oval-shaped structure filled with nuclei and is involved with the regulation and processing of somatic functions. The thalamus is often described as the "sensory relay center" and receives information containing somatosensory, visual, auditory and gustatory inputs and transfers that information to specific regions of the cortex. All incoming sensory information, except for the olfactory system, makes a synapse within a specific nucleus within the thalamus. For example, visual inputs project to the medial geniculate nucleus of the thalamus (Chapter 5). In addition to sensory inputs, the thalamus receives information regarding motor function from subcortical regions as well as diffuse information from other limbic regions. All projections to and from the cerebral cortex make reciprocal connections with the thalamus.

The hypothalamus is involved in viseromotor, viscerosensory and endocrine functions. The hypothalamus is involved in the regulation of mood and emotions (fear, rage, happiness, etc...), coordination of sleep and wake states, regulation of food and water intake, and control of hormone release (Chapter 10). The hypothalamus is located just anterior and caudal to the thalamus. The pituitary gland is attached to the hypothalamus via the infundibular stalk and is intricately connected in both anatomy and function to the pituitary gland. The optic nerve, cranial nerve II, enters the brain just anterior to the infundibular stalk and projects back toward the thalamus. Axon collaterals of the optic nerve are sent into the hypothalamus and are involved in regulation of circadian rhythms and to the midbrain for reflex activity.

The epithalamus is in the posterior region of the diencephalon and contains the pineal gland and the habenular nucleus. The pineal gland is a highly vascularized tissue containing pinealocytes which are NOT neuronal and are indirectly sensitive to light. Their main function is to produce and secrete melatonin in a rhythmic fashion. The secretion is coordinated to a 24 hours photic input related to light hitting the retina. Some ganglion cells of the retina project to the suprachiasmatic nucleus which in turn connect to the paraventricular nucleus of the hypothalamus. These hypothalamic neurons project to sympathetic neurons of the upper thoracic spinal cord. The pre-ganglionic neurons synapse project to the superior cervical ganglion and synapse with post-ganglionic neurons. The neurons travel along the carotid artery back into the brain and synapse onto pinealocytes. The downstream signaling cascade inhibits the enzyme serotonin-N-acetyltransferase which slows down the production of melatonin from its precursor, serotonin. Therefore, pinealocytes release less melatonin during the daylight hours due to decreased enzymatic activity. During the nighttime, sympathetic activity is reduced which enhances the enzymatic activity which converts serotonin to melatonin. Thus, melatonin levels peak toward the end of night. The pineal gland is involved with activities associated with circadian rhythms as well as the onset of puberty. In animal in which the reproductive status is seasonal and dependent on daylight hours, the pineal gland plays important roles in the regulation of reproductive status. The epithalamus also contains the habenular nucleus which is part of the limbic system and is involved in the emotional and visceral responses to food.

The subthalamus or ventral thalamus contains many of the ascending sensory and descending motor tracts. Several nuclei are involved in motor control are also found in the subthalamus.

Telencephalon

The telencephalon is the largest part of the human brain and contains 2 large cerebral hemispheres that are separated by the longitudinal fissure. Each hemisphere contains cortical tissue and underlying fiber tracts and a few subcortical nuclei. The cortex forms many folds and invaginations over the surface of the brain which increase the surface area and allows for a greater number of cell bodies to be packaged within the cerebrum. The folds on the surface of the brain are called gryi and the valleys between the folds are called sulci. Each cerebral hemisphere is divided into several lobes (Figure 3.29). The frontal lobes sits most anteriorly and are separated from the parietal lobe via the central sulcus. The most posterior lobe is called the occipital lobe, and on each side of the brain is a temporal lobe.

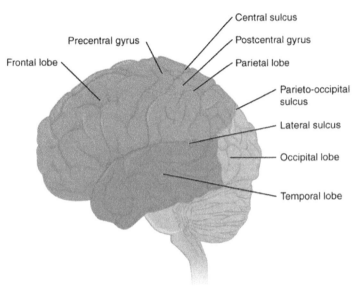

Figure 3.29

The frontal lobe is associated with multiple functions including intellect, creativity, motivation and voluntary motor movement. Broca's area is a region, usually limited to the left side of the brain that controls the movement of the mouth as it relates to speech formation. The gyrus in front of the central sulcus is called the pre-central gyrus and contains a large number of upper motor neurons, or neurons that are sent down the spinal cord to control motor neuron activity. This area is called the primary motor cortex. Additional upper motor neurons can be found nearby in the frontal (and parietal) lobes. The premotor area is an area involved in the coordination and preparation of intended motor movements. The frontal lobe also receives some inputs from the olfactory nerve, cranial nerve I, and is involved in the perception of smell.

The parietal lobe is involved in the perception of somatic sensations. Sensory inputs from the thalamus project to the primary somatosensory cortex situated in the post-central gyrus. Wernicke's area is found in the left parietal lobe and is a region involved in the understanding of speech and the ability to form coherent speech patterns.

The occipital lobe is the most posterior lobe and is involved with the perception of visual inputs. Eyes receive visual information through the retina which passes through the optic nerve and a specific path back to the occipital lobe. Eyes are constantly moving in order to focus light in a specific region of the retina. The coordination of eye movements related to vision also occur in the occipital lobe.

The temporal lobes are found on each lateral aspect of the brain. The temporal lobe is separated from the frontal and parietal lobes by a large gap, the lateral fissure. The temporal lobe contains areas involved in the perception of smell and hearing. Deep inside the temporal lobe is a region called the hippocampus, a region involved in the formation of short-term memory. Within the lateral fissure sits a region called the insula. The insular cortex is continuous with the frontal, parietal and temporal lobes and it receives some nociceptive and viscerosensory inputs.

In the entire cerebral cortex, the cell bodies are located on the edges of the cortical tissue, the gray matter and the nerve tracts are running underneath and form the white matter. The white matter is comprised of tracts of fibers which connect individual gyri and lobes together; these are called association fibers. Commissural fibers are fibers that connect structures on each side of the neuraxis. The largest branch of commissural fibers is the corpus callosum which connects the two cerebral hemispheres together. Around the corpus callosum is a circular region of cortical tissue and deep nuclei which are involved in regulating complex functions such as emotion, behavior, and memory.

CHAPTER 3, SECTION 4 – SUMMARY

➢ The CNS is comprised of the neural tissue in the brain and spinal cord.

➢ Sensory information travels through the dorsal root to enter the dorsal horn of the spinal cord and the motor information exits the ventral horn through the ventral root. All sensory and motor information that travels up and down the spinal cord is found in the outer regions of the spinal cord (white matter) whereas the cell bodies and dendrites are located in the central region of the spinal cord and form the dorsal, lateral and ventral horns.

➢ The brainstem is continuous with the spinal cord and contains the medulla oblongata, the pons and the midbrain. Most centers involved with basic vital functions can be found in this region; control of heart rate, blood pressure, ventilation, and swallowing.

➢ The cerebellum, the "little brain" is found on the posterior aspect of the brainstem. It is primarily involved with fine tuning and correction of errors in all motor movements.

➢ The diencephalon contains 4 regions, the thalamus, hypothalamus, epithalamus and subthalamus. The thalamus is the major sensory relay station and all incoming sensory information (except olfaction) makes a synapse in this region before projecting to the cerebral cortex. The hypothalamus is involved with many autonomic and endocrine functions and influences most every aspect of human physiology. The epithalamus contains the pineal gland which is involved in the regulation of circadian rhythms. And the subthalamus contains many sensory and motor tracts as well as some nuclei involved in the regulation of motor control.

➢ The telencephalon contains the 2 large cerebral hemispheres. The cerebral cortex is divided into distinct lobes both anatomically and functionally. The frontal lobes are involved with intellect, creativity, motivation and somatic motor function. The parietal lobes are involved with somatic sensory processing. The temporal lobes are involved with hearing and memory and the occipital lobes are involved with visual processing.

References and Suggested Readings

Funakoshi K, Nakano M. 2007. The sympathetic nervous system of anamniotes. *Brain, Behavior, and Evolution* 69:105-113.

Hodgkin AL, Huxley AF, Katz B. 1952. Measurement of current-voltage relations in the membrane of the giant axon of *Loligo*. *Journal of Physiology* 116:424-448.

Hodgkin AL, Huxley AF. 1952. Currents carried by sodium and potassium ions through the membrane of the giant axon of *Loligo*. *Journal of Physiology* 116:449-472.

Hodgkin AL, Huxley AF. 1952. The components of membrane conductance in the giant axon of *Loligo*. *Journal of Physiology* 116:473-496.

Hodgkin AL, Huxley AF. 1952. A quantitative description of membrane current and its application to conduction and excitation in nerve. *Journal of Physiology* 116:500-544.

Hoyle CHV. 2011. Evolution of neuronal signaling: Transmitters and receptors. *Autonomic Neuroscience: Basic and Clinical* 165:28-53.

Kimelberg HK. 2010. Functions of mature mammalian astrocytes: a current view. *The Neuroscientist* 16(1):79-106.

Langmoen IA, Apuzzo ML. 2007. The brain on itself: Nobel laureates and the history of fundamental nervous system function. *Neurosurgery* 61(5):891-908.

Miljkovic-Licina M, Gauchat D, Galliot B. 2004. Neuronal evolution: analysis of regulatory genes in a first-evolved nervous system, the hydra nervous system. *Biosystems* 76:75-87.

Nilsson S. 2011. Comparative anatomy of the autonomic nervous system. *Autonomic Neuroscience: Basic and Clinical* 165:3-9.

Palay SL, Sotelo C, Peters A, Orkand PM. 1968. The axon hillock and the initial segment. *The Journal of Cell Biology* 38:193-201.

Roots BI. 2008. The phylogeny of invertebrates and the evolution of myelin. *Neuron Glia Biology* 4(2):101-109.

Shepard GM, Erulkar SD. 1997. Centenary of the synapse: from Sherrington to the molecular biology of the synapse and beyond. *Trends in Neuroscience* 20(9):385-392.

Yeager M, Harris AL. 2007. Gap junction channel structure in the early 21st century: facts and fantasies. *Current Opinion in Cell Biology* 19:521-528.

Young HM, Can KN, Anderson CR. 2011. Development of the autonomic nervous system: a comparative view. *Autonomic Neuroscience: Basic and Clinical* 165:10-27.

Zalc B, Goujet D, Colman D. 2008. The origin of the myelination program in vertebrates. *Current Biology* 18(12):R511-R512.

Chapter 4: Sensory Physiology

Sensory receptors and systems have evolved along with the nervous system to help detect external and internal stimuli. Evolution of single receptors and receptor units have evolved into large sensory organs. Detection of certain physical modalities within the body, such as chemical, mechanical, and thermal stimuli help to regulate homeostasis and normal cellular function. Detection of light, sound and taste help organisms to understand their external environments. And detection of balance, acceleration, and proprioception (knowing where your limbs are located in space) help organisms to navigate through their external environments. Throughout the animal kingdom, various types of specific sensory organs have developed to help detect and capture prey and elude predators. For example, electric sensing has developed in some aquatic animals such as sharks and eels to help animals detect objects and it is used for types of communication. In birds, sensing of magnetic fields help birds navigate through the environment; this sensory input helps birds perceive their location, direction of flight and altitude. This chapter will limit the sensory receptors to highlight those senses found in humans.

The conscious awareness of sensation or feeling is a cortical process; without the sensory cortex of the brain, we could not "sense" anything. The sensory system is comprised of receptors located in the PNS which project, in very specific patterns, into the CNS and up to the brain. The term receptor can be confusing at times. In sensory physiology, a receptor is defined as a specific structure that is receptive to a particular stimulus (touch, light, etc...). The perception of sensation varies from individual to individual and is a higher order brain function. This chapter will cover the mechanical processing of the senses from localization and activation of the sensory receptors in the PNS to the ascending paths through the CNS, up to the sensory cortex of the brain. It will not, however, cover the psychology of sensation or our perception and understanding of senses.

Section 1 - General Properties of Sensory Systems

In the body, our senses can be divided into two broad categories, general senses and special senses. The general senses are distributed throughout the entire body. Somatic receptors provide information regarding touch, pressure, temperature, proprioception and pain from the skin and muscles. Visceral information arises from the organs and provides information primarily from pain and pressure receptors. The special senses provide information regarding smell, sight, taste, hearing and balance. In all senses, sensory reception begins within a stimulus acting on a single cell. The sensory receptor can either be directly on the ending of a sensory neuron or the receptor can be a specialized cell closely associated with a sensory neuron (Figure 4.1). Sensory neurons project into the dorsal horn of the spinal cord/brain and follow a particular path throughout the neuraxis. All sensory neurons are excitatory and release glutamate onto second order neurons. All sensory information synapses in the thalamus (except the olfactory system) before projecting to the cerebral cortex.

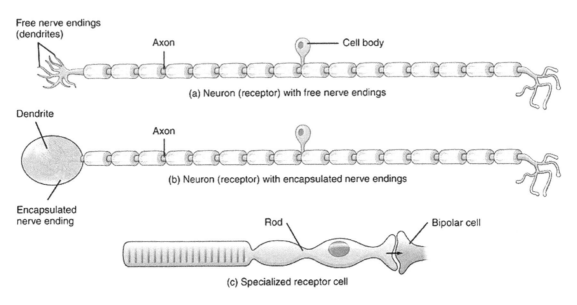

Figure 4.1

Sensory coding

The sensory system converts a stimulus energy into something that the CNS can interpret; i.e., sensory coding. The sensory system is organized in such a way as to isolate and detect sensory information. Sensory receptors are sensitive to a specific modality or have a unique ability to sense a particular stimulus. There are 5 types of sensory receptors in the body that detect various stimuli.

9) *Photoreceptors* are specialized receptors localized to the retina of the eye that respond directly to photons of light and are involved in our perception of sight or vision. Some photoreceptors, the cones, only detect specific wavelengths or colors of light, i.e., photons in the red, green or blue spectrums and are involved with color vision. Other photoreceptors, the rods, detect a larger light spectrum and are involved in the perception of light or no light.

10) *Thermoreceptors* detect temperature. Some thermoreceptors are specialized to detect warm temperatures and others are specialized to detect cold temperatures. These receptors are involved with the regulation of body temperature.

11) *Chemoreceptors* are specialized to sense various chemicals. For example, the olfactory epithelium in the nasal cavity is involved in detecting molecules in

the air which give us the sense of smell. Gustatory receptors on the tongue are specialized to detect chemicals and are involved with our perception of taste. And still other types of chemoreceptors in the body detect O_2, CO_2 and pH in the blood. These chemoreceptors are involved in the regulation of the respiratory and cardiovascular systems.

12) *Mechanoreceptors* are specialized receptors that are sensitive to compression, bending or stretching of the receptor. The body also contains a large number of mechanoreceptors which are involved with the sensation of touch, pressure, proprioception, balance, hearing, and blood pressure regulation.

13) *Nociceptors* are special receptors that respond to extreme mechanical, chemical and thermal stimuli. Nociceptors provide information regarding pain.

Sensory receptors are also described in terms of their location in the body. Exteroreceptors are receptors associated with skin and somatic sensation of touch and pain. These provide information regarding the external environment of the organism. Visceroreceptors are associated with organs and provide conscious awareness of pain and pressure in the internal organs. And proprioreceptors are associated with muscles, joints and tendons and provide information regarding the location of your limbs in relationship to your body. For example, if you close your eyes, you still know where your arms and legs are located. You can reach up and touch your nose with your finger. Proprioreceptors allow for this conscious understanding of where your limbs are located.

The receptor potential

A sensory receptor is either a specialized cell associated with a sensory neuron or the specialized ending of the sensory neuron itself. Specialized sensory cells don't typically generate action potentials, but are depolarized after activation. Activation of the receptor by a specific stimulus will result in the opening of channels (typically Na^+ channels) that allow the cell to depolarize. Depolarization of the sensory cell leads to the opening of voltage-gated Ca^{2+} channels followed by an influx of Ca^{2+}. Ca^{2+} promotes exocytosis and the release of vesicles filled with neurotransmitter. Neurotransmitters cross a synapse to bind to receptors on the sensory neuron leading to excitation of the neuron. Sensory receptors that are located on the ending of a sensory neuron are activated in a similar manner. The stimulus is detected by special receptors (mechanoreceptor, photoreceptor, etc...) which lead to the opening of a channel and subsequent depolarization. The depolarization in the sensory neuron is similar to an EPSP, except that it is located not at a synapse, but on the ending of a sensory receptor and is therefore called the receptor potential. The receptor potential decays with a certain time constant and length constant and is a type of graded response. Many sensory neurons contain large-diameter, heavily myelinated axons and are considered type 1 fibers. Voltage-gated Na^+ channels are found in high density at the first node of Ranvier. If the cell is depolarized enough to reach threshold and activate the voltage-gated Na^+ channels, then an action potential will be activated. This is called an adequate stimulus.

Factors that influence the magnitude of the receptor potential are 1) the strength of the stimulus, 2) the summation of multiple receptor potentials, 3) the duration of the stimulus, and 4) a phenomenon called adaptation. We will use light touch as an example to demonstrate how these factors influence the size of the receptor potential. A very light touch to the skin with a thin filament can evoke a small receptor potential that decays over distance. If the receptor potential is not adequate to induce an action potential at the first node of Ranvier, then there is nothing perceived by the brain; i.e., no touch. Increasing the intensity of stimulus by pressing the thin filament down on the skin will increase the number of individual ion channels that open allowing an increased influx of Na^+. This increased depolarization could lead to the formation of an action potential and the perception of light touch. Further increases in the intensity of the stimulus can cause more channels to open on the individual axon increasing the number of action potentials that are fired. The increased numbers of action potentials project ultimately to the cerebral cortex and is perceived as a stronger stimulus. Sensory coding of intensity occurs via changes in the frequency of action potentials.

A sensory unit is a single sensory neuron and all of its receptor endings. The sensory neuron contains multiple axon collaterals that converge onto a single axon which projects into the dorsal horn of the spinal cord. The cell bodies of sensory neurons are located in the dorsal root ganglia. The receptive field is the entire area which is covered by the nerve endings of the sensory unit. If the thin filament is pressed into the skin with a greater intensity, multiple nerve endings of a single sensory unit can get activated. This will result in multiple receptor potentials on each axon collateral which converge and summate at the first node of Ranvier. This can also increase the frequency of the action potentials that are fired by the sensory neuron.

If a stimulus is applied for a long period of time, then action potentials will continue to fire in some sensory neurons. These allow for the sensation of continuous touch. However, some sensory neurons undergo a phenomenon called adaptation in which the neuron "adapts" to the stimulus and stops firing action potentials. Neurons can either be rapidly-adapting or slowly-adapting which indicates how quickly the neuron stops firing action potentials. If a neuron remains in a depolarized state, multiple action potentials are activated. Recall that depolarization is due to the opening of voltage-gated Na^+ channels which then inactivate after a short period of time. In order for the inactivation gate to be removed, the voltage-gated channels need to be sufficiently hyperpolarized. If the channels are not exposed to a hyperpolarizing current then they can be "stuck" in an inactivated state and the frequency of action potentials slows or can even stop.

In different areas of the body, sensory units can occur with varying densities. In some areas, such as the fingers and face there is a greater number of sensory units with a smaller receptive field. This allows for a greater sense of acuity whereas other areas such as the legs or torso contain a low density of sensory units with large receptive fields. In these large receptive fields, if one sensory unit is simultaneously touched in two areas, the brain perceives this a single touch to one area; only one neuron was activated. However, if receptor fields overlap sufficiently, this will help provide some general information regarding the location of the stimulus.

Lateral inhibition

Lateral inhibition increases the acuity or sharpens the contrast of the sensory inputs when multiple sensory inputs are simultaneously stimulated (See Figure 4.2). In essence, lateral inhibition allows one to identify the exact localization of a stimulus although multiple sensory neurons might be activated. Lateral inhibition decreases the inputs from the periphery which highlights the center region. Lateral inhibition occurs in many sensory systems. For example sensory neurons involved with light touch, temperature and pressure enter the dorsal horn of the spinal cord and make synapses with other neurons and interneurons. Lateral inhibition is a process in which each sensory neuron inhibits the surrounding neurons. If three neurons are simultaneously activated by a single stimulus, action potentials are triggered in each neuron. The center neuron fires action potentials at a higher frequency due to the increased numbers of nerve endings that get activated. The surrounding neurons on each side also fire action potentials, but at a reduced frequency because fewer nerve endings were activated. The action potentials travel along the primary axons and enter the spinal cord. Each neuron also projects to an inhibitory interneuron which inhibits the neighboring axons. This inhibits the peripheral axons and increases the contrast between the three inputs. Lateral inhibition is an important feature of somatic sensation as well as vision.

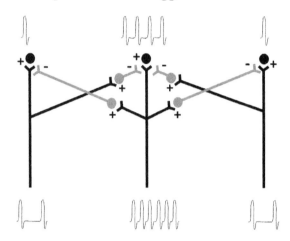

Figure 4.2

CHAPTER 4, SECTION 1 – SUMMARY

➢ The senses evolved to detect external stimuli to help detect and capture prey and avoid predators as well as to detect internal stimuli to help regulate homeostasis.

➢ The senses are divided into the general senses and the special senses. The general senses include somatic sensory information which carries information about touch, pressure, temperature, proprioception and pain. The special senses include the ability to sense smell, sight, taste, hearing, and balance.

➢ Five types of sensory receptors can be found in the human body: 1) photoreceptors respond to photons of light, 2) thermoreceptors respond to hot or cold temperatures, 3) chemoreceptors respond to various chemicals such as blood gases or molecules in the mouth that confer the sensation of taste, 4) mechanoreceptors respond to stretch, compression, and bending and are involved in the sense of touch, hearing, balance, proprioception, blood pressure, etc... 5) nociceptors respond to extreme mechanical or chemical or thermal stimuli and are involved with the sense of pain.

➢ Sensory receptors can be the specialized ending of a sensory neuron or a special cell with an associated sensory neuron. A sensory unit is a single sensory neuron and all of its receptor endings.

➢ All sensory neurons respond to their specific stimuli by depolarization. This is called the receptor potential.

➢ If a receptor potential is large enough, an action potential travels along the sensory axon into the spinal cord. The cell bodies of all sensory neurons are found in the dorsal root ganglia along the spinal cord or a ganglia associated with a specific cranial nerve.

➢ The magnitude of the receptor potential is influenced by 1) the strength of the stimulus, 2) the summation of multiple receptor potentials, 3) the duration of the stimulus and 4) adaptation.

➢ Lateral inhibition is the process that increases the acuity or sharpens the contrast of sensory inputs when multiple sensory units are activated. It involves inhibitory interneurons which inhibit the inputs of surrounding sensory units.

Section 2 – Somatic and Visceral Sensation

Sensation in skin

Skin is the largest organ in the body. The skin makes the closest contact with the outside environment and is designed to protect the body and provide sensory information about the external environment. Skin has an outer epidermis which is comprised of a stratified squamous epithelium that is keratinized. Keratinization is a process by which cells create a tough barrier to water, chemicals and bacteria. Strong keratin fibers, lipids, and keratohyalin proteins are secreted by keratinocytes and are found sandwiched between dead cells. Under the epidermis is the dermis, a connective tissue layer that contains a superficial papillary layer made of areolar connective tissue and a larger reticular layer comprised of dense irregular connective tissue. Under skin is the hypodermis, another layer of connective tissue that connects skin to the underlying organs and structures, such as muscles. Skin contains multiple sensory receptors that are found scattered throughout, from the basal layer of the epidermis all the way through skin and into the hypodermis (See Figure 4.3). Specific sensory receptors are located at certain layers in order to detect the specific modalities that activate them. Sensory receptors of skin are sensitive to multiple types of mechanical and chemical perturbations, temperature and nociception.

The most common sensory nerve ending in the body is a free nerve ending. In skin, free nerve endings are sensitive to either temperature, nociception or are a type of mechanoreceptors or chemoreceptor. There are two types of temperature receptors, those that are sensitive to warm and those that are sensitive to cold. The cold temperature receptors are 10-15 times more numerous in the body than those that are sensitive to warm temperatures and are involved in regulating body temperature. Nociceptors that are sensitive to hot are a separate type of neuron. Warm temperature-sensitive neurons respond to temperature

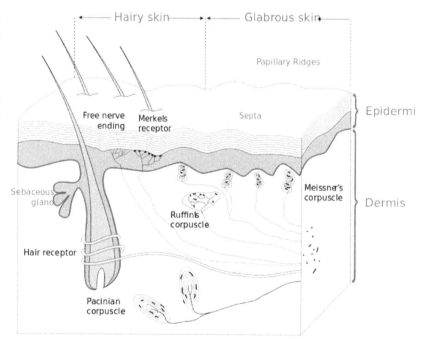

Figure 4.3

up to ~43°C at which time nociceptors which are sensitive to hot temperatures begin to get stimulated. Temperature receptors are scattered throughout the epidermis and dermis in skin. In this manner, the body can distinguish between cold, warm and hot.

Within skin, there are multiple types of receptors that provide information about touch. There are receptors that are sensitive to light touch such as free nerve endings, Merkel corpuscles (or discs) and Meissner's corpuscles, receptors that are sensitive to texture such as the Meissner's corpuscles, and receptors that are sensitive to deep pressure and vibration such as the Ruffini end organs and the Pacinian corpuscle.

Merkel discs are a type of sensory receptor that contains a specialized epithelial cell found sitting on the basement membrane. The axon of a sensory neuron makes a specialized flattened nerve ending which contacts the special Merkel cell. Merkel sensory receptors are a type of slowly-adapting mechanoreceptor and thus provide some information regarding the duration of touch. Meissner corpuscles are found under the epidermis in papillary ridges in highly sensitive areas of the body such as the lips and fingers. Meissner corpuscles are a type of encapsulated nerve ending associated with a gel-filled structure. Meissner corpuscles are involved in the determination of texture, and along with Merkel discs, they are involved in the ability to discriminate two-points that are simultaneously applied to the skin.

Deep pressure and vibration are sensed by receptors that are found deeper in the dermis and the hypodermis. Ruffini end-organs are found in the dermis of hands and are a type of receptor that is sensitive to continuous touch or pressure. Ruffini end-organs are also a type of neuron that is associated with a specialized gelatinous structure. The Pacinian corpuscle is a large structure found in the deep dermis and hypodermis (and in joints between bones). The Pacinian corpuscle is a round or oval structure that has many layers of a gelatinous protein layered with nerve endings. The Pacinian corpuscle is a type of rapidly-adapting mechanoreceptor and detects the onset and offset of stimulation or touch.

All spinal sensory receptors have their cell bodies located in the dorsal root ganglia and the axons project into the dorsal horn of the spinal cord where they enter certain ascending paths based on their specific sensory modality. For example, all of the information regarding temperature whether that information comes from the leg or the arm is carried through a path called the spinothalamic tract. Information carrying somatic sensation will project to the thalamus and on to the post-central gyrus of the parietal lobe. Areas in the brain, including the post-central gyrus are anatomically arranged such that the information from the hand is next to the information from the forearm and so on. Areas which have fine areas of discrimination such as the hands and the face have more neurons that arise from these areas and they each project to a neuron in the brain (See Figure 4.4). These areas of the brain that are designated for the hand and face are therefore larger.

Proprioception

Proprioception provides sensory information from muscles, tendons and joints. This allows individuals to recognize where there limbs and their bodies are located in space. This information also uses sensory information regarding balance for perception. Pacinian corpuscles, Golgi tendon organs and muscle spindles are the types of receptors that provide this information. Golgi tendon organs and Pacinian corpuscles are found in the tendons and joint space and help to localize joint position. Muscle spindles are a sensory receptor found in skeletal muscles which help to recognize muscle length and tension (Chapter 5). Many of these receptors convey unconscious

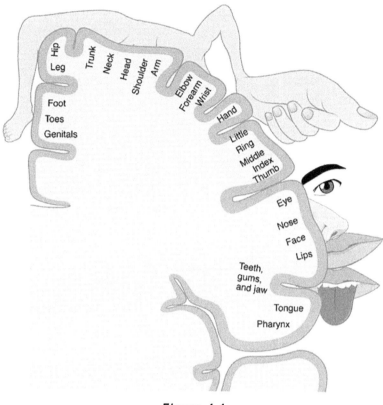

Figure 4.4

sensory information to help with balance and basic motor function and project to the cerebellum and other deep nuclei, but they also convey information to the cerebral cortex for conscious awareness of the limb location relative to your body.

Visceral receptors

Visceral receptors are receptors that are found in the viscera or organs. The majority of the receptors in the viscera that allow conscious awareness of the viscera are pain and pressure receptors. For example, gas bloating in the large intestine presses on the pain and pressure receptors activating the receptor and provide you with a sensation of discomfort. There are many other types of receptors that are involved in the homeostatic regulation of organ function. These specific types of receptors will be covered in each organ system.

Ascending sensory paths

Perception of our senses is our general understanding and awareness of what the sensation means and occurs in the cortex of the brain. Non-conscious sensation also occurs in our body and is involved in maintaining homeostasis. Each sensory modality travels through a unique pathway to reach a specific area in the cerebral cortex (See Figure 4.5, on the next page). In general, most neural paths use 3 neurons to project from the periphery to their target area in the cerebral cortex. In some cases, the first portion of the name of the ascending path denotes its starting location and the second portion of the name describes its target location. For example the spinothalamic tract arises from the spinal cord and projects to the thalamus.

Figure 4.5

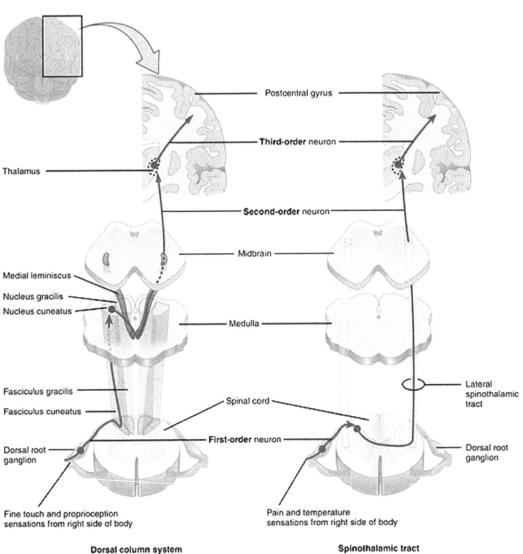

Dorsal column system

Spinothalamic tract

The anterolateral system contains the spinothalamic tract and carries sensory information regarding pain, temperature, and light touch from the periphery to the post-central gyrus of the parietal lobe. The primary neuron is the sensory neuron that arises from sensory receptor and travels into the dorsal horn (its cell body located within the dorsal root ganglia) (Figure 4.5). The primary neuron connects to the secondary neuron which crosses to the opposite side of the spinal cord (the contralateral side) and enters the anterolateral tract to ascend the spinal cord. The anterolateral tract is a collection of sensory fibers that span a region on the edge of the anterior and lateral columns of the white matter. The primary and secondary neurons may connect directly or in many cases there may be interneurons that connect the two neurons. The secondary neuron projects up to the thalamus where it synapses in a region called the ventral posterolateral nucleus. The third order neuron projects from the VPL nucleus to the post-central gyrus of the parietal lobe. The sensory information is organized and grouped by specific locations in the body as well as specific types of sensory receptors.

The medial lemniscal system (dorsal column pathways) carries proprioceptive and two point discriminative information up to the cerebral cortex (Figure 4.5). The primary neuron again is the sensory neuron that projects from the sensory receptor into the dorsal horn of the spinal cord. In this case, however, the sensory neuron does not make a synapse, but instead enters the dorsal columns to ascend to the medulla oblongata on the same side of the spinal cord (the ipsilateral side). In the dorsal horns there are two tracts running up the spinal cord, the medial tract is called the fasciculus gracilis and the lateral tract is the fasciculus cuneatus. The fasciculus gracilis carries information from below T6, whereas information above T6 enters the dorsal columns and enters the lateral edge of the dorsal column and forms the fasciculus cuneatus. Each tract ascend together to make synapses in a nucleus in the medulla, the nucleus cuneatus and the nucleus gracilis. The secondary neurons from these two nuclei cross to the contralateral side and enter the medial lemniscal tract. The secondary neuron ascends through the pons and midbrain to enter and synapse within the ventral posterolateral nucleus of the thalamus. From the thalamus, the third order neuron projects to the post-central gyrus of the parietal lobe for conscious awareness of sensation.

The spinocerebellar system carries non-conscious proprioceptive sensory information regarding muscle length and tension, balance and joint location to the cerebellum. The posterior spinocerebellar tract is a two neuron system. The primary neuron enters the spinal cord through the dorsal horn of the spinal cord and synapses with a neuron located in dorsal horn (dorsal nucleus of Clarke). The second order neuron enters the posterior spinocerebellar tract on the ipsilateral side of the spinal cord and ascends to enter the cerebellum through the inferior cerebellar peduncle.

There are more additional sensory paths that carry specific types of sensory information to specific areas of the brain. In general, sensory inputs that provide conscious awareness of sensation project to the cerebral cortex and other inputs carrying unconscious sensory signals project to other areas of the brain. We will cover specific sensory information concerning homeostatic regulation of specific organ systems as they arise. For example, we will cover the sensation of blood pressure during the cardiovascular system, the sensation of blood gases in the respiratory system and the sensation of osmolarity in the endocrine system. The special senses are covered below.

CHAPTER 4, SECTION 2 – SUMMARY

➤ Sensory receptors in skin provide information about the external environment. These receptors include free nerve endings, Merkel corpuscles, Meissner's corpuscles, Ruffini end-organs and Pacinian corpuscles and convey information regarding touch, pain, vibration and pain.

➤ Proprioception involves the sensation of spatial recognition of your limbs and body. Sensory receptors can be found in muscles, tendons and joints.

➤ Visceral sensory receptors are found in the organs and respond to pressure and pain.

➤ Sensory information is carried up to the brain through a variety of neural pathways that are specific to the different sensory modalities.

➤ The anterolateral system carries sensory information regarding pain, temperature, and light touch from the periphery to the brain. This path arises from the sensory neuron, makes contact with a secondary neuron in the dorsal horn of the spinal cord and crosses to the opposite side to ascend the spinal cord. The secondary neuron synapses in the thalamus before projecting to the primary sensory cortex located in the parietal lobe.

➤ The medial lemniscal system carries information regarding proprioception and two-point discrimination from the periphery to the brain. The sensory neuron enters the dorsal horn of the spinal cord and directly enter the dorsal columns to ascend the spinal cord on the same side as it entered. The sensory neuron synapses in the medulla before crossing to the opposite side of the cord to ascend to the thalamus. The tertiary neuron projects from the thalamus to the primary sensory cortex.

➤ The spinocerebellar system carries non-conscious proprioceptive information to the cerebellum. Sensory information enters the dorsal horn and synapses with a second neuron. The secondary neuron ascends on the same side of the spinal cord to make its final synapse in the ipsilateral cerebellum.

Section 3 - Special Senses

The special senses include the sense of taste, smell, vision, hearing and balance. These specific senses are carried through cranial nerves directly into the brain without entering the spinal cord. Some cranial nerves however, also carry general somatic afferents. For example, the trigeminal nerve carries sensory information from receptors located on the skin covering the face and neck.

Gustatory System

The sense of taste or gustation is achieved by specialized sensory organs located on the tongue and other surfaces of the oral cavity. The taste bud is a collection of three cell types that are embedded into the stratified squamous epithelium lining the tongue and surface of the mouth. Each taste bud contains ~40-60 gustatory cells, along with supporting cells (sustentacular cells) and basal cell. The supporting cells provide nourishment and mechanical support for the gustatory and basal cells. The basal cells undergo mitosis every10-14 days to replace old worn-out, gustatory cells. The gustatory cells are columnar cells that project long microvilli, or gustatory hairs toward the surface of the epithelium into a taste pore. The pore contains aqueous saliva. The molecules in food dissolve and enter the pore to activate specific taste receptors located on the gustatory hairs.

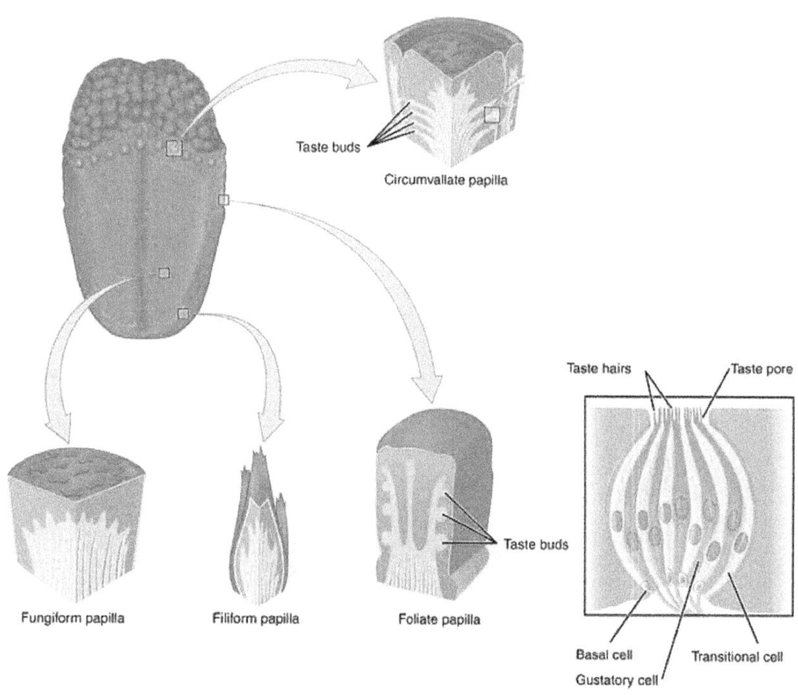

Taste buds are found on the surface of the tongue associated with specific structures called lingual papillae (Figure 4.6). Lingual papillae form the bumpy surface of the tongue and are a prominent projection. The majority of the lingual papillae are called filiform papillae and have no taste receptors associated with them. The majority of the taste buds are found associated with foliate lingual papillae which can be found along the lateral and anterior edges of the tongue. The taste buds are most often found on the lateral aspects, or the side of each papillae. There are some additional taste buds associated with fungiform papillae which are found scattered over the superior aspect

Figure 4.6

Taste buds
Circumvallate papilla

Taste hairs
Taste pore

Fungiform papilla
Filiform papilla
Foliate papilla
Taste buds

Basal cell
Transitional cell
Gustatory cell

of the tongue and the vallate papillae which are the largest papillae and form a row of 8-12 papillae at the most posterior aspect of the tongue. The distribution of taste receptors is based on the types and numbers of receptors for the various modalities of taste, sweet, sour, bitter, salty and umami. There are many types of receptors for the various modalities of taste. Multiple receptor types can be found can be found on each individual gustatory cell.

Gustatory cells have a negative resting membrane potential which is due, in part, to leak K^+ channels. Some signal transduction pathways for the detection of salts, NaCl and KCl, may be due to the direct movement of ions, i.e., Na^+ into the gustatory cell resulting in depolarization. Similarly, ingested K^+ increases the extracellular K^+ concentration and results in less K^+ leak and cellular depolarization. Detection of sour tastes may be due to the acidic nature of sour components. The high extracellular positive acidic (H^+) environment may block the outward K^+ movement causing cellular depolarization. Some sweet, sour and bitter molecules activate receptors that belong to the family of G-protein coupled receptor proteins. For example, sucrose can activate G-protein coupled receptors and enhance the formation of intracellular cAMP leading to activation of PKA and the phosphorylation of K^+ channels. Closure of K^+ channels leads to cellular depolarization. Another known mechanism includes the activation of bitter receptors and the subsequent activation of a G_q coupled receptor. PLC gets activated and leads to the formation of DAG and IP3 which directly leads to an increase in intracellular Ca^{2+} levels leading to cellular depolarization. A final example is the umami receptor which responds directly to glutamate (found in protein, i.e., meat) acting through a special metabotropic glutamate receptor. Activation of mGluR leads to the activation of Gi and inhibits the formation of cAMP. The cAMP usually is binding to a Ca^{2+} channel and keeps it closed. By decreasing cAMP levels the Ca^{2+} channel opens and Ca^{2+} flows into the cell causing cellular depolarization. In all of the above mechanisms, depolarization of the gustatory cell leads to the opening of voltage-gated Ca^{2+} channels and enhances exocytosis of vesicles which release neurotransmitter onto neurons innervating the gustatory cell.

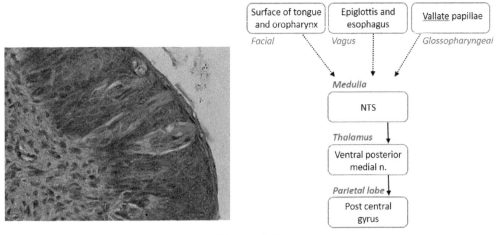

Figure 4.7

The taste buds located on the surface of the tongue and the soft palate and scattered throughout the oropharynx are innervated by neurons of the facial nerve (cranial nerve VII). The taste buds located in the vallate papillae are innervated by a branch of the glossopharyngeal nerve (cranial nerve IX) and taste buds located on the epiglottis and in the esophagus are innervated by the vagus nerve (cranial nerve X) (See Figure 4.7). The sensory neurons of the facial, glossopharyngeal and vagus terminate in the nucleus of the solitary tract (or nucleus of the tractus solitarius, NTS) located in the medulla. Axons from the NTS travel to the ipsilateral thalamus (the ventral posterior medial nucleus) where they synapse. Thalamic neurons of the gustatory pathway ultimately project to the post-central gyrus of the parietal lobe for perception of taste and higher cortical processing. Cortical processing of taste perception involves influences from many other factors such as smell, tactile sensations (textures), temperature, age, as well as visual inputs.

Olfactory System

Olfaction or the sense of smell is carried out by a specialized epithelium located in the nasal cavity (Figure 4.8). The olfactory epithelium contains three types of cells which help influence and control the sense of olfaction. The primary sensory receptor is the olfactory neuron and it is surrounded by supporting sustentacular cells and basal cells. The olfactory neuron is a bipolar cell that contains a single dendrite which extends up into a thick mucus layer that lines the nasal cavity. Several olfactory hairs or cilia are found on the tips of dendrites and contain many membrane bound odorant receptors. Odoriferous molecules get trapped in the mucus and come into contact with the odorant receptors on olfactory hairs. Different olfactory neurons have different sensitivities to odorants based on the numbers of receptors to specific molecules. There are over 1000 different types of possible receptors which belong to the G-protein family of proteins. The majority of G-proteins

Figure 4.8

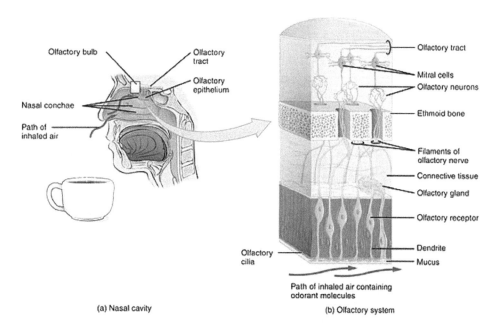

(a) Nasal cavity　　　　(b) Olfactory system

appear to associate with G_s and activate adenylyl cyclase and increase intracellular cAMP levels leading to the opening of cationic channels. The dendrites on the olfactory neurons depolarize in response to activation by odorant molecules and action potentials are generated on the unmyelinated axon of the olfactory neuron. The olfactory neuron extends an axon into small holes or olfactory foramina of the cribiform plate on the ethmoid bone. The axon extends into the cranial cavity and synapses with either the tufted cells or mitral cells within the olfactory bulb. This collection of axons comprise the first cranial nerve I, the olfactory neuron. Within the bulb, olfactory neurons with similar odorant receptor subtypes synapse with tufted cells and mitral cells to form a small, ball-like structure called a glomerulus. The tufted and mitral cell axons enter the frontal and temporal lobes of the brain which form reciprocal connections. Neurons also project to other areas such as the hypothalamus and other limbic structures which provide information related to emotional aspects of smell and to the hippocampus for memories of smell.

Along with the olfactory neurons, two additional types of cells can be found in the olfactory epithelium, sustentacular cells and basal cells. Basal cells undergo cell division or mitosis and replace olfactory neurons approximately every 30-60 days. The olfactory neurons are considered true neurons because they are derived from the CNS. The sustentacular cells provide mechanical support for the olfactory neurons as well as secrete substances that contribute to the mucus covering the luminal surface of the olfactory epithelium. In addition, mucus comes from specialized glands lying under the epithelium as well as from the goblet cells of the pseudostratified columnar epithelium covering the rest of the nasal cavity.

In humans the sense of smell is carried out by several million olfactory neurons which are found in the nasal cavity in a small area of the superior aspect of the nasal cavity, ~5cm2. Many animals such as the dog have a much keener sense of smell and their nasal cavities are covered by a large percentage of olfactory epithelium.

Visual System

The eyes are adapted to collect photons of light and convert them into action potentials for processing and visual perception which occurs in the visual cortex of the occipital lobe. On earth, most of the visible light comes from the sun. Other sources of light include fire, bioluminescence created by some animals, and man-made electrical light. Human eyes can detect electromagnetic radiation in the 400-750nm range and is therefore called visible light (See Figure 4.9).

The mammalian eye is adapted to collect and focus photons of light onto the sensory receptors, the retina. The eyeball contains three major layers, an outer fibrous layer, the middle vascular layer and the inner nervous layer (Figure 4.10). The outermost fibrous layer is comprised of dense, regular connective tissue. It is comprised of the sclera, the white part of the eyeball, and the cornea which sits in the front and is transparent to allow light to enter the eye. The sclera is the site where muscles attach to the eye and allow for eye movement. Each eye has 6 skeletal muscles whose movement is controlled by 3 cranial nerves; the oculomotor, trochlear and abducens nerves. The eyes move in response to conscious effort and reflex activity.

The middle layer of the eye is the vascular layer. The vascular layer contains the iris, the ciliary body and the choroid. The iris contains pigmented cells and is the colored portion of the eye.

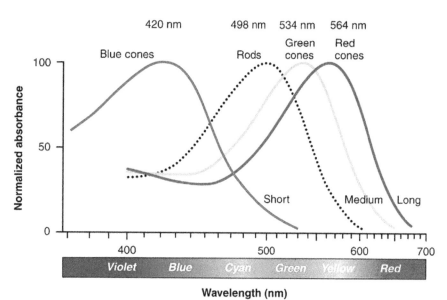

Figure 4.9

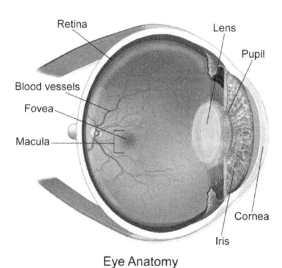

Eye Anatomy

Figure 4.10

Two layers of smooth muscle sit under the pigmented portion of the iris and control the diameter of the pupil, the open center of the iris which allow light to pass through. The size of the opening or the pupil is under both sympathetic and parasympathetic control (See Figure 4.11, on the next page). The sphincter pupillae is a circular muscle encompassing the circumference of the pupil and the dilator pupillae muscle fibers radiate outward. Sympathetic stimulation causes mydriasis or dilation of the pupil. Release of norepinephrine onto the dilator pupillae muscle causes contraction and increases the size of the pupil. Parasympathetic stimulation causes miosis or constriction of the pupil. Release of ACh from the oculomotor nerve (cranial nerve III) onto sphincter pupillae muscle causes smooth muscle contraction, decreasing the size of the pupil.

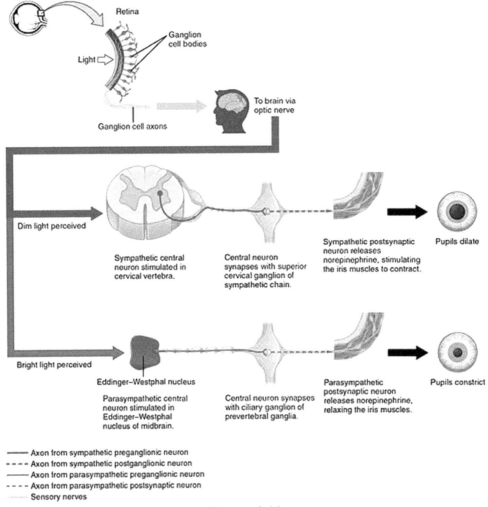

Figure 4.11

The ciliary body produces the aqueous humor, a fluid that fills the anterior chamber of the eye or the space behind the cornea and in front of the lens. The aqueous fluid drains out of the anterior chamber through the canal of Schlemm which is found in front of the iris where the iris and the cornea converge. If the drainage slows down, the pressure of the anterior chamber increases resulting in glaucoma. If left untreated glaucoma can cause blindness. The ciliary body also controls the shape of the lens. The ciliary body contains long processes that attach to suspensory ligaments which attach directly to the lens itself. When the ciliary body is relaxed, tension is applied to the suspensory ligaments and the lens is flattened. Activation of parasympathetic fibers (cranial nerve III) cause the ciliary muscles to contract, the suspensory fibers are slackened and the lens becomes rounded. This allows for accommodation of near objects. As we age, the ability to accommodate lessens and thus, the need for reading glasses increases.

Finally, the choroid is continuous with the ciliary body which sits behind the retina and contains pigmented cells and blood vessels that supply the eye. The pigmented cells absorb any light that gets past the retina to prevent light scattering in the eye. The blood vessels provide the retina and sclera with proper nutrient and gas exchange.

The innermost layer of the eye is the retina (Figure 4.12). The retina contains two layers, the sensory layer and a single layer of cells called the pigmented layer. The pigmented layer is the outermost layer of the retina and sits closest to the choroid. It is comprised of a single layer of pigmented cuboidal cells and is important in reducing light scattering. It is also important in the recycling of the photoreceptors that are located on the rods and cones, the cells receptive to light. The sensory layer contains multiple cell layers. Starting from the outermost edge, next to the pigmented epithelium, sits the rods and cones. The rods and cones are connected to a bipolar cell which is in turn connected to the ganglion cell which is found in the innermost layer. Two types of interneurons are found in the sensory retina. Horizontal cells make connect the rods and cones to the bipolar cells and amacrine cells connect the bipolar cells to the ganglion cells. An additional, supporting cell can be found in the retina that extends the length of the sensory layer, the Müller cells. In front of the retina is a large posterior chamber filled with the vitreous body, a gelatinous filled sac that presses on the retina and helps to adhere the sensory retina to the pigmented retina.

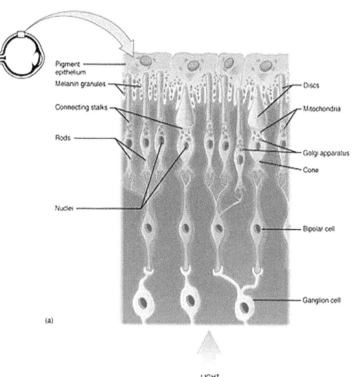

Figure 4.12

As light enters the eye, it passes through many structures before hitting the photoreceptors located in the retina. Light passes through the cornea into the anterior chamber and is modified by the diameter of the pupil. Light passes through the lens which changes its focal length and through the vitreous body of the posterior chamber. Once it hits the retina, light must extend through multiple cell layers, the ganglion cell layer and the bipolar layer, (and the interneurons) before finally reaching the photoreceptors, the rods and cones. One function of Müller cells is to act as an optic fiber and they carry the photons of light directly to the rods and cones.

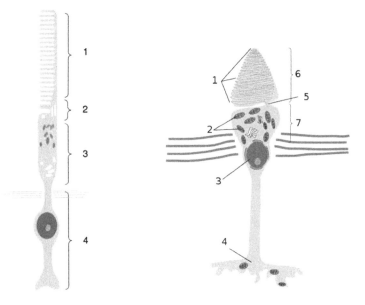

Figure 4.13

In the retina, the rods and cones are highly organized (Figure 4.13). The cones can be found in the highest density in a more centralized region called the fovea. In bright light, the lens focuses the light onto the fovea which enhances visual acuity. As you move away from the fovea, the number of cones decreases and the number of rods increase, such that at the edges of the retina are filled only with rods. The rods and cones contain the photoreceptors which detect photons of light. Rods are 1000X more sensitive to light than cones and this allows vision to occur in very dim light. Rods contain only one type of photopigment. The cones are less sensitive to light, therefore they are only active in bright light. Cones have three types of photopigments which allow for color discrimination. The photopigments are found in the outer segment of the rod or cone. The outer segment is embedded into the pigmented epithelium and contains stacks of membranes which contain the photopigments. The outer segment of the rod is rod-shaped whereas the cone outer segment is cone-shaped.

Figure 4.14

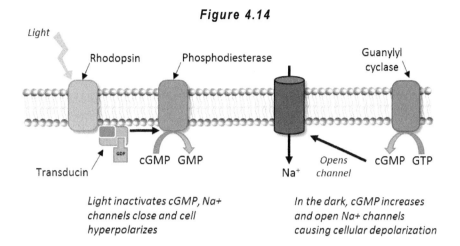

Light inactivates cGMP, Na+
channels close and cell
hyperpolarizes

In the dark, cGMP increases
and open Na+ channels
causing cellular depolarization

The photopigments are special G-protein-linked receptors with an attached ligand complex (Figure 4.14). The receptor is called opsin which is the light sensor and the ligand is retinal (a derivative of vitamin A). In the dark, retinal is in an inactive form (11-cis-retinal). Photons of light, change the retinal to an active form (all-trans retinal). The ligand then activates its receptor, opsin, and causes a conformational change. The rhodopsin molecule activates a specific G-protein called transducin. The α-subunit of transducin activates a phosphodiesterase, an enzyme which inactivates cGMP by breaking it down to GMP.

In the dark, photoreceptors (rods and cones) have a constitutively active guanylyl cyclase which produces cGMP from GTP. cGMP activates and opens a Na^+ channel. Na^+ moves down its concentration gradient into the photoreceptor and causes cellular depolarization. When light hits the photoreceptor, it activates rhodopsin. Retinal changes shape from 11-cis to the all-trans position and activates opsin and in turn, transducin. Transducin stimulates phosphodiesterase which breaks down cGMP to GMP. Thus, light causes a reduction in the cytosolic cGMP levels and this will cause the Na^+ channels to close and cause the cell to become hyperpolarized.

In all photoreceptors, rods and cones, light activates the mechanisms described above and light results in less glutamate released. The rods and cones synapse onto bipolar cells. Horizontal cells are interneurons which help create lateral inhibition of visual receptive fields. Visual receptive fields are circular with a center-surround arrangement of cells. A group of photoreceptors in the "center" of the circle converge onto a single bipolar cell. The photoreceptors which "surround" the center are attached via horizontal cell connections (GABAergic). Together, the center and surround fields create a single receptive field. Some of these bipolar cells create an ON pathway (and are turned on in light) and some create an OFF pathway (turned off in light). This helps discriminate exactly where the most light is directed.

The ON and OFF pathways are dependent upon two types of bipolar cells. Bipolar cells which exhibit the ON pathway contain metabotropic glutamate receptors (mGluR6). In the dark, when the photoreceptor is depolarized, it is releasing glutamate. Glutamate acts on mGluR6 which results in the hyperpolarization of the bipolar cell. Therefore, the bipolar cell will be inhibited and will NOT stimulate the ganglion cell. In the light, less glutamate is released from the photoreceptor; the bipolar cell is no longer inhibited and therefore will depolarize and release neurotransmitter and stimulate the ganglion cell. Thus, in the light, the bipolar cell of the center receptive field and its pathway is turned ON. The ganglion cells generate action potentials which will be sent to the brain for processing. In the retina, only ganglion cells generate action potentials, the bipolar cells and photoreceptors (rods and cones) only respond by depolarizing or hyperpolarizing.

Bipolar cells of the center of the OFF pathway contain AMPA receptors at the synapse between the photoreceptor and the bipolar cell. In the light, photoreceptors release less glutamate onto the bipolar cell and the AMPA receptors are not activated. Thus these bipolar cells and pathway is turned OFF in the light.

Visual receptive fields are organized with an ON center/OFF surround arrangement or an OFF center/ON surround arrangement. A ganglion cell receives the collective information from a receptive field (Figure 4.15) to determine the location of the light source. Photoreceptors that are located in the surround region of the receptive field are not connected directly to the center bipolar cells but they are connected to horizontal cells which influence the state of the center bipolar cells. Horizontal cells get stimulated by light hitting the photoreceptors. The horizontal cells release GABA onto nearby bipolar cells (lateral inhibition). For example, in an ON center/OFF surround arrangement, stimulation of light into the center will stimulate the center ON path and the horizontal cells will inhibit the surround. If the light hits the surround region, the horizontal cell will inhibit the center and thus the ganglion cell will be inhibited increasing the acuity and detection of light (light did not hit the center). A similar event happens in the OFF center/ON surround configuration. The retina has overlapping visual receptive fields which help detect and decipher light.

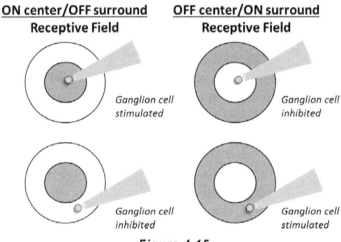

Figure 4.15

In the dark, eyes adapt to the changing light intensity. Dark adaptation takes approximately 20-25 minutes for full adaptation to take place. The sensitivity to light increases due to multiple events occurring in the eyes. The pupil dilates which allows light to hit a larger portion of the retina, specifically the rods which are located more in the periphery of the eye. The pigments in the rods are regenerated. When rods are exposed to bright light they become "bleached" so that the information from these areas is "ignored" by the brain. In addition, there is a slight adjustment of the circuitry of the retina, so that the brain now starts to use the information coming from the rods.

Light adaptation is much faster (~ 5-10min). The pupils constrict and decrease the amount of light allowed in the eye. The rods become "bleached" and there is some adjustment to the functional circuitry so that the brain stops paying attention to the rods and pays attention to the cones.

The optic disc is the location in the eye where the axons of the ganglion cells and the blood vessels converge. The optic nerve (cranial nerve II) enters the brain just inferior to the hypothalamus. Some of the axons cross before entering the brain and form the optic chiasm. The inputs that arise from the right visual field from both eyes project back to the left side of the brain and inputs that arise from the left visual field project to the right brain. The axons of ganglion cells synapse with neurons of the lateral geniculate body of the thalamus which then project back to the visual cortex located in the occipital lobe. Some collaterals of the ganglion cells project to the superior colliculus in the midbrain for reflex eye movements and to the hypothalamus for regulation of circadian rhythms.

Auditory System

The sense of hearing allows organisms to hear sounds within a certain range of frequencies. Sound is a complex mixture of pure tones and random related waves called noise. Sound waves in air are simple sine waves moving at a certain frequency and are recoded in cycles/second (Hertz, Hz). In humans, the normal range of sounds can be heard between 50 and 16,000 Hz. Different animals have ranges of sounds that can be heard outside of the range of human sounds. The intensity of sound or the loudness of sound is measured in decibels and is the amount of force or pressure that the wave exerts on the tympanic membrane and the hair cells within ear. Sounds outside of the normal range of decibels can cause irreparable damage to the hair cells within the inner ear.

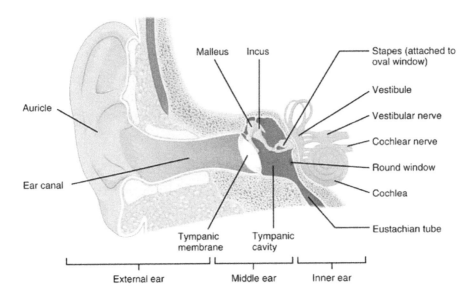

Figure 4.16

Sound waves through the air are captured by external ears or the pinna or auricles (Figure 4.16). In humans, the pinna play only a minor role in collecting sound waves, but in animals, the pinna play a major role in sound wave collection. For example, many animals can turn their ears independently to capture sound waves around the body. You can mimic this action by using your hands to capture sound waves next to the ears. You can even hear sounds behind your body by directing the hands in a backward direction. It is easy to recognize that in animals with large ears, this helps with survival, either in search of its prey or avoidance from predators. In animals, large ears can also play additional physiological functions such as thermoregulation. Ears are relatively thin structures that can be perfused with a large blood supply and exposed to the environment to enhance cooling.

Sound waves are collected by the pinna and transferred into the external auditory meatus where they hit the tympanic membrane. The external auditory meatus contains hairs and modified sweat glands called ceruminous glands. Cerumen is a waxy substance that is secreted into the lumen of the external auditory meatus and keeps the tympanic membrane supple. The hairs and cerumen also prevent bacteria and insects from inhabiting the space (especially important in animals other than humans). The tympanic membrane is a very thin membrane which easily vibrates when sound waves hit it. The membrane is comprised of two epithelia, a simple squamous epithelium and a simple cuboidal membrane, separated by a little connective tissue. On the inner surface of the tympanic membrane, three bony ossicles are attached in series, the malleolus, incus and stapes to another membrane, the oval window. The ossicles contain synovial joints which move easily and allow them to vibrate when sound waves move the tympanic membrane. The ossicles sit in a space called the middle ear which is filled with air and is open to the nasopharynx by way of the Eustachian or auditory tube. In children, middle ear infections are common because infections in the nose and throat can easily migrate up the Eustachian tube into the middle ear. Fluid can fill up the space and cause the tympanic membrane to burst or rupture. This relieves the pressure of the middle ear and the pain usually subsides. In adults, middle ear infections are rarer because the tube narrows with development and it is oriented on an angle, thus gravity helps prevent the migration of fluid upward.

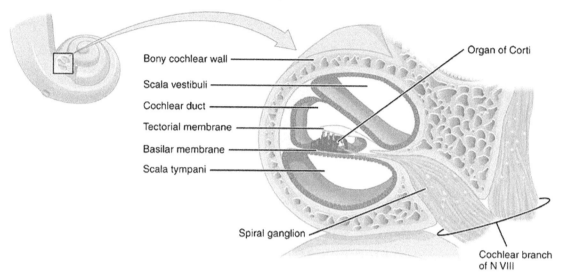

Figure 4.17

The stapes is attached to another thin membrane, the oval window. The oval window is the beginning of the inner ear where the cochlea is located. The oval window is smaller than the tympanic membrane and thus amplifies the size of the wave that is transmitted into the cochlea. The cochlea is a coiled snail-shaped structure that contains three chambers (Figure 4.17). The oval window is attached to the first chamber, the scala vestibuli, which is filled with perilymph. The scala vestibuli winds up the snail-shaped structure 2 ½ times to reach the tip or helicotrema. The chamber that moves in the downward spiral is called the scala tympani. The scala tympani is continuous with the scala vestibuli and therefore is also filled with perilymph. The scala tympani ends at another membrane, the round window. The entire cochlea is surrounded by hard bone. The round window provides a soft region to allow the compression and expansion of fluid and helps to deaden the wave. Sandwiched between the scala vestibuli and tympani is a third chamber called the scala media or the cochlear duct which contains the sensory organ of Corti.

Sound waves are gathered by the external ears and directed into the external auditory meatus and hit the tympanic membrane. The vibration of the membrane causes the ossicles to vibrate and push on the oval window. The oval window vibrates and pushes on the fluid filled chamber and causes a wave to flow through the perilymph of the scala vestibuli. The fluid wave will move through the fluid of the scala vestibuli at a certain frequency and will hit the floor of the scala vestibuli or the vestibular membrane at various frequencies. The vestibular membrane is also the roof of the chamber beneath, the scala media. The endolymph of the scala media moves and bends the basilar membrane which contains the sensory organ of Corti.

Figure 4.18

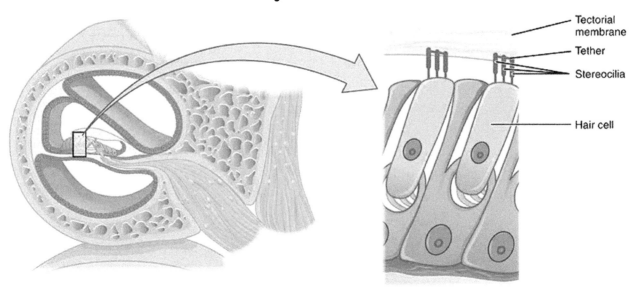

Within the cochlear duct of humans, there are two regions of hair cells, a single layer of inner hair cells and a couple of layers of outer hair cells. More than 90% of the afferent inputs arise from the inner hair cells. The apical surface of the hair cells contain a stereocilia and a kinocilum which are embedded into a tectorial membrane (Figure 4.18). When a sound wave bends the basilar membrane it causes the tips of the hair cells to bend. The cilia are connected to each other through tip linker proteins, such that the bending of one cilia causes a domino effect and bends all subsequent cilia on an individual hair cell. Mechanosensitive K^+ channels are found on the tips of the cilia and when the tip bends it causes the channel to open. The endolymph contains an extremely high concentration of K^+ compared to other extracellular spaces and is in higher concentration compared to the intracellular K^+ concentration of hair cells. Opening of a K^+ channel therefore causes an influx of K^+ down its concentration gradient and causes

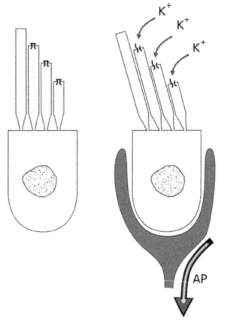

Figure 4.19

depolarization of the hair cells. Depolarization spreads down the cell and causes the opening of voltage-gated Ca^{2+} channels and subsequent exocytosis of glutamate. Release of glutamate stimulates the sensory neurons of the cochlear nerve (See Figure 4.19, on the next page). The cochlear neurons that arise from the cochlear duct have their cell bodies located in the cochlear ganglion (or spiral ganglion) found inside the cochlea. The cochlear nerve joins the vestibular nerve to form cranial nerve VIII, the vestibulocochlear nerve and enters the brainstem at the pontomedullary border. All cochlear inputs make a synapse within the cochlear nucleus and then the superior olivary nucleus of the brainstem. Inputs into the superior olivary nucleus are subjected to a type of lateral inhibition. Inputs from various regions of the cochlea are compared and only the strongest inputs are projected onward. Neurons project through multiple paths to synapse within the inferior colliculus for reflex activity before reaching the medial geniculate nucleus of the thalamus. Auditory thalamic neurons target the auditory cortex located in the temporal lobe.

Activation of the cochlear duct occurs at certain vibrations and resonance frequencies. These frequencies activate the cochlear duct at certain locations. These neurons are mapped in a highly organized tonotopic map within the brain and allow the brain to detect certain notes and sounds.

Vestibular System

The vestibular system is also located within the inner ear. It is specialized to detect head tilt, acceleration and rotational body movement; i.e., the sense of balance and body motion. Like the auditory system, the sensory receptor cell that transduces the stimulus into an action potential is the hair cell. In vertebrates, all sensory hair cells appear to originate from a phylogenetic precursor and the evolution of the structure and function of the inner ear changes throughout the phyla. Throughout the vertebrate phyla, the number of epithelia and chambers associated with the vestibular system and hearing varies, from 3 to 9 epithelia existing in a number of different chambers. The least complex structure resides in the hagfish and contains three sensory epithelia which detect sensations of body movement. It is believed that the auditory hair cells and neurons were derived from vestibular hair cells and neurons. In mammals, the vestibular system is comprised of 8 separate epithelia located in different chambers of the inner ear which are filled with endolymph. The hair cells of the epithelia are innervated by the vestibular nerve, a branch of the vestibulocochlear nerve (cranial nerve VIII).

Static equilibrium

The vestibule is a large opening which contains two chambers involved with detection of static equilibrium or head tilt and acceleration. In mammals, the saccule and utricle are 2 chambers that are found sitting at right angles in the vestibule (See Figure 4.20). The utricle sits in the vertical orientation or the transverse plane whereas the saccule is oriented in the horizontal or coronal plane. The chambers are filled with endolymph and hair cells are found in a specialized epithelium called the macula. The macula contains hair cells with many stereocilia and a single kinocilum along with supporting columnar cells. On top of the macula sits a gelatinous mass containing crystals and is called the otolithic membrane. The hair cells of the macula bend in the direction that the head is tilted. When the kinocilum is bent down away from the stereocilia the membrane potential becomes depolarized. Hair cell activation in the vestibular system is by the same mechanism as the auditory hair cell activation. Bending of the kinocilum and stereocilia result in the opening of mechanosensitive K^+ channels which are connected via tip linker proteins at the surface of the cilia. K^+ enters the hair cell down its concentration gradient from the high K^+ concentration of the endolymph into the hair cell. K^+ entry depolarizes the cell and opens voltage gated Ca^{2+} channels and cause the cell to release glutamate at the synapse of the vestibular neurons. If however, the hair cell is bent in the opposite direction, and the kinocilium is bent toward the stereocilia, the membrane potential is depolarized, most likely due to the closing of more K^+ channels.

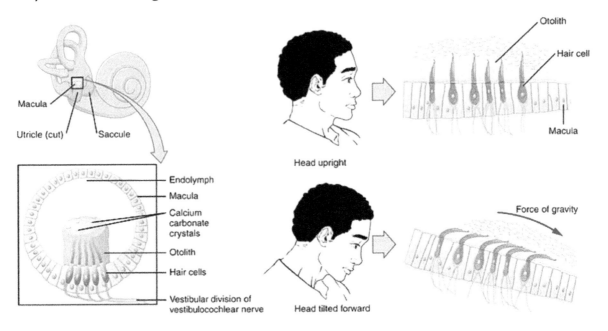

Figure 4.20

Inputs from the vestibular neurons that arise from the utricle and saccule are integrated to determine head position and acceleration. For example sitting upright, the hair cells of the saccule are being bent in a downward fashion and the hair cells of the utricle are in a stationary position. The moment you bend over to touch the ground to pick up a pencil, the hair cells in the utricle begin to bend and get activated whereas the amount of action potentials from the saccule begin to decrease. The relative abundance and location of the inputs provide information to the brain to decipher head position relative to gravity. Under water, the effect of gravity is not as strong and thus confusion about direction is not uncommon.

Acceleration works in the same manner. When your body moves forward quickly such as when a car accelerates quickly, there is a lag between the movement of car and the movement of your body. In other words, your body moves slightly before the fluid in the ear moves. This difference between movements causes the otholithic membrane to slide over the hair cells causing activation. In addition, pressure receptors in the skin and body get activated as your body is pressed into the seat. Together this information is integrated in the brain and provides the sensation of acceleration. Once your body (and hair cells and endolymph) and the car are moving at a constant speed, the hair cells are no longer being activated. Any further detection of movement in the car is detected by visual information along with changes in speed (acceleration and deceleration) which comes from the activation of hair cells as well as proprioceptive and somatic sensory inputs.

Dynamic or rotational equilibrium

Sensory information regarding motion or dynamic or rotational equilibrium is provided by specialized epithelium of the semicircular canals. Three circular canals are found in each inner ear situated in the transverse, coronal and sagittal planes (Figure 4.21). Each circular canal has two enlarged bulges near the base of the circle and found close to the vestibule. These enlarged sections are called the ampulla and contain the specialized sensory epithelium, the crista ampullaris. The crista ampullaris contains hair cells supported by columnar epithelial cells. A gelatinous matrix, the cupola, sits atop the crista ampullaris and acts as a float which gets displaced due to the motion of the endolymph. Not only is simple motion detected, but also the rate of the movement.

Figure 4.21

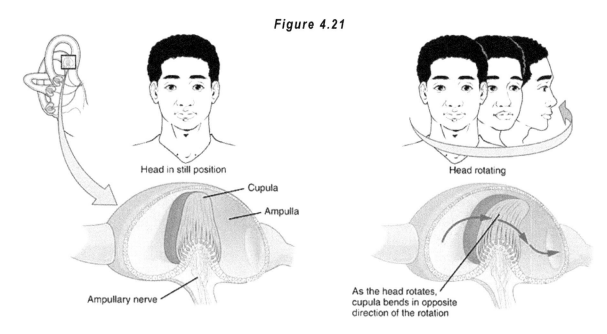

If you move in a clockwise direction, the endolymph in the semicircular canal (of the same plane) lags behind and the hair cells bend backwards or to the right (Figure 4.22). If your body continues to move in a circle at the same rotational speed, eventually the body and the fluid will be moving at the same rate and the hair cells will not get bent. If you stop moving your body, the endolymph will continue to circulate and the hair cells will bend in the opposite direction (to the left). The information that comes from the sensory neurons that arise from the crista ampullaris of all semicircular canals is projected via the vestibular nerve into the brainstem. The brain senses how the body is moves.

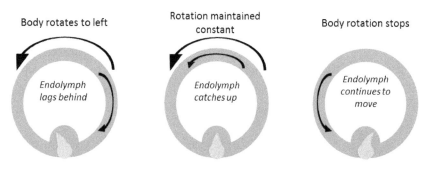

Figure 4.22

Activation of the hair cell in any region of the utricle, saccule and circular canals results in the release glutamate and stimulation of the vestibular branch of the vestibulocochlear nerve (cranial nerve VIII). All of the vestibular neurons project into the brainstem at the pontomedullary border and synapse within the vestibular nucleus. Second-order neurons of the vestibular nucleus synapse in the posterior ventral nucleus of the thalamus. Third-order neurons from the thalamus project to the vestibular sensory cortex located in the parietal lobe for conscious awareness of movement. Neurons in the vestibular pathway also send axon collaterals to multiple areas involved with visual movements, (the abducens motor nucleus, the trochlear motor nucleus and the oculomotor nucleus) and to areas that are involved with postural control such as the cerebellum and neurons of the vestibulospinal tract.

CHAPTER 4, SECTION 3 – SUMMARY

- ➢ Gustation or the sense of taste is accomplished by special sensory receptors located on the tongue and surrounding surfaces of the mouth. Gustatory cells have chemoreceptors that get activated when eating specific foods. Depolarization leads to the release of neurotransmitters and excitation of sensory neurons (facial, glossopharyngeal and vagus). Impulses project to neurons in the ipsilateral NTS, to the VPM of the thalamus and to the post-central gyrus of the parietal lobe for final processing.

- ➢ Olfaction or the sense of smell is carried out using a special epithelium lining the superior portion of the nasal cavity. Airborne molecules are trapped in mucus and activate chemoreceptors located on special bipolar cells. Action potentials travel to neurons located in the olfactory bulb which then project directly to the frontal and temporal lobes for the conscious awareness of the sense of smell.

- ➢ The visual system is a complex organ system. The eye itself contains three tissue layers. The outermost fibrous layer contains the sclera and cornea. The middle vascular layer contains the choroid, the ciliary body and the iris. The innermost layer contains the pigmented and neural retina.

- ➢ Light enters the cornea and passes through the pupil, an opening controlled by the iris, and the lens, which is regulated by the ciliary body. Light passes through the vitreous body to activate photoreceptors located on the rods and cones of the retina. The retina contains three layers of cells, the rods and cones are the outermost cell, followed by the bipolar cell and the ganglion cell is the innermost cell.

- ➢ Photons of light activate rhodopsin molecules on cones and rods and result in the activation of transducin, a G-protein. Transducin activates phosphodiesterase and deceases the amount of available cAMP. A Na+ channel closes due to the lack of cAMP (which normally keeps the channel open) causing cellular hyperpolarization. Less glutamate is released on bipolar cells and the cells are disinhibited. They begin to depolarize and release neurotransmitter to stimulate the ganglion cell.

➢ Visual inputs project through the optic nerve (ganglion cell axons) and project back to the lateral geniculate body of the thalamus before synapsing in the primary visual cortex located in the occipital lobe.

➢ The auditory system allows us to hear sounds from the environment. Sound waves are collected in the external auditory meatus by pinna and bend the tympanic membrane. The ear ossicles vibrate and cause vibrations of the oval window. This causes waves in the perilymph of the internal ear which propagate through the cochlea and activate hair cells of the cochlear duct.

➢ In the inner ear, the tips of hairs on special hair cells and cause the opening of K+ channels. The extracellular fluid is high in K+ concentration and the opening of channels cause the K+ to flow into cells and cause depolarization. Hair cells release glutamate onto the cochlear branch of the vestibulocochlear nerve (cranial nerve VIII).

➢ Impulses from the cochlear nerve synapse with neurons in the cochlear nucleus of the medulla and the superior olivary nucleus. Inputs then project to the medial geniculate nucleus of the thalamus and the temporal lobe for conscious awareness of sounds.

➢ The vestibular system confers the sensation of balance. Inputs from the saccule and utricle provide information regarding static equilibrium and acceleration and inputs from the semicircular canals provide information regarding rotational equilibrium. All of these chambers are filled with endolymph and contain specialized epithelial tissue containing hair cells. Stimulation of hair cells causes activation of the vestibular nerve (part of cranial nerve VIII).

References and Suggested Readings

Burighel P, Caicci F, Manni L. 2011. Hair cells in non-vertebrate models: lower chordates and molluscs. *Hearing Research* 272:14-24.

Demb JB. 2008. Functional circuitry of visual adaptation in the retina. *Journal of Physiology* 586(18):4377-4384.

Dounglas RJ, Marin KAC. 2007. The butterfly and the loom. *Brain Research Reviews* 55:314-328.

Duncan JS, Fritzsch B. 2012. Transforming the vestibular system one molecule at a time: the molecular and developmental basis of vertebrate auditory evolution. In: Sensing in Nature, ed C. Lopez-Larrea. Landes Bioscience and Springer Science. Pp. 173-186.

Glowatzki E, Fuchs PA. 2002. Transmitter release at the hair cell ribbon synapse. *Nature Neuroscience* 5(2):147-154.

Kaas JH. 2008. The evolution of the complex sensory and motor systems of the human brain. *Brain Research Bulletin* 75:384-390.

Liman ER. Changing senses: chemosensory signaling and primate evolution. In: Sensing in Nature, ed C. Lopez-Larrea. Landes Bioscience and Springer Science. Pp.206-217.

Martin JP, Beyerlein A, Dacks AM, Reisenman CE, Riffell JA, Lei H, Hildebrand JG. 2011. The neurobiology of insect olfaction: sensory processing in a comparative context. *Progress in Neurobiology* 95:427-447.

Molnar Z, Brown RE. 2010. Insights into the life and work of Sir Charles Sherrington. *Nature Reviews: Neuroscience* 11:429-436.

Nilsson DE. 2009. The evolution of eyes and visually guided behaviour. *Philosophical Transactions of The Royal Society B* 364:2833-2847.

Niven JE, Laughlin SB. 2008. Energy limitation as a selective pressure on the evolution of sensory systems. *The Journal of Experimental Biology* 211:1792-1804.

Renard E, Vacelet J, Gazave E, Lapébie P, Borchiellini C, Ereskovsky AV. 2009. Origin of the neuro-sensory system: new and expected insights from sponges. *Integrative Zoology* 4:294-308.

Chapter 5: Muscle Physiology

Movement is an essential function for the survival of most animals. Very small and primitive animals are not motile and can gather food and exchange gases, nutrients and waste products with their environment primarily through simple diffusion mechanisms. They can accomplish this because their environment (the water) moves around and through them. As animals evolved and became larger, they developed the ability to move through their environments in order to gather food and evade predators. Movement of animals is due to the formation of skeletal muscles that can be voluntarily controlled by nerves. Therefore the nervous and muscle systems appeared to have co-evolved. Muscles also evolved to move substances throughout bodies and evolved to help coordinate and control organ function. Muscles are a necessary component for survival. There are three types of muscle tissue found in vertebrates: skeletal muscle, smooth muscle and cardiac muscle. The primary role of skeletal muscle is to produce movement and maintain posture and body position, and in doing so, it is also involved with stabilizing joints. Skeletal muscle is also important in the generation of body heat and creating respiratory movements to allow for gas exchange with the environment. Smooth muscle is found in many organs and is involved in moving substances through an organ, such as peristaltic movement of chyme throughout the digestive tract or changing the resistance of tubes such as in the regulation of blood flow to organs. Cardiac muscle is found in the heart proper and its primary function is to generate pressure and move blood throughout the systemic and pulmonary circulations to aid in gas, nutrient and waste exchange. All muscle cells have several common characteristics. All muscle cells are excitable tissues. This means that they can respond to nervous stimuli and generate action potentials along their plasma membranes. All muscle cells have the ability to shorten in length or contract. All muscle cells are extensible; i.e., they can be stretched, usually by opposing muscle groups and gravity. And finally, all muscle cells are elastic and can return to their original shape. This chapter will be primarily dedicated to describing the characteristics and mechanics of skeletal muscle. Smooth muscle will be covered at the end of this chapter and cardiac muscle will be covered in Chapter 6.

Section 1 – Skeletal Muscle

In vertebrates, the development of skeletal muscles arise from the fusion of multiple cells called myoblasts. Myoblasts fuse together and form a long tubular structure which then fills with contractile filaments which allow for cellular shortening. Skeletal muscle cells are therefore multinucleated and very long; some muscle cells extending many centimeters in length. In most mammals, skeletal muscle makes up 40-60% of the total body weight. Most of the research that has described what we know about skeletal muscles was performed on frogs and rabbits. Classical studies described the anatomy, the cellular organization and the basic mechanisms underlying contraction and relaxation of skeletal muscle.

Skeletal Muscle Organization

Each skeletal muscle in the body is a discrete organ. The outermost edge of a muscle is surrounded by a layer of protective, fibrous connective tissue called the epimysium or the fascia (Figure 5.1). Muscles are comprised of bundles of skeletal muscle cells collected together into discrete collections called fascicles. These fascicles are wrapped in another layer of strong connective tissue sheath, the perimysium. Within each fascicle are the individual muscle cells. Each individual muscle cell is covered in a thin, light connective tissue sheath called the endomysium. Nerves and blood vessels travel through the connective tissue sheaths to help innervate muscle cells and provide nutrients and remove waste from muscle cells.

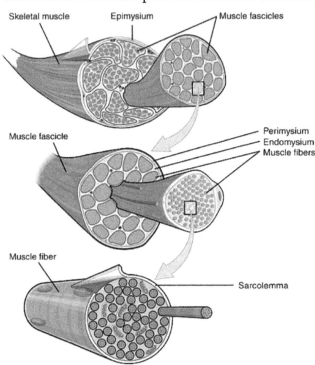

Figure 5.1

In vertebrates, skeletal muscles attach to bones through tendons and often cross a joint space. The most proximal connection and the stationary attachment is referred to the origin of the muscle whereas the most distal portion or the portion that moves in response to muscle contraction is known as the insertion. The epimysium of the muscle is continuous with the tendons which are attached to bones. The tendon itself is a very tough, dense regular connective tissue which penetrates deep into the fibers of the bone at both the origin and the insertion. These penetrating fibers are called Sharpey's fibers.

Individual muscle cells (also called muscle fibers or myofibers) are small in diameter (10-100uM) however, they can be extremely long in length (mm to up to 30+cm in length) (See Figure 5.2). Each muscle cell is enclosed in a plasma membrane called the sarcolemma and contains thousands of cylindrical structures called myofibrils. The myofibrils run in parallel to the length of muscle cells and each myofibril is comprised of repeating individual units called sarcomeres. A sarcomere is the functional unit of muscle; i.e., the unit that shortens in response to nervous stimulation.

Under the light microscope, skeletal muscle looks striped in appearance or striated. This is due to the parallel arrangement of muscle cells and the highly organized arrangement of the myofilaments within each sarcomere. Each sarcomere is a composed of thin myofilaments called actin and thick myofilaments called myosin. Actin is anchored at each end of the sarcomere to a protein scaffold called the Z disk because, three-dimensionally, it is shaped as a round, flattened disk at the end of a cylinder. In cross section, the disk shape becomes a distinct line and is often called the Z line (Figure 5.3). Myosin myofilaments are attached in the middle of the sarcomere by a light delicate filamentous protein scaffold called the M line. The myosin myofilaments are surrounded by 6 filamentous actin myofilaments. In cross section, a single sarcomere extends from Z line to Z line and the myosin and actin myofilaments overlap one another to some degree. The entire region which encompasses the myosin myofilament in a sarcomere is called the A band (which refers to anisotropic because this region polarizes visible light). The actin and myosin myofilaments overlap one another to some extent (more or less) depending on the state of contraction. The center region is called the H band. The H-band is the region in which myosin myofilaments do not overlap with actin and the M-line runs down the middle. This region contains enzymes important in generating the energy necessary for contraction such as creatine kinase. The region that contains the actin myofilaments alone is called the I-band and extends across two sarcomeres (I refers to isotropic because these bands are non-polarizing to light). During the contraction of skeletal muscle, the actin and myosin myofilaments form connections called cross bridges.

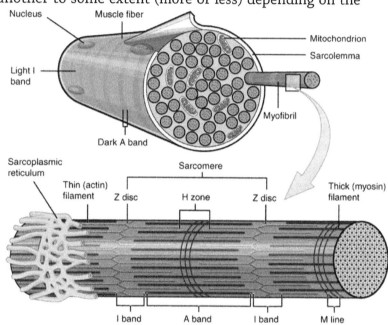

Figure 5.2

A.

B.

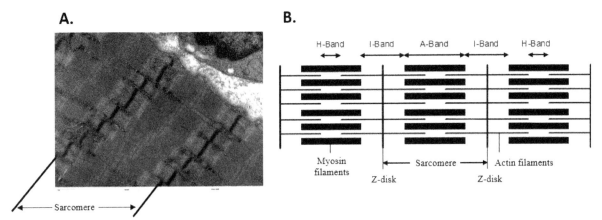

Figure 5.3

Actin, the thin myofilament, is comprised of two filamentous strands of actin (F actin) twisted together in a double helix (Figure 5.4). F actin is formed by stringing together many globular actin proteins (G actin). Actin attaches to the Z line through various proteins including α-actinin. Associated with the strands of F actin are two other proteins, tropomyosin and troponin. Tropomyosin is an elongated protein that sits in each groove of the double helix of actin. Troponin is a three subunit protein that attaches to both the actin and the tropomyosin molecules. Troponin is comprised of three subunits, TnC which is the center subunit and has Ca^{2+} binding sites, TnT which binds to tropomyosin, and TnI which refers to "inhibit" and interacts with actin to prevent myosin from binding to actin. The troponin/tropomyosin complex is involved in the regulation of the actin-myosin interactions and thus contraction of the muscle. When Ca^{2+} is NOT present, the troponin/tropomyosin complex blocks the myosin binding sites on actin. In the presence of Ca^{2+}, troponin undergoes a conformational change and moves tropomyosin exposing the myosin binding sites allowing contraction to take place.

Myosin is considered the thick filament. Myosin molecules consist of two light meromyosin chains and two heavy meromyosin chains. The peptide chains also twist together in a double helix (Figure 5.4). At the end of the heavy meromyosin chain, the peptides form a globular head region which contains several other globular proteins called myosin light chains. The types of polypeptides that make up the globular heads influence the ATPase activity and thus the speed of muscle contraction. Many individual myosin molecules aggregate together with their

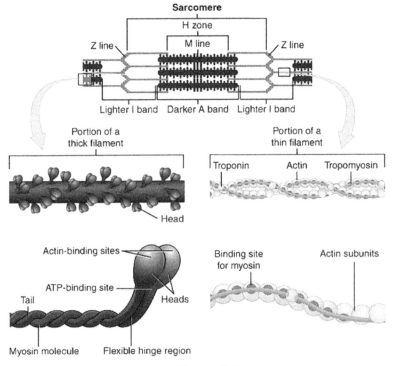

Figure 5.4

globular head regions facing outward on the ends and the meromyosin chains in a common center region. This center region of myosin molecules connect at the M-line and is bare of the globular heads. On both ends of the myosin, the globular heads overlap with the actin filaments and can form cross bridges during contraction.

Titin, the largest protein in the body (34,350 amino acids in length) runs from the Z line to the M-line. Titin attaches to multiple proteins including α-actinin at the Z line and connects the myosin molecule to the Z line on each end helping to stabilize its location within the sarcomere to keep in close proximity with actin molecules. Titin is coil-shaped and functions like a long spring or rubber band and can spring back to its original length when stretched. This springing action plays a role in the passive elasticity of muscles.

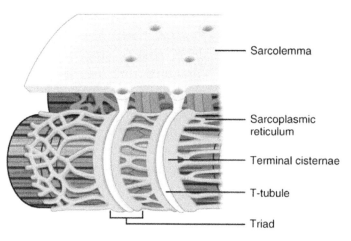

Sarcolemma

Sarcoplasmic reticulum

Terminal cisternae

T-tubule

Triad

Figure 5.5

The actin and myosin myofilaments are highly organized within each muscle cell into sarcomeres, the functional unit of contraction. The sarcomeres are stacked up on top of each other to form myofibrils and the myofibrils are lined up in parallel to fill the majority of the muscle cell's interior. The cytoplasm of each cell, the sarcoplasm, is a minor component of the cell and the cell's organelles (nucleus, mitochondria, etc..) are found on the outside edges of the cell. The endoplasmic reticulum, or sarcoplasmic reticulum, is highly specialized in skeletal muscles. The plasma membrane of the cell surrounds the cell and creates a system of transverse tubules which extend from the surface of the plasma membrane and delve deep into the muscle cell to surround each sarcomere (See Figure 5.5). Each sarcomere has two transverse tubules (T-tubule) which surround each sarcomere and each T-tubule is associated with the thickened endings of two portions of sarcoplasmic reticulum. This thickened portion is called the terminal cisternae. Two terminal cisternae plus a centrally located T-tubule is called a triad. The triad is important in the regulation and release of Ca^{2+} that occurs during the contraction phase.

Sliding Filament Model

The sliding filament model describes the relationship between actin and myosin molecules during contraction. During contraction of the muscle, the size of the actin and myosin molecules do NOT change size, but rather the amount of overlap between the two filaments change. During contraction, each sarcomere within each myofibril has the ability to change length or shorten due to the amount of overlap between the actin and myosin molecules. Contraction or the sliding of the filaments past one another occurs within each sarcomere in every myofibril within muscle cells. In

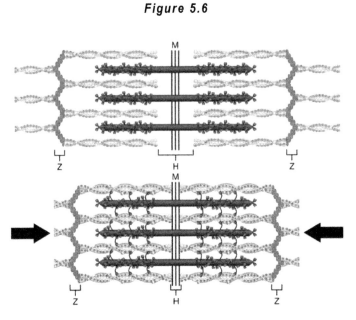

Figure 5.6

general, the myosin heads attach to actin and the globular head of the myosin bends pulling the actin toward the M-line, thus shortening the length of the sarcomere (Figure 5.6). The myosin heads pull the actin filaments and move the Z lines toward the center M-line and shorten the length of the sarcomere. During contraction, the H zone disappears and the I-band shortens but the A-band stays the same length.

Excitation-contraction coupling

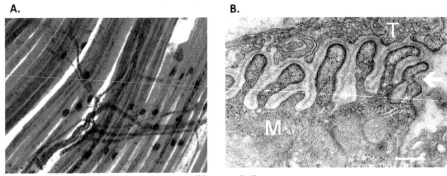

A.   B.

Figure 5.7

Skeletal muscles are innervated by α-motor neurons, also called somatic motor neurons. The cell soma of somatic motor neurons are located in the ventral horn of the spinal cord. The muscles of the face and neck, however, are innervated by cranial nerves and their somatic motor neurons are located in specific brainstem nuclei. The axons of the somatic motor neurons project out of the brain or spinal cord and travel through nerves to reach their target skeletal muscle. At the muscle, the neurons send multiple axon collaterals to multiple muscle cells. Thus, when a single motor neuron fires an action potential, multiple muscle cells will contract. This unit is called a motor unit and is comprised of one neuron and all of the muscle cells that it innervates. At each muscle cell, the axon synapses with the muscle and is called the neuromuscular junction (NMJ) (Figure 5.7). The NM J contains a specialized nerve ending of the motor neuron and the site of the synapse on the muscle is called the motor end plate. The end of the axon has multiple branches with thickenings or swellings along the motor end plate. Below each swelling or synaptic bouton, there are multiple junctional folds in the sarcolemma. Each junctional fold is associated with one active site or synapse in which neurotransmitters are released into the synaptic cleft. Nicotinic ACh receptors are found at the crest of the junctional folds and the depths of the folds are rich with voltage gated Na⁺ channels (See Figure 5.8). An action potential in the motor neuron will release ACh which crosses the synaptic cleft to bind to the cationic nACh receptors. Associated with the synaptic cleft is acetylcholinesterase. Acetylcholinesterase is the enzyme responsible for the degradation of ACh and can be found associated with the post-synaptic membrane. The enzyme

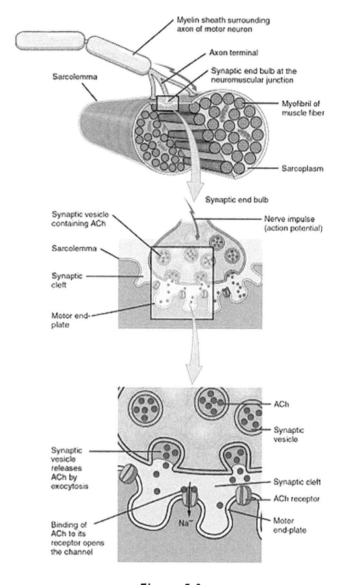

Figure 5.8

cleaves acetylcholine into acetic acid and choline. Choline transporters can be found in high numbers on the pre-synaptic membrane and can be used to synthesize more neurotransmitters.

Once the nACh receptor is activated on the muscle cell, Na⁺ flows into the cell and K⁺ flows out of the cell through the channel and results in cellular depolarization. The rapid influx of Na⁺ activates the rich source of voltage-gated Na⁺ channels in the clefts and is sufficient to activate an action potential along the sarcolemma of the muscle cell. Along the entire sarcolemma, voltage-gated Na⁺ and voltage-gated K⁺ channels contribute to the formation of an action potential. The action potential quickly spreads away from the neuromuscular junction in every direction throughout the entire muscle cell. The action potential courses down through the T-tubules extending deep into the interior of the muscle cell surrounding each sarcomere. Associated with the T-tubules are the terminal cisternae of the sarcoplasmic reticulum. At the triad, depolarization associated with the action potential activates a dihydropyridine (DHP) receptor on the plasma membrane. The DHP receptor is an L-type voltage-gated Ca^{2+} channel, however, in skeletal muscle, the amount of calcium that enters this channel is not significant and does not play a role in contraction (this is different in cardiac muscle, see Chapter 6). If extracellular Ca^{2+} is removed or the channel is altered so that it is impermeable to Ca^{2+}, activation of DHP by a change in voltage still initiates contraction of skeletal muscle. This is because the DHP receptor is mechanically linked to ryanodine receptors (RyR) located on the membranes of the terminal cisternae of the SR. The mechanism of activation of RyR appears to be a direct mechanical interaction between DHP and RyR. The RyR is also a Ca^{2+} channel and once activated, the channel opens and Ca^{2+} rushes down its concentration gradient from the SR to the sarcoplasm and the surrounding sarcomeres. Ca^{2+} binds to the TnC subunit of troponin which undergoes a conformational change and moves the tropomyosin to expose a myosin binding site on the actin. Once the active site is exposed, myosin is free to interact with actin and allows contraction or cross bridge cycling to take place.

Ca^{2+} is continually being pumped back into the SR through a Ca^{2+}-ATPase. The SR Ca^{2+}-ATPase, (sarcoplasmic endoplasmic reticulum Ca^{2+}-ATPase, SERCA), is found in virtually all cells and pumps 2 Ca^{2+} ions into the lumen using one molecule of ATP. In skeletal muscles, there are many SERCA present in large numbers on the longitudinal tubules of the SR and a smaller amount present in the terminal cisternae. Within the SR, the Ca^{2+} is shuttled from the longitudinal tubules into the terminal cisternae and held in large concentrations within the terminal cisternae due to the presence of Ca^{2+}-binding proteins such as calsequestrin and histidine-rich calcium-binding protein (HRC).

Cross bridge cycling

Once Ca^{2+} enters the sarcoplasm and binds to troponin, the active sites on actin become exposed and allow myosin to interact with actin. In the resting state, myosin is in an energized state and has ADP and P attached to the "globular" head region. When myosin comes into contact with actin it forms what is called a cross bridge (Figure 5.9). Once the myosin head comes into contact with the actin, the myosin undergoes a conformational change and loses its affinity for ADP causing ADP to detach. As ADP detaches, another

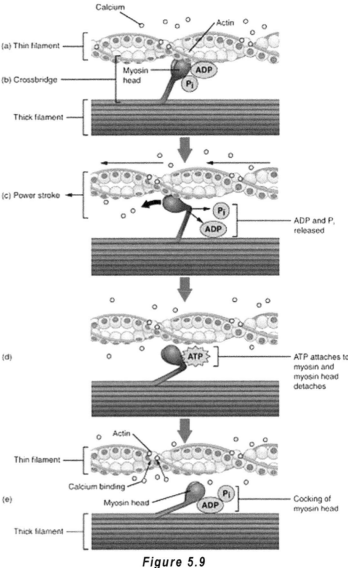

Figure 5.9

conformational change causes the myosin head to bend. The bending of the head is called the power stroke and allows for myosin and actin to slide past one another. The bending action of the myosin head causes the release of the phosphate. Once ADP and P have fallen off the globular head, there is an open binding site for ATP. If ATP is readily available, ATP binds to the myosin head resulting in a decrease in its affinity for actin and causes the myosin and actin molecules to disengage. There is an enzyme on the myosin head, an ATPase which causes the hydrolysis of ATP into ADP and P. This reaction causes the myosin head to bend back to its original resting position. This is one cross bridge cycle and requires 1 ATP molecule. Each of the myosin heads are independent structures and will bind and unbind independent of one another. The cross bridge cycling will continue as long as Ca^{2+} and ATP are present.

When muscle cells become fatigued, the levels of available ATP decreases. This prevents activation of the power stroke and the normal function of the Ca^{2+}-ATPase. The speed and force of contraction are both decreased. In the case of death, ATP levels fall, but Ca^{2+} becomes readily available. When the heart stops beating and breathing stops, the oxygen levels in blood begin to decrease rapidly. As oxygen levels fall, cells can no longer make ATP. Cells become leaky and Ca^{2+} slowly leaks into the sarcomeres and allows myosin to bind to actin. The lack of ATP prevents 1) SERCA from working which enhances intracellular Ca^{2+} levels and 2) prevents the myosin from disengaging from the actin. Thus, skeletal muscles get stuck in a contracted state or "rigor mortis."

In a normal, relaxed state, the myosin head is not attached to actin and is sitting in an energized state ready for action. In order to activate skeletal muscle contraction, an action potential from somatic motor neurons is required. The time of the action potential in skeletal muscle is very fast, ~1msec. The action potential precedes the release of Ca^{2+} from the SR but once Ca^{2+} is released, contraction can occur. The action potential is finished by the time skeletal muscle begins to contract. A single muscle twitch or contraction of the muscle is much slower than the action potential and can last as long as 100-200msec. When action potentials stop firing, then muscle quickly relaxes due to the removal of Ca^{2+} by SERCA and the removal of ACh by acetylcholinesterase in the synaptic cleft. Muscle lengthening is due to the actions of an antagonist muscle contracting or gravity pulling and lengthening the muscle fiber.

Summary of the sequence of events that lead to contraction
1. Action potential is generated along the somatic motor neuron
2. Release of ACh from the motor neuron and activation of nicotinic ACh receptors on post-synaptic membrane
3. Depolarization of muscle cell leads to activation of action potential generation and propagation along sarcolemma
4. Action potential propagates down T-tubules
5. Activation of DHP receptors on sarcolemma and subsequent activation of ryanodine receptors on terminal cisterna of SR
6. Release of Ca^{2+} from SR through ryanodine receptors
7. Ca^{2+} binds to troponin, causing conformational change in shape

8. Troponin moves tropomyosin and uncovers the active site on actin molecule
9. Myosin can bind to actin to start contraction
10. The myosin binds to actin and a phosphate ion falls off
11. This starts the power stroke and the myosin head bends causing ADP to fall off
12. When ATP binds to the myosin head, the myosin detaches from actin
13. ATPase hydrolyzes ATP into ADP and P causing the myosin head to return to its starting position
14. As long as calcium and ATP is present contraction continues

Mechanical properties of contraction

Classical experiments on isolated muscles have revealed how muscles respond to electrical stimulation. All skeletal muscles require neuronal activation in order to contract. If you stimulate a nerve that projects to a muscle with a very low voltage, threshold may not be reached and nothing happens; no action potential and therefore no muscle contraction. If the voltage is increased and threshold is reached, a single action potential in the nerve will result in a single muscle twitch of the muscle. Threshold is the point at which a single action potential is generated and leads to contraction of the muscle cells that are innervated by that neuron. Only the neurons with the lowest threshold will fire an action potential and only those muscle cells that are innervated by those neurons will contract. If you increase the stimulus strength and send another stimulus, more neurons will reach threshold and fire action potentials. Therefore, more muscle cells will contract and the single muscle twitch will be larger and the whole muscle will generate more tension. The size of the muscle twitch generated by a whole muscle will continue to enlarge until all of the neurons that are projecting to the muscle get activated. At this point all of the muscle cells contract and generate tension and the single muscle twitch is at its largest size. This is called the maximal response. Any greater voltage will not elicit a greater response, because all of the muscle cells are already generating a muscle twitch. The amount of tension generated by a muscle is dependent on how many single muscle cells are contracting. The increase in the size of the muscle twitch as voltage increases is called a graded response and is a type of population coding. Increases in the number, or population, of muscle cells determine, or codes for, a given size of muscle twitch. Each motor unit or the individual neuron and the muscle cells that it innervates functions as "all or none." Whereas, the entire muscle functions as a graded response.

Single Muscle Twitch

A single action potential applied to a nerve innervating a muscle will induce a single muscle twitch (Figure 5.10). A muscle twitch contains three phases, a latent or lag phase, a contraction phase and a relaxation phase. Each phase of the muscle twitch has very specific neural mechanisms that underlie each phase.

The start of the lag phase begins when a stimulus is applied to the α-motor neurons. The motor neurons release ACh at the NMJ which activates nACh receptors and cause the muscle cell to depolarize. This leads to the opening of voltage-gated Na⁺ channels and activation of an action potential along the sarcolemma. The action potential propagates over the entire the skeletal muscle from the site of the synapse and moves down the

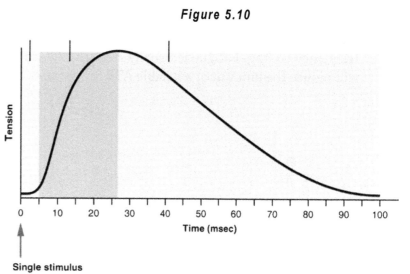

Figure 5.10

Single stimulus

T-tubules surrounding each sarcomere. In the T-tubules, depolarization leads to the activation of the DHP receptor which in turn activates the RyR allowing Ca^{2+} to flow out of the SR. Ca^{2+} moves into the sarcomere, binds to troponin and pulls tropomyosin away from the active sites. This allows myosin to contact the actin molecule. This is the end of the lag phase and the beginning of the contraction phase. The entire lag phase runs ~5 msec. The contraction phase is the time when the myosin heads bind to actin resulting in cross bridge formation. The bending of the myosin head and cross bridge cycling is dependent on ATP and the amount of time that the active sites are exposed. The myofilaments slide past one another and muscle shortening occurs. Ca^{2+} is constantly being taken back into the SR via SERCA and as the amount of Ca^{2+} decreases, less tension is generated and the contraction phase ends and the relaxation phase begins. The relaxation phase ends when the muscle returns back to its original length.

Summation and Tetanus

If more than one action potential is sent to the muscle in quick succession, then summation can occur (See Figure 5.11). Summation refers to the combination of several individual muscle twitches adding onto each other creating an even greater muscle tension than a single muscle twitch. When a single muscle twitch is initiated, a single action potential results in a distinct amount of Ca^{2+} released from the SR. The Ca^{2+} binds to troponin and exposes a certain amount active sites on actin which is dependent on how much Ca^{2+} is released. Contraction followed by full relaxation occurs. If a second action potential is initiated before full relaxation has finished, then summation occurs. The second action potential comes down the T-tubule and activates the DHP and RyR receptors again, releasing another burst of Ca^{2+} from the SR, before the Ca^{2+} from the previous action potential has been resequestered. This means that more Ca^{2+} is available for binding and exposes even more active sites. If more active sites are exposed, then myosin can slide past actin even farther and cause a greater amount of muscle tension. This is summation. If the frequency of action potentials is slow enough that you can see a small relaxation preceding the next contraction, this is called unfused tetanus (a phenomenon observed in experimental conditions). Most normal contractions in the body however, are controlled by a high frequency of action potentials being sent down from the brain to initiate fused tetanus or a smooth increase in muscle contraction (Figure 5.11). This is referred to as frequency coding. Fatigue is usually a result of continued high frequency stimulation. This will reduce the amount of available ATP for muscle contraction and result in a reduced

Figure 5.11

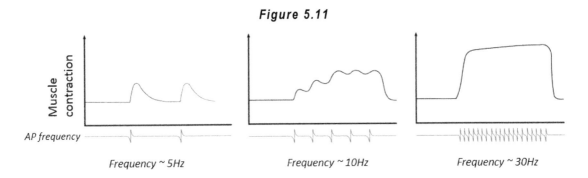

Frequency ~ 5Hz   Frequency ~ 10Hz   Frequency ~ 30Hz

Energy sources for contraction

In muscles ATP is necessary for many cellular functions, including 1) cross bridge cycling where a single ATP molecule is needed for the bending action of each myosin head, 2) pumping Ca^{2+} back into the SR via SERCA, and 3) running the Na^+/K^+ pumps on the sarcolemma and maintaining the negative interior of the muscle cell. In working muscles, ATP is in high demand. There are 4 sources for ATP; free cytosolic ATP, creatine phosphate, and aerobic and anaerobic metabolism.

Figure 5.12

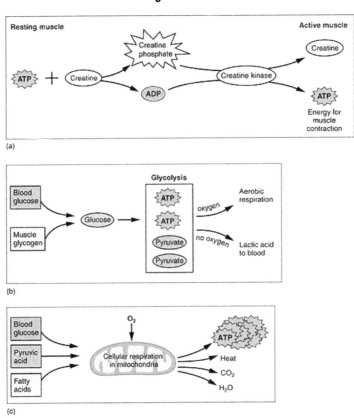

In all cells there is a small amount of free ATP in the cytosol that helps normal cell function, but cells must be able to generate more ATP as needed (Figure 5.12). Most ATP that is generated in cells comes from oxidative metabolism which uses glucose and oxygen to form ATP. Oxidative metabolism is relatively slow, but it is very efficient and requires oxygen to produce 38 ATP molecules. Cells can also utilize anaerobic metabolism or glycolysis to generate ATP. Glycolysis is very fast but can only generate 2 ATP molecules at a time and cannot by utilized for long periods of time (only short durations). Skeletal muscles also contain creatine phosphate which can create a single ATP.

Heat generation

Each time a cross bridge forms between actin and myosin, a single molecule of ATP is needed. Most energy in muscle cells is produced using oxidative phosphorylation. Oxidative phosphorylation is a process which utilizes many steps and gives off heat as a by-product. As glucose is converted to ATP, the excess heat is used to help maintain homeostasis of body temperature in mammals. When body temperature begins to fall, shivering thermogenesis can be activated to generate heat. Shivering thermogenesis is the rapid contraction and relaxation of motor units to activate muscle contraction and give off heat as a by-product. Shivering thermogenesis is not coordinated body movements but rather shaking muscle movements created to generate heat. This is strikingly evident in hibernating animals in which they utilize shivering thermogenesis (and other mechanisms) to increase body temperature from very low temperatures (~5°C) back to normal body temperature (~37°C).

Length-tension relationship

The outside forces that are applied to a muscle or the amount of weight that a muscle is trying to move is called the load. The muscle must generate a certain amount of tension in order to move the load and contraction is the muscles attempt to shorten against a load. The active component of skeletal muscle is to contract or shorten. If the tension is greater than the load then the muscle will shorten. If the tension is less than the load then the muscle will lengthen. An isometric contraction is a type of contraction where the muscle does NOT change length, but the tension that the muscle is applying to the load changes. For example, if you lift a heavy bag and hold the bag at your chest, the muscle is no longer changing length, but the muscle is still working to hold the bag up in a set position. The muscle is continuing to contract and this is called an isometric contraction. Cross bridge cycling is

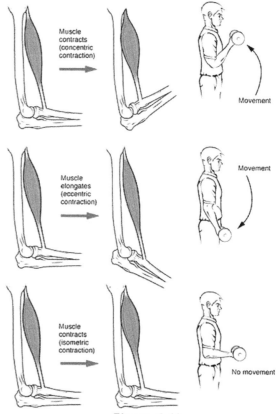

Figure 5.13

being activated continually in order to generate enough tension to hold the weight. Another type of contraction is when the length of the muscle is changing, this is called an isotonic contraction. When the length of the muscle changes, the tension that the muscle generates remains the same. For example, lifting a weigh in a biceps curl moves the same weight while the muscle changes length.

Another way to describe contractions is based on the direction of the contraction (Figure 5.13). A concentric contraction is when you simply lift a weight upward such as such as the biceps curl. However, when you sit into a chair, you don't simply relax your muscles and flop into the chair, rather you slowly set your body down; this is called an eccentric contraction. In general, more injuries occur during the eccentric contractions than the concentric contractions.

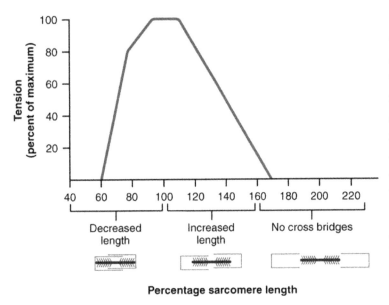

Percentage sarcomere length

Figure 5.14

In muscles, the amount of tension that can be developed is dependent on the starting length of the muscle (See Figure 5.14, on the next page). Contraction is accomplished by the sliding of the myofilaments within each sarcomere, therefore the amount of overlap that can be accomplished will determine the amount of tension that the muscle can generate. For example, if you take a muscle and stretch it out so that there is NO overlap between the actin and myosin filaments and then send an action potential down the sarcolemma, will there be any contraction? No, because the myosin heads cannot come into contact with the actin and thus no cross bridge formation and no muscle shortening. At the opposite extreme, if you squish a muscle such that the sarcomere is in its shortest state, where the actin filaments are slightly overlapped and the H-zone is completely disappeared, if you stimulate the muscle, no tension and no shortening will occur because you are already at the shortest possible state. In between, these two extremes the muscle will be able to generate some tension. The maximal tension can be generated when the muscle is at its normal resting length. At this time, the actin and myosin heads are in full contact and can generate the most motion along the sarcomere.

The total tension that a muscle can generate is due to the active tension combined with the muscle's passive tension. Whole muscles have some natural elasticity component. Titin molecules found in sarcomeres and elastic fibers in the connective tissue fibers surrounding the muscles act like rubber bands and store energy as they are stretched. This is the passive component of tension. Active tension is due to the myosin actin cross bridge formation. When muscles contract, they must generate enough tension to overcome the elasticity and create enough force to shorten.

Force-velocity relationship

As muscles work, the amount of load (or the weight) influences the speed of the contraction phase. For example, you can pick up a penny off the floor very quickly whereas if you pick up a 50lb weight, the speed of the contraction is slower. In order for muscles to generate greater tension to pick up a heavy load, they need to utilize more actin and myosin cross bridges. In addition, more myosin heads need to stay "locked" in order to prevent slippage against a heavy load. So, in light loads, the speed of contraction is relatively fast whereas the speed of contraction during heavy loads is relatively slow.

Types of muscle fibers

In general, there are two categories of muscle fibers; slow twitch (Type I) and fast twitch (Type IIa and Type IIb). The name slow twitch and fast twitch refers to the speed of the muscle twitch that is recorded in each of these fiber types. Some muscles have an extremely fast muscle twitch, such as the muscles that move the eye and some muscles have a very slow muscle twitch, like muscles that control posture. And then there are some muscles that have muscle twitches that are intermediate in speed such as the calf muscle, the gastrocnemius. In humans, each muscle is comprised of a mixture of fiber types, whereas in other vertebrates, each muscle is comprised of a single fiber type. This accounts for the "white meat" and "red meat" in animals like chicken.

Slow twitch muscle cells use oxidative metabolism to generate the majority of their ATP. These muscle cells tend to have more mitochondria and a higher capillary density. Large amounts of myoglobin bind and store oxygen for oxidative metabolism. Slow twitch muscles have a slower ATPase activity on the myosin heads and a higher activity of enzymes involved in oxidative phosphorylation, thus, they contract more slowly. They also contain a different form of SERCA (1) in the sarcoplasmic reticulum which pumps calcium back into the sarcoplasmic reticulum relatively slowly and contributes to a slower relaxation time. These muscle cells tend to be smaller in diameter and are more fatigue resistant compared to fast twitch muscles. Slow twitch muscle cells can be found in greater numbers in postural muscles and muscles that are specialized for endurance; i.e., more slow twitch muscle fibers found in the lower limbs compared to the upper limbs.

Fast twitch muscle cells respond quickly to nervous stimulation and the contraction and relaxation phases are relatively fast. The primary cause of this increased contraction time is due to the myosin ATPase and the speed of breaking down ATP into ADP and P which increase the cross bridge cycling phase. In general, fast twitch muscles are more adapted to anaerobic respiration; they contain fewer and smaller mitochondria, very little myoglobin and large stores of glycogen. Fast twitch muscle fibers have larger diameters and fatigue more quickly than slow twitch muscles. Fast twitch fibers tend to be found in muscles specialized for quick muscle activities over short durations (i.e., sprinting). There are two types of fast twitch muscles; a glycolytic form (type IIb) and an oxidative form

(Type IIa). The glycolytic form of fast twitch fibers (type IIb) are relatively rare in humans and primates and are highly specialized for generating fast muscle contractions. The enzymatic activity of glycolytic enzymes is very high and they contain the SERCA2 isoform which pumps calcium back into the SR quickly and speeds up relaxation times. The type IIa oxidative form of fast twitch muscles is an intermediate form of muscle fiber. The muscle fibers have higher activities of the enzymes for oxidative phosphorylation and are more fatigue resistant than the type IIb form of fast twitch muscles. During training, the type IIa can be converted to a type IIb or vice versa. This allows muscles to change and adapt to different needs of the body.

Response to exercise

Regular exercise and training protocols improves athletic performance. Regular training results in changes in the neural, cardiovascular, respiratory and the muscular systems. Together, these responses elicit an improvement in exercise performance. Muscles respond to training by altering function at multiple levels.

In skeletal muscles, many changes occur at the cellular level. Muscles do not duplicate or make new cells, rather muscle cells increase their size or exhibit cellular hypertrophy. Small cells located in the endomysium, the satellite cells, fuse with existing muscle cells and provide an additional nucleus and cellular machinery to an existing cell. Muscle cells can create new sarcomeres and myofibrils and SR and mitochondria. The muscle cells enlarge and will be able to generate greater tension due to the increase in the number of sarcomeres. This will allow muscles to lift greater weight. . At the cellular level, the activity of enzymes involved with glycolysis or oxidative phosphorylation also change. Muscles can convert Type IIa and IIb fibers; depending on the type of exercise. For example, if the muscles are training to be quicker the types of ATPases found on the myosin head change and allow the muscles to cycle cross bridges faster. Other changes in muscles include, better coordination of muscle use, better circulation and blood supply to muscle cells and less restriction by adipose cells. The brain is able to recruit motor units more efficiently and more effectively to control motor movement.

CHAPTER 5, SECTION 1 – SUMMARY

> Skeletal muscle cells are long cylindrical cells filled with actin and myosin myofilaments organized into sarcomeres, the functional unit of skeletal muscle. Each cell contains many sarcomeres stacked on top of each other and form a cylindrical structure called a myofibril.

> Filamentous actin myofilaments are alpha helical proteins attached to each end of a sarcomere called the Z-disk. Tropomyosin molecules are situated within each groove of the helix and are attached to the actin via the protein troponin.

➢ Myosin myofilaments are grouped together in a bundle in the center of each sarcomere. The myosin head regions stick out toward, and overlap with, the actin myofilaments.

➢ Within each cell is a tubular network that is continuous with the outer sarcolemma and projects deep within the cell and surrounds each sarcomere.

➢ Somatic motor neurons release ACh at the neuromuscular junction and stimulate nicotinic ACh receptors leading to the depolarization of the plasma membrane. Voltage-gated Na^+ channels are activated and lead to the formation of an action potential. The action potential spreads across the sarcolemma and down the T-tubular network.

➢ The sarcoplasmic reticulum is associated with T-tubule. The depolarization of the action potential activates the DHP receptor on the plasma membrane which stimulates RyR located on the sarcoplasmic reticulum and causes the release of internal Ca^{2+} stores.

➢ Ca^{2+} binds to troponin which pulls away the tropomyosin and exposes the myosin binding sites on actin. Myosin binds with the aid of ATP and the myofilaments slide past one another and cause muscle tension. Muscle relaxation occurs when the Ca^{2+} in resequestered back into the sarcoplasmic reticulum.

➢ A single muscle twitch is initiated by a single action potential. However, in normal physiology, a series of high frequency action potentials results in summation and tetanus and initiates muscle contraction. As each successive action potential migrates down the T-tubules, RyR activation results in more and more Ca2+ release such that more active sites are exposed and they stay exposed for longer periods of time. This causes a greater force of contraction than a single muscle twitch.

➢ The starting length of the muscle will influence the maximum amount of tension that it can generate. This is due to the amount of actin and myosin overlap.

➢ The amount of the load that is applied to the muscle will influence the velocity of the contraction phase. Greater weights applied to the muscle slow down the speed of the contraction phase.

➢ Muscle fibers come in two primary types, slow twitch (Type I) oxidative and fast twitch (type II) fibers. Fast twitch muscle fibers can be either an oxidative form (Type IIa) or glycolytic form (Type IIb).

➢ Muscle fibers respond to training and exercise and change their internal structure. In general, the cells will enlarge or hypertrophy, there will be more myofibrils, more mitochondria, the enyzmes will change and allow muscles to become more efficient, etc...

Section 2 – Somatic Motor Transduction and Descending Motor Paths

Voluntary movement and postural control is regulated by the activation of somatic motor neurons. The α-motor neurons that innervate each skeletal muscle are located in specific columns of the ventral horn of the spinal cord and they receive inputs from many different sources which influence their activity (Figure 5.15). In order for motor neurons to fire action potentials, they must get stimulated from some outside source. The signals that converge onto α-motor neurons come from a variety of locations. Locally within the spinal cord there are multiple interneurons that connect motor neurons to one another and help control and coordinate muscle function. For example, if you go outside and start running, your legs will alternate very easily, without much thought from your brain to activate each leg as you step forward. In addition, your arms swing forward and back in a particular rhythm that matches your running speed. This happens without even thinking about swinging your arms. The motion for arm swing is built in to central pattern generators that help control coordinated arm and leg movements. Next time you run, try to swing your arms in the opposite direction. It is very hard to accomplish because of the activation of the central pattern generators. Essentially you have to use higher brain regions to actively change or move each arm in the direction that "YOU" want to move the arms.

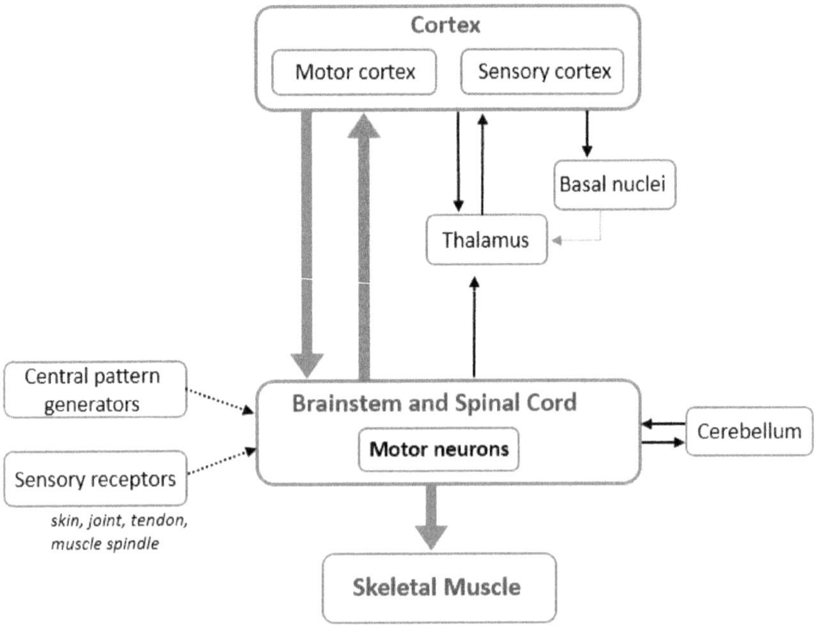

There are also multiple types of sensory afferents that converge onto α-motor neurons from the muscles, joints and skin that can also influence muscle contraction. Muscle spindles (sensory afferents) located within muscles give information about the length and tension that is being applied to a muscle. The withdrawal reflex allows for you to quickly move away from noxious stimuli in skin, such as pulling your hand off of a hot stove. And the Golgi tendon organs help to initiate reflexes to prevent you from putting too much force on a muscle. These sensory afferents cause stimulation of some muscle groups and inhibit other muscle groups to carry out a specific motor movement.

Figure 5.15

The α-motor neurons also receive information from higher brain regions. Everyone has the ability to control their muscles voluntarily; i.e., you can raise your hand any time you wish. These inputs arise from brain regions located in the frontal lobe. As you initiate a voluntary muscle movement, many other areas of the brain also get activated to coordinate the smooth muscle movement. In addition to the frontal cortex, multiple higher brain regions are involved in the regulation and production of smooth and precise motor movements. One neural loop projects through the basal nuclei and thalamus and another loop projects through the cerebellum. If these centers are damaged, motor control is altered and tremors and spasticity are possible. This is evident in patients with Parkinson's disease in which areas of the basal nuclei are altered creating the motor symptoms of the disease.

Spinal Reflexes

Skeletal muscles maintain posture, they move the limbs and trunk, they move the head and neck and control facial expression and they control speech. Voluntary movements are movements that are consciously activated to achieve a specific purpose. When a voluntary movement is initiated, many motor neuron pools are simultaneously activated and/or inhibited in a coordinated fashion to achieve a common goal. Reflexes are movements that utilize skeletal muscle and are unconscious movements. Reflex activity is initiated under many conditions, including normal muscle movement and helps to coordinate muscle movement.

A simple reflex arc requires several key components in order to function properly. A sensory receptor is needed to detect a specific stimulus. The sensory receptors are located out in the periphery. The sensory neuron projects into the dorsal horn of the spinal cord through the dorsal root. The sensory neuron synapses with interneurons which in turn synapses onto motor neurons. Motor neurons are stimulated to activate a target tissue. Reflexes are however, more complicated than this simple reflex arc demonstrates. Usually many muscle groups are targeted through both excitatory and inhibitory neurons to carry out a motor movement.

Muscle stretch reflex

Skeletal muscles contain two types of muscle cells or fibers, extrafusal fibers and intrafusal fibers. Extrafusal fibers are the muscle cells that are responsible for contraction of skeletal muscles (the type I and type II fibers described earlier in this chapter) and are innervated by α-motor neurons. Intrafusal fibers are a type of modified muscle cell associated with sensory afferents that provide information about the length and tension of the muscle. The intrafusal fibers have center regions with little to NO actin and myosin myofilaments but contain a gelatinous-like sac that is associated with a sensory neuron. On the ends of the intrafusal fibers, there are sarcomeres which can be activated to contract and can change the length of the intrafusal fiber. The ends of the intrafusal fibers are innervated by a smaller type of motor neuron, the γ-motor neuron. There are two types of intrafusal fibers, nuclear bag fibers which sense the degree of muscle stretch and the nuclear chain fibers which detect the speed and magnitude of the stretch. These two types of muscle cells are clustered into a sensory receptor called the muscle spindle.

The muscle stretch reflex is the only monosynaptic reflex in the body; a synapse forms directly between the sensory afferent neuron and the motor efferent neuron (with no interneuron). The muscle spindle actively provides information about the state of the muscle at all times. For example, if you catch a tossed ball, there is an initial small force applied to the muscle and the biceps brachii will get stretched (slightly). As the muscle lengthens, the muscle spindle gets stretched and the sensory afferents will increase their firing rate. The sensory afferents project into the dorsal horn and synapse directly with α-motor neurons located in the ventral horn. The response of this afferent feedback is to contract the muscle upward to its original starting position; i.e., the stimulated α-motor neuron activates extrafusal fibers causing the muscle to contract. The muscle spindle slackens and a reduced firing of action potentials originate from the sensory afferent fiber. The γ-motor neuron is activated to return the muscle spindle length back to its original length and the frequency of action potentials originating from the sensory neuron return to normal and resets the sensory receptor. This activity that originates from the muscle spindle helps to determine muscle length and position.

The patellar tendon reflex is a classic muscle stretch reflex which is commonly used to clinically determine normal neuron-muscle function. If the patellar tendon is hit with a hammer, the quadriceps muscles are quickly stretched. This activates the muscle stretch reflex. The sensory neurons associated with muscle spindles in the quadriceps muscle fire action potentials due to the quick and rapid stretch. The sensory neurons project into the dorsal horn of the spinal cord and release glutamate directly onto the α-motor neuron of the same muscle. This causes the muscle to contract and the leg kicks outward.

Golgi tendon reflex

The tendons that attach muscles to bones also contain specialized sensory receptors which detect the amount of stretch and monitor the tension applied to the tendons. A simple passive stretch of muscles (lengthening the muscle fibers) will stretch the tendons and the Golgi tendon organ and results in an increase in the firing rate of its associated sensory afferent neuron. However, if the muscle contracts and the muscle shortens in length, the tendon is stretched to even greater lengths and the Golgi tendon organ is even stretched to a greater degree. This results in an even greater increase in the firing rate of the sensory neuron. When this happens, the sensory afferent neuron enters the dorsal horn of the spinal cord and stimulates an inhibitory interneuron by releasing glutamate at the synapse. The inhibitory interneuron fires action potentials and releases inhibitory neurotransmitters onto the α-motor neurons. This inhibits the motor neurons and they stop firing action potentials. The load placed on the muscle is quickly dropped. This prevents muscles from applying too much force to tendons.

Withdrawal reflex

The withdrawal reflex allows for the quick movement of a limb away from a noxious or painful stimulus. The withdrawal reflex is also a polysynaptic reflex and utilizes interneurons to simultaneously activate and inhibit specific muscles. The withdrawal reflex is initiated by nociceptors located in skin. These are specialized receptors that are free nerve endings. They are sensitive to extreme mechanical, chemical and thermal stimuli. For example, if you step on a sharp object, nociceptor(s) located in the skin get activated. The axon of the nociceptor enters the dorsal horn of the spinal cord and synapses with multiple interneurons to diverge and send signals to multiple areas in the CNS. 1) Neurons of the spinothalamic tract are activated which project up the contralateral spinal cord along the anterolateral tract to allow conscious perception of pain (Chapter 4). 2) Excitatory interneurons get activated to excite some muscle groups and 3) inhibitory interneurons get activated to inhibit antagonist muscles to ensure proper motor movement.

The simple withdrawal reflex includes a sensory neuron which enters the spinal cord. It synapses and stimulates an excitatory interneuron. The excitatory interneuron stimulates α-motor neurons to cause a muscle to contract, which will pull a limb away from a noxious stimulus. Reciprocal inhibition ensures that the antagonist muscle group does not contract. This occurs through an inhibitory interneuron. The sensory neuron sends axon collaterals to inhibitory interneurons which get excited. The inhibitory interneuron fire action potentials and release inhibitory neurotransmitter onto α-motor neurons of antagonist muscle groups. In the example of stepping on a sharp object, you realize that in order to pull the leg away from the noxious stimulus, you must step on the opposite foot. This activates the crossed extensor reflex. The sensory neuron also connects to interneurons which project to the opposite side of the body. Excitatory interneurons excite muscle groups to cause contraction of some muscles and inhibitory interneurons inhibit antagonist muscle groups.

Hierarchy of motor control

All voluntary motor movements are controlled by a variety of local and higher brain regions. The forethought and initiation of voluntary movement arises from areas in the pre-frontal lobe. This area projects to the pre-central gyrus or the somatic motor cortex to initiate upper motor neurons. The upper motor neurons descend through specific paths to activate motor neuron pools and central pattern generators associated with motor movement. Within the spinal cord the motor neuron is influenced by the descending projections as well as the sensory information that is arising from muscle spindles, joint receptors and Golgi tendon organs. The sensory information also projects upward to the cerebellum and thalamus and are involved with modifying the descending motor projections. The complex neuronal descending and ascending loops ensure smooth calculated movements by the body. We will only review the major descending paths that control motor function here.

Descending motor pathways

In order to initiate voluntary motor movement, action potentials must arise from the primary motor cortex. Many of the pre-motor fibers originate in the pre-central gyrus located in the frontal lobe of the brain. These fibers course down the brain and spinal cord to innervate motor neurons and activate motor movement. These fibers course through specific paths based primarily on location.

Figure 5.16

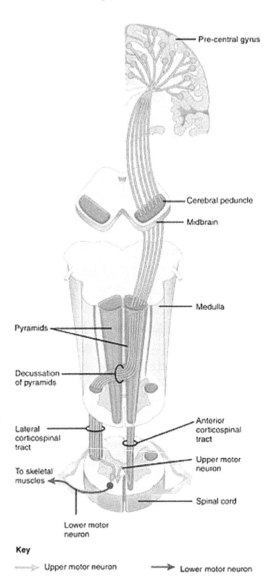

Corticospinal tract

This is the primary motor pathway that controls most voluntary movement of the muscles of the body (limbs primarily) (Figure 5.16). The corticospinal neurons originate in the primary motor cortex located in the frontal cortex. These neurons descend through the internal capsule of the telencephalon, course through the subthalamus and enter the cerebral peduncles located in the midbrain. They pass through the cerebellum and send axon collaterals to pontine nuclei for cerebellar processing. The axons then enter the medulla oblongata. In the medulla, the corticospinal fibers comprise the pyramids and the majority of the fibers cross in the pyramidal decussation. The axons that cross to the contralateral spinal cord enter the lateral corticospinal tract. They descend the spinal cord to synapse with α-motor neurons located in the ventral horn of the spinal cord. The axons that did not cross the pyramidal decussation stay in the anterior column and form the anterior corticospinal tract. The axons descend the spinal cord through the anterior corticospinal tract until they reach the level of the spinal cord at which their target motor neuron is located. At this level of the spinal cord, the axon crosses the spinal cord to target α-motor neurons on the contralateral spinal cord.

Other descending tracts

Motor neurons that control the voluntary muscles of the face and neck originate in nuclei of brainstem cranial nerves and not spinal nerves. The upper motor neurons arise in the primary motor cortex of the frontal lobe with all voluntary control neurons. The upper motor neuron course through the same path as described above for the corticospinal tract. The upper motor neurons that innervate the face and muscles project to cranial nuclei located in the brainstem (therefore they do not continue down the spinal cord). Muscles that control mastication or chewing are controlled by neurons that arise from the trigeminal motor nucleus and the muscles that control facial expression are controlled by neurons of the facial motor nucleus. These motor neurons project to the ipsilateral side of the face (no crossing of motor fibers). These descending paths are called the corticobulbar pathways; the upper motor neuron arises from the cortex and projects to the "bulb" or the brainstem.

Other descending tracts include the bulbospinal paths. These originate in the "bulb" and project down the spinal cord. Some of the tracts include the vestibulospinal, reticulospinal tectospinal and the rubrospinal paths. Many of these pathways are involved with postural control.

CHAPTER 5, SECTION 2 – SUMMARY

➤ Somatic motor neurons are under descending control from inputs that arise from the primary motor cortex. They are also under regulatory control from many other inputs including interneurons for the coordination of complex motor movements and sensory afferent inputs from muscles, skin, and joints.

➤ Spinal reflexes allow limbs to quickly respond to noxious stimuli as well as help control normal muscle function.

➤ Special sensory receptors found in muscles provides information regarding the length and tension applied to muscles. These muscle spindles respond when a muscle is stretched. A classic example of the stretch reflex is the patellar tendon reflex. Hitting the patellar tendon with a hammer causes the quadriceps muscles to stretch. Sensory afferents associated with the muscle spindle are stimulated and make a synapse with the motor neurons that innervate the same muscle. The sensory neuron stimulates the motor neuron and it fires an action potential and causes the muscle to contract. The muscle stretch reflex is a monosynaptic reflex.

➤ The Golgi tendon reflex detects the amount of stretch or tension applied to tendons. As muscles contract, the forces applied to the tendon increases and stimulates the Golgi tendon organs found in tendons. The sensory neuron from the Golgi tendon organs project into the spinal cord and synapse with inhibitory interneurons. The inhibitory interneurons inhibit the same muscle from which the sensory organs originated and cause the muscle to stop contracting. The Golgi tendon reflex is a polysynaptic reflex.

➤ The withdrawal reflex is also a polysynaptic reflex and allows for the quick removal of a limb from a noxious stimulus. Activation of nociceptors in the skin cause action potentials to propagate along sensory neurons into the dorsal horn of the spinal cord. The sensory neuron synapses with both excitatory and inhibitory interneurons to excite and inhibit specific muscle groups which allow for the withdrawal of a limb.

➢ Motor neurons are activated by specific neural pathways that descend from the cerebral cortex. The corticospinal tract (both lateral and anterior) control most voluntary movement of muscles. Other pathways help control muscles of the face (bulbospinal) and postural muscles (vestibulospinal, reticulospinal, tectospinal).

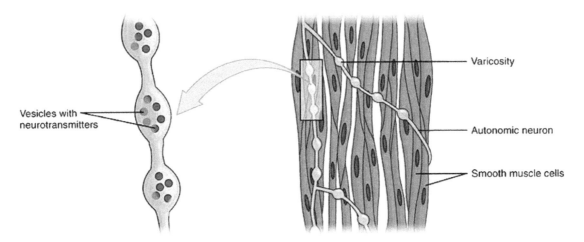

Figure 5.17

Section 3 - Smooth Muscle

Non-striated or smooth muscle is found in many types of organs (Figure 5.17). Smooth muscle is traditionally categorized as either single unit or multi-unit. Single unit refers to conditions where the smooth muscle cells are electrically coupled with many gap junctions and thus the whole muscle contracts or relaxes as a single unit. Multi-unit smooth muscle describes conditions in which muscle cells are not electrically connected (as much) and thus act as multiple units within the organ. In fact, many smooth muscles are more complex and these two terms can be thought of as the extremes and most smooth muscles are a mixture of the two terms with some cell to cell communication and some neural modulation to coordinate smooth muscle contraction in any particular organ.

Smooth muscle cells are small spindle shaped cells with a centrally located nucleus. Smooth muscle cells contain actin and myosin filaments, however, the arrangement of the myofilaments is NOT in sarcomeres and thus the muscle does NOT have a striated appearance. There are no Z-disks, but actin is attached to a proteinaceous structure called the dense bodies. The myosin filaments overlap with the actin myofilaments, however, the organization is more of a star-array shape. When smooth muscle contracts, the cells become shorter, but they also get slightly fatter in the middle (Figure 5.18). The cells do not contain a T-tubular system but they do have small depressions into the cell called caveolae. These small depressions are somewhat associated with the sarcoplasmic reticulum but not to the extent that is observed in skeletal muscle. Ca^{2+} is still needed for contraction.

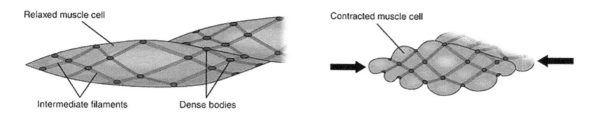

Figure 5.18

In smooth muscle, Ca^{2+} comes from two sources. One source of Ca^{2+} is from the external environment. Ca^{2+} channels embedded in the surface of the plasma membrane of smooth muscle cells can get activated or turned off to help regulate intracellular Ca^{2+} levels. Ca^{2+} also comes from internal stores, the sarcoplasmic reticulum (Figure 5.19). In smooth muscle, Ca^{2+} does not bind to troponin, but rather Ca^{2+} binds to a protein called calmodulin. The Ca^{2+}-activated calmodulin can then activate myosin kinase which is an enzyme which utilizes ATP to phosphorylate the myosin head. Phosphorylation of the

Figure 5.19

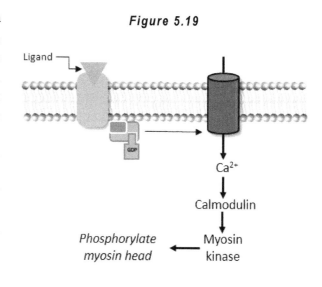

myosin head causes the head to bend and initiates the power stroke. Another enzyme, myosin phosphatase, removes the phosphate group and causes the recovery stroke. As long as Ca^{2+} is present, contraction can take place.

The contraction and relaxation times are slower in smooth muscle compared to skeletal muscle. This is due to the long distances that Ca^{2+} has to diffuse through the cytoplasm both to get to calmodulin and then the time it takes to resequester the Ca^{2+} back into the SR.

Smooth muscle is regulated by the autonomic nervous system, the enteric nervous system, or by hormones. Unlike skeletal muscle, smooth muscle can have a multitude of receptors located on its plasma membrane which can influence the contraction or relaxation of smooth muscle. For example, a single smooth muscle cell might have mACh receptors to respond to parasympathetic nerves, adrenergic receptors to respond to sympathetic stimulation and receptors for the hormone, oxytocin. Recall that the autonomic nervous system is always "on." This indicates the smooth muscle is always under some sort of regulatory control and maintains a certain tone; it is never fully relaxed like skeletal muscle. Smooth muscle can also be regulated by auto-rhythmic signals which originate from within the smooth muscle cell. Smooth muscle can also maintain constant tone for very long periods of time without fatigue. And unlike skeletal muscle, length does not influence the force of contraction.

CHAPTER 5, SECTION 3 – SUMMARY

> ➤ Smooth muscle is under involuntary control and is regulated by neurons of the autonomic nervous system; i.e., most smooth muscle cells are innervated by both sympathetic and parasympathetic fibers which regulate the tone (or contraction state) of smooth muscle.

> ➤ Actin and myosin myofilaments are the proteins used for shortening, but they are not organized into sarcomeres.

> ➤ Contraction of smooth muscle is regulated by the amount intracellular Ca^{2+}. Ca^{2+} binds to calmodulin which activates myosin kinase. Myosin kinase phosphorylates the myosin head and causes the head to bend. Myosin phosphatase removes the phosphate and allows the head to return to its original shape.

References and Suggested Readings

Barbara JG, Clarac F. 2011. Historical concepts on the relations between nerves and muscles. *Brain Research* 1409:3-22.

Batters C, Veigel C, Homsher E, Sellers JR. 2014. To understand muscle you must take it apart. *Frontiers in Physiology* 5:1-14

Baylor SM, Hollingworth S. 2012. Intracellular calcium movements during excitation-contraction coupling in mammalian slow-twitch and fast-twitch muscle fibers. *Journal of General Physiology* 139(4):261-272.

Endo M. 2009. Calcium-induced calcium release in skeletal muscle. *Physiological Reviews* 89:1153-1176,

Franzini-Armstrong C, Protasi F. 1997. Ryanodine receptors of striated muscles: a complex channel capable of multiple interactions. *Physiological Reviews* 77(3)699-729.

James RS. 2013. A review of thermal sensitivity of the mechanics of vertebrate skeletal muscle. *Journal of Comparative Biochemistry B* 183:723-733.

Jevsek M, Mars R, Mis K, Grubic Z. 2004. Origin of acetylcholinesterase in the neuromuscular junction formed in the in vitro innervated human muscle. *European Journal of Neuroscience* 20:2865-2871.

Lehrer SS. 2011. The 3-state model of muscle regulation revisited: is a fourth state involved? *Journal of Muscle Research and Cell Motility* 32:203-208.

Millet GY. 2011. Can neuromuscular fatigue explain running strategies and performance in ultra-marathons? *Sports Medicine* 41(6):489-506.

Ohtsuki I. 1999. Calcium ion regulation of muscle contraction: the regulatory role of troponin T. *Molecular and Cellular Biochemistry* 190:33-38.

Ogawa Y. 1985. Calcium binding to troponin C and troponin: effects of Mg^{2+}, ionic strength and pH. *Journal of Biochemistry* 97:1011-1023.

Rebbeck RT, Karunasekar Y, Board PG. 2014. Skeletal muscle excitation-contraction coupling: who are the dancing partners? *The International Journal of Biochemistry and Cell Biology* 48:28-38.

Seipel K, Schmid V. 2005. Evolution of striated muscle: jellyfish and the origin of triploblasty. *Developmental Biology* 282:14-26.

Chapter 6: Cardiovascular Physiology

The cardiovascular system includes the heart and all of the vessels that carry blood to and from the heart. Its main function is to transport blood to the various tissues in order to aid in the exchange of gases, nutrients and wastes, transportation of hormone, and provide a means for heat transfer and temperature control. In this regard, the cardiovascular system works intricately with every other organ and organ system in the body and plays a vital role in each of their functions. In single-celled and very small organisms, the distance between cells and their environment are extremely short and, therefore, exchange of gases, nutrients and waste products can be achieved by diffusion properties alone. As animals evolved and became larger, the need for a circulatory system to help aid in gas, nutrient and waste exchange became necessary. Most invertebrates maintain an open circulatory system in which blood (or hemolymph) circulates through a heart and artery into a large chamber called the hemocoel. The movement of the blood or hemolymph is achieved by not only the heart but also by the contraction of the limbs and peristaltic movement of smooth muscle in the body. The flow of blood is maintained by valves as well as pump control mechanisms. In vertebrates, the circulatory system is closed and blood is 1) pumped by a heart to distribute blood throughout the body, 2) carried away from the heart through an arterial system which acts as a pressure reservoir, 3) flows through capillaries to allow gas, nutrient and waste exchange with tissues, and 4) is carried back to the heart by a venous system and acts a blood reservoir. Much of what we know about the heart and cardiovascular system is due to research on the mammalian heart.

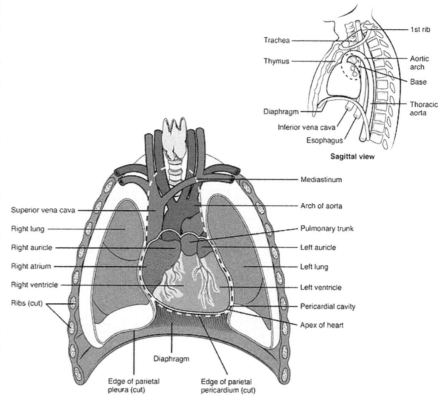

Figure 6.1

169

Section 1 - Heart

The Mammalian Heart

In mammals, the heart along with the large blood vessels coming and going to the heart is situated in the middle portion of the thoracic cavity, or the mediastinum (See Figure 6.1). The mammalian heart is divided into four chambers separated by complete septa. The upper two chambers are called the right and left atria and are separated by a complete interatrial septum. The lower two chambers are called the right and left ventricles and are separated by a complete interventricular septum (Figure 6.2). Between the atria and ventricles sits a ring of tough connective tissue called the heart skeleton which serves to isolate the electrical activity of the atria and ventricles and provides an attachment site for the valves that separate these chambers. The blood leaves the heart through vessels called arteries and blood returns to the heart through veins. The right atrium receives blood from the body through two major veins, the superior vena cava and the inferior vena cava as well as blood from the heart tissue itself through the coronary sinus. Blood travels from the right atrium through an atrioventricular valve, the tricuspid valve into the right ventricle (Figure 6.3). Blood is pumped through the pulmonary semilunar valves into the pulmonary trunk and carries deoxygenated blood to the lungs for gas exchange.

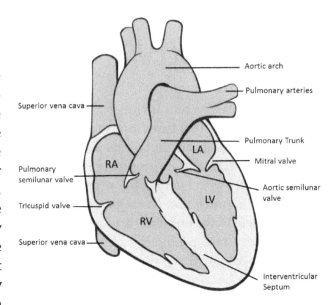

Figure 6.2

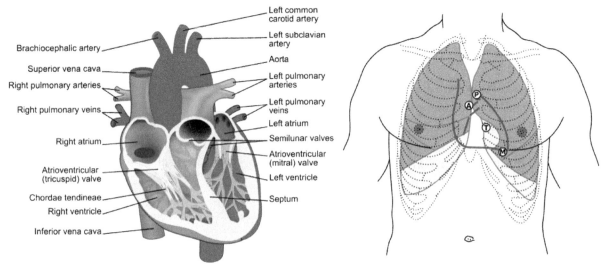

Figure 6.3

As blood passes through capillaries within the alveoli of the lungs, carbon dioxide (CO_2) is released and oxygen (O_2) is picked up. The oxygenated blood returns to the heart through 2 right and 2 left pulmonary arteries which empty into the left atrium. From the left atrium, blood passes through another atrioventricular valve, the bicuspid valve which is commonly called the mitral valve to enter the left ventricle. Finally, oxygenated blood is pumped out of the left ventricle through the aortic semilunar valve into the aorta to carry oxygenated blood to the tissues of the body. The opening and closing of the valves are controlled by passive changes in pressure and ensure that blood flow is in one direction. The atrioventricular valves are attached to papillary muscles in the ventricles through tough fibrous, chordae tendinae which prevent relapse of the valves when the pressures increase during ventricular contraction (See Figure 6.3). The organization of the mammalian heart allows blood to be separated into two distinct systems, the pulmonary circulation and the systemic circulation.

The majority of the wall of the heart chamber is comprised of striated, contractile cardiac muscle and is called the myocardium. There are three types of muscle fibers distributed throughout the myocardium. The smallest muscle fibers are the least contractile, but are extremely auto-rhythmic. These cells are found in small, special regions of the heart (the sinoatrial node and the atrioventricular node) and are referred to as nodal cells. The primary function of the nodal cells is to generate action potentials and spread these action potentials to the intermediate-sized, contractile muscle cells. The largest cells are found in the ventricles and are also not very contractile. The Purkinje cells are specialized to conduct the action potential throughout the ventricles quickly. The intermediate-sized muscle cells constitute the majority of the myocardium and they are highly contractile myocardial cells.

The inside of the heart is lined with the endocardium which consists of a simple squamous epithelium, its basement membrane and a small amount of connective tissue lying beneath. The epithelium is continuous with all of the vessels that emerge from the heart, including the arteries, veins and capillaries. This specialized epithelium of the cardiovascular system is called the endothelium.

The outside of the heart is covered in a flexible, fibrous pericardium. There are two parts of the pericardium, the visceral pericardium which is attached to the heart itself and the parietal pericardium which makes up the wall of a pericardial chamber. The chamber is lined with a serous epithelium which produces and secretes the pericardial fluid and acts as a lubricant to prevent abrasion as the two surfaces pass one another as the heart beats continuously throughout life.

The heart has multiple functions. First, the heart is involved in generating blood pressure which allows blood to travel through the entire circulatory system; blood flows from high to low pressure. The heart is involved with routing blood and separating the circulation into the pulmonary and systemic circulations. Finally, the heart ensures that blood flows in one direction; the valves prevent backflow and are involved with regulating the blood supply.

Electrical activity of the heart

Action potentials are generated spontaneously due to special membrane properties within pacemaker cells of the heart. The pacemaker initializes and controls the underlying heart rhythm. The nervous system and hormones modify the pace or rhythm and the contractility of the heart muscle. Once an action potential is generated in one cardiac muscle cell, the action potential will spread throughout the heart in a coordinated manner. This is achieved by a specialized conduction system spread throughout the myocardium of the heart and placement of gap junctions between cells (Figure 6.4). The action potential is first generated in a collection of cells located just medial to the opening of superior vena cava, the sinoatrial node (SA node). The action potential spreads quickly throughout the left and right atria and to the atrioventricular node (AV node) located in the right atrium just medial to the right AV valve. The action potential passes through the AV node slowly which allows for atrial contraction and ventricular filling before the ventricles contract. The action potentials pass from the atria to the ventricles through a collection of nodal cells called the AV bundle or bundle of His. The AV bundle passes through a structure called the cardiac skeleton which is a ring of tough connective tissue which separates the atria from the ventricles. The cardiac skeleton provides a site for the valves to attach as well as a site for cardiac muscle attachment. It also serves to separate the electrical activity of the atria and the ventricle. Once the AV bundle passes through the cardiac skeleton it separates into right and left bundle branches that course down under the endocardium of the interventricular septum toward the apex of the heart. The action potential is spread quickly through the bundle branches to the Purkinje fibers which conduct the action potential to the ventricular cardiac myocytes of the ventricles and upward toward the base of the heart.

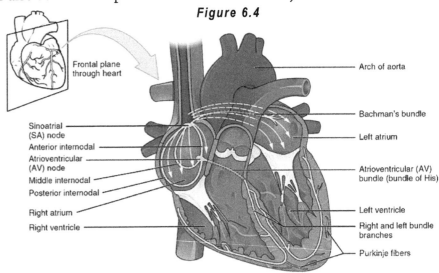

Figure 6.4

Anterior view of frontal section

In mammals, the nodal cells that generate the pace of heart originate in a structure called the SA node. In fish, amphibians, and some reptiles, the cells that spontaneous generate the action potential are found in a large venous sinus which sits just prior to the atrium. In these vertebrates, the first chamber to beat is the sinus venosus, followed by the atria, and then the ventricle(s).

Action potential generation in nodal cells

By definition, pacemaker cells do not maintain a constant resting membrane potential. All pacemaker cells undergo a steady depolarization called the pre-potential or pacemaker potential which leads to an action potential and sets a "pace." In the heart, the pacemaker potential of the SA node cells is faster than all other cells that contain pacemaker properties and so it is termed the pacemaker of the heart (See Figure 6.4); i.e., it sets the pace of the heart because it fires first and is transmitted to the entire heart through the conduction system. The membrane potential of SA nodal cells slowly depolarize due to the activation of an F-type Na^+ channel (See Figure 6.5, below). This unusual type of Na^+ channel is activated, NOT by depolarization like most traditional voltage-gated channels, but rather, hyperpolarization. Because of its unusual mechanism of activation it was called the "funny" channel or the F-type Na^+ channel. When the cell hyperpolarizes, the membrane potential becomes more negative and the F-type Na^+ channels open and allow Na^+ to move inside the cell down their concentration gradient. The influx of Na^+ causes a slow steady depolarization and leads to the opening a "transient" or T-type Ca^{2+} channel. Ca^{2+} flows in the cell down its concentration gradient further depolarizing the cell membrane. Subsequently, the steady depolarization causes the F-type Na^+ channels to close. The slow depolarization of the pre-potential phase brings the cell to threshold activating the "long-acting" or L-type voltage-gated Ca^{2+} channels. The repolarization phase of the action potential occurs due to the inactivation of the L-type Ca^{2+} channels and the opening of voltage-gated K^+ channels and the efflux of K^+. As the cell becomes more negative, the cycle starts over; the F-type Na^+ channels become activated and the depolarization of the pre-potential starts again. The action potential is spread to other nodal cells and to contractile cardiac myocytes of the atria via gap junctions. The action potential spreads across the atria and quickly to the AV node.

Figure 6.5

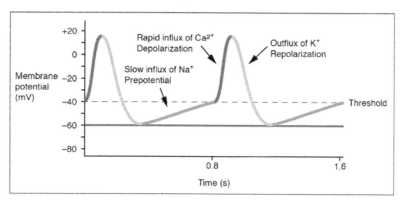

The shape and the underlying mechanism of the action potentials of cells in the AV node are similar to the SA node, except that the rise phase of the pre-potential is much, much slower. In fact, the speed of the action potential through the AV node slows considerably and allows the atria to contract and thus pushes some blood into the ventricles. The speed of the action potential in the AV node slows because 1) the diameter of the cells is smaller which increases the resistance of the cell, 2) the arrangement of the cells is complex and intermixed with extensive connective tissue, 3) the expression of F-type Na^+ channels is poor which slows the upswing of the pre-potential, as well as 4) possible differences in connexin expression patterns (i.e., the gap junction proteins) which may slow the propagation from cell to cell. The action potential is then spread to the AV bundle, bundle branches and Purkinje cells. The action potential speeds up and passes quickly throughout these conducting cells as well as the ventricular myocardium.

Action potential generation in cardiac myocytes

The conducting nodal cells are connected to contractile cardiac myocytes of the atria and ventricles. The profile of the action potential in the contractile cardiac myocytes is different compared to the nodal cells due to different channels in the plasma membrane (Figure 6.6). Once the nodal cells depolarize due to Na^+ and Ca^{2+} influx, these ions are free to flow through gap junctions into cardiac myocytes. This positive charge brings the cardiac myocytes cell to threshold and opens fast voltage-gated Na^+ channels and cause a rapid depolarization of the cell membrane. This opens L-type voltage-gated Ca^{2+} channels and causes a subsequent influx of Ca^{2+} into the cell. The voltage-gated Na^+ channels quickly become inactivated, but there is a long

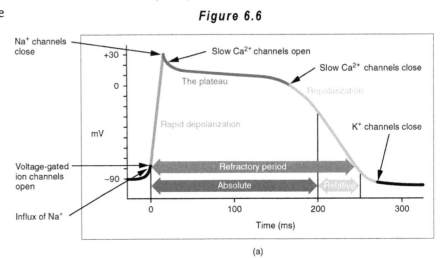

Figure 6.6

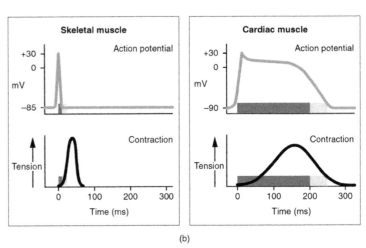

plateau phase of depolarization due to the long opening phase of the L-type Ca^{2+} channels. The Ca^{2+} channels eventually begin to close and voltage-gated K^+ channels open up. This results in the repolarization phase. The long length of the action potential (up to 500msec) results in a long refractory period and ensures that the contraction phase of the myocardium is almost finished by the time another action potential can be generated. This prevents summation and tetanus in the heart myocardium.

Electrocardiogram (ECG)

The electrocardiogram (ECG) is a clinical measurement of the sum of all of the electrical currents that are generated by the action potentials that spread across the cells of the heart. This electrical current can be detected by electrodes placed at the surface of the skin. Clinicians use information from the ECG to determine a number of parameters of heart function such as abnormalities in the spread of action potentials as they move throughout the myocardium. These can be due to rhythm disturbances or damage of the myocardium due to ischemia or a lack of blood flow. Remember that the ECG is a measurement of the electrical activity on the outside of the heart cells and does not measure the contraction or relaxation of the heart muscle.

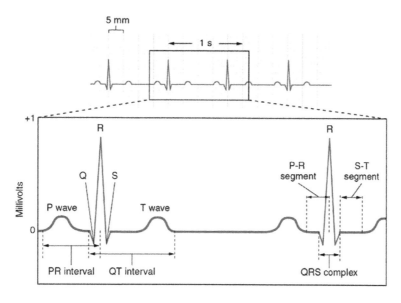

Figure 6.7

In general, the ECG trace is divided into several deflections and intervals (Figure 6.7). The deflections include a P wave, a QRS complex and a T wave. The P wave is due to the depolarization of the action potentials as they spread across the cells of the atria. The QRS wave is due to the depolarization phase of the action potentials in the cells of the ventricles. The atria are repolarizing during the time that the QRS complex is occurring and are therefore masked by the QRS complex. The T wave is the repolarization phase of the action potential in the cells of the ventricles. Several intervals of importance are the P-R interval which indicates the time that is needed for the action potential to spread from the atria through to the AV node. Most of this time is due to the spread of action potentials through the AV node and thus an elongation of this period most likely indicates an AV blockage of some sort. The length the QRS wave indicates the time that it takes the action potential to spread through the ventricles. Usually an elongated QRS wave indicates a block in the bundle branches. The ST segment is the time spent after the depolarization has spread through the ventricles and then repolarization occurs. An elongation of the ST segment often is due to ischemic damage in the ventricles.

An arrhythmia is any abnormal rhythm that the heart displays (See Figure 6.8, on the next page). This can be due to disturbances in the initiation of the impulse or during the propagation of the impulse through the myocardium. Increases in heart rate that do not alter the normal sequence or progression of action potentials throughout the heart are referred to as tachycardia, and decreases in heart rate below normal are called bradycardia. Other forms of tachycardia can arise from an ectopic foci or a site of rhythm generation other than the SA node. Usually these ectopic foci are located in the ventricle. Ectopic tachycardias can last a few beats to hours to days.

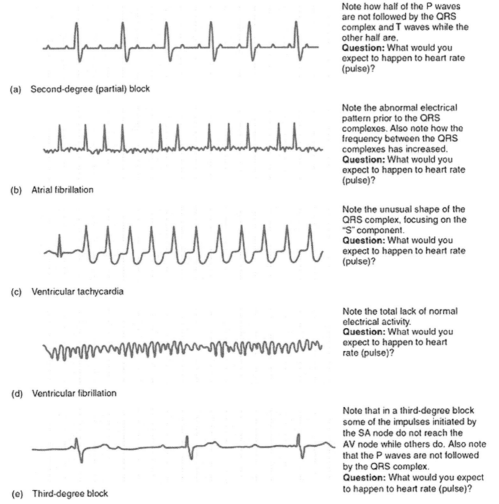

(a) Second-degree (partial) block

Note how half of the P waves are not followed by the QRS complex and T waves while the other half are.
Question: What would you expect to happen to heart rate (pulse)?

(b) Atrial fibrillation

Note the abnormal electrical pattern prior to the QRS complexes. Also note how the frequency between the QRS complexes has increased.
Question: What would you expect to happen to heart rate (pulse)?

(c) Ventricular tachycardia

Note the unusual shape of the QRS complex, focusing on the "S" component.
Question: What would you expect to happen to heart rate (pulse)?

(d) Ventricular fibrillation

Note the total lack of normal electrical activity.
Question: What would you expect to happen to heart rate (pulse)?

(e) Third-degree block

Note that in a third-degree block some of the impulses initiated by the SA node do not reach the AV node while others do. Also note that the P waves are not followed by the QRS complex.
Question: What would you expect to happen to heart rate (pulse)?

Figure 6.8

Ectopic foci can also cause premature ventricular contractions (PVCs). PVCs are a common occurrence in most individuals but can increase during times of stress or from an abnormal condition such as the side effect of some medications. A PVC arises in the ventricle and causes the ventricle to beat earlier than its normal rhythm (prematurely). When this happens, the extra ventricular contraction is called an extrasystole (or extra contraction). After the extrasystole a long pause, or compensatory pause is observed. Since the normal rhythm of SA node depolarization is not altered, the SA node fires and sends an action potential down the AV node and into the ventricles. Since the PVC was the result of a premature ventricular depolarization, the ventricles are in their absolute refractory period and thus cannot depolarize during the normal rhythm. The subsequent pause is due to the natural lag between SA node pacemaker activities and the time that action potential arrives at the ventricles.

Another common type of arrhythmia is an AV block. An AV block is a serious disturbance in the natural rhythm. If the action potential does not travel through the AV node or is blocked at the AV node or bundle of His, then the ventricles will not depolarize or contract. First degree AV block is simply a delay between the P wave and the QRS complex. This indicates that the signal is having a hard time traversing the AV node. Second degree AV block is when the signal from the AV node does not reach the ventricles some of the time. Usually the block occurs in a specific pattern; for example 3 P waves followed by one depolarization getting through and a normal QRS wave and T wave follow. The rhythm may be 3:1 or 2:1 or even 3:2. A third degree AV block is when none of the signals that arise from the SA node make it to the ventricles. In this case, an atrial rhythm and a very slow ventricular rhythm can be observed but the rhythms are not connected to one another. An AV block is one of the most common reasons for the implantation of an artificial pacemaker.

Myocardial cell contractility

Contractile myocardial cells are rectangular cells that can have 1 or 2 branches (Figure 6.9). The cells contain a centrally located nucleus (or two), and actin and myosin myofilaments arranged in sarcomeres which form myofibrils similar to skeletal muscle cells. Since cardiac muscle cells need to continuously contract for an entire lifetime, the cells contain a large amount of mitochondria specialized in oxidative cellular respiration. The mitochondria contain the enzymes needed to maintain a rapid use of substrates to produce high levels of ATP. Subsequently, there is a very extensive

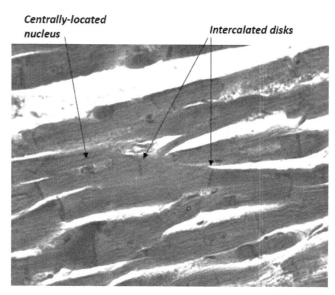

Figure 6.9

capillary network through the myocardium; essentially one capillary for every myocytes in order to meet the high demand for oxygen. Any interruption in blood flow for even short times will alter cardiac function.

All cardiac muscles, both nodal cells and cardiac myocytes, are connected to one another via low resistance gap junctions. Therefore, if one muscle cell fires an action potential, it will easily spread through to all of the muscle cells in the heart. Cardiac muscle excitation-contraction is very similar to skeletal muscle with a few exceptions (See Figure 6.10, on the next page). In cardiac muscle, as an action potential spreads across the sarcolemma, it will open up L-type Ca^{2+} channels which enhances Ca^{2+} entry into the cell. In skeletal muscles, there is a direct coupling of the dihydropyridine receptor (DHP or L-type Ca^{2+} channels) to the ryanodine receptors (RyR) and the release of Ca^{2+} from SR is necessary for contraction (See Figure 6.11, also on the next page). In cardiac muscles, Ca^{2+} must come from the external environment in order to activate internal stores in order to sufficiently

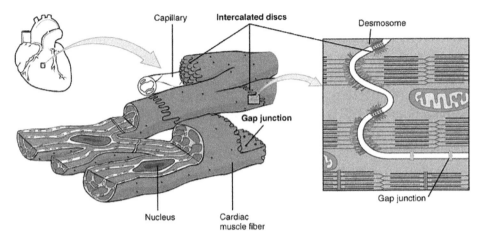

Figure 6.10

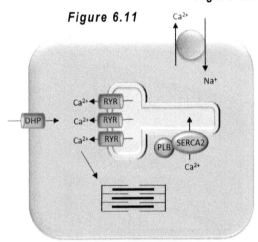

Figure 6.11

induce contraction. Ca^{2+} comes from both L-type Ca^{2+} channels on the plasma membrane and from L-type Ca^{2+} channels (DHP) connected to RyR located on the sarcoplasmic reticulum (SR). In cardiac muscle, the Ca^{2+} influx through the L-type Ca^{2+} channels induces Ca^{2+} release from RyR. This so called Ca^{2+}-induced Ca^{2+} release (CICR) is necessary for excitation-contraction coupling. As action potentials spread across the sarcolemma and move down T-tubules, the L-type Ca^{2+} channels get activated and intracellular Ca^{2+} levels rise. The SR is associated with the t-tubules as well as at the sarcolemma and the increased intracellular Ca^{2+} activates RyR located on the SR. In cardiac muscle, between 14 and 100 RyRs cluster together next to many L-type Ca^{2+} channels and form a unit of calcium release. Like in skeletal muscle, the terminal cisterna contain Ca^{2+} binding proteins such as calsequestrin which concentrates Ca^{2+} in the SR for quick release.

Once Ca^{2+} enters the cytosol, Ca^{2+} is free to bind to troponin which exposes active sites and allow actin and myosin to interact and cause contraction. Cytoplasmic Ca^{2+} is removed by Ca^{2+}-ATPases (SERCA2) located on the sarcoplasmic reticulum which pump Ca^{2+} back into the SR as well as a Na^+/Ca^{2+} exchanger located on the sarcolemma (1 Ca^{2+} is exchanged for 3 Na^+). Na^+/K^+ pumps are also located on the sarcolemma control intracellular Na^+ and K^+ levels.

Mechanical properties of the heart

The heart is made up of 4 muscular chambers that contract and cause blood to flow from the atria to the ventricles and from the ventricles to the circulatory systems. The heart functions as two separate pumps that work simultaneously to pump blood to the systemic and pulmonary circulations (Figure 6.10). As the heart chambers fill with blood and contract, pressure differences are generated which allow blood to flow from high pressure to low pressure. The heart is responsible for generating the initial high pressures of the systemic and pulmonary circulations and the arterioles are important for regulating pressure changes throughout the system and control blood flow to and within organs and tissues.

Cardiac Cycle

The time during which the ventricles are actively contracting is referred to as the systolic period or systole and the time during ventricular relaxation is called the diastolic period or diastole. The systolic period has two phases; the period of isovolumetric contraction and the period of ejection (See Figure 6.12). When systole begins, approximately 120-130mls of blood have emptied into the ventricles; this volume is referred to as the end-diastolic volume. As the ventricles start contracting, blood is pushed upward and will collect in the atrioventricular valves and cause them to snap shut. This is the start of the period of isovolumetric contraction. As the contraction phase continues, the pressure within the ventricles continues to rise rapidly. At this point, both the atrioventricular valves and the semilunar valves are closed and the volume in the ventricles remain constant. Once the pressure in the ventricles exceed the pressures in the aorta and the pulmonary trunk, the semilunar valves will open and blood will flow into the outgoing arteries. This is the end of the period of isovolumetric contraction and the start of the period of ejection. As blood is pushed out or ejected from the ventricle into the aorta or the pulmonary trunk, the pressure in the large arteries increases. The pressures in the ventricle and large vessels rise for a short period and then as the volume of blood begins to decrease, the pressures also decrease. The ventricles stop contracting and the relaxation period or diastole begins. There is a small amount of blood left in the ventricles at the end of the systolic period and is therefore called the end-systolic volume. At rest, the end-systolic volume is approximately 50-60mls. The maximum pressures that the right and left ventricles create are not equal; ~120mmHg in the left ventricle and ~25mmHg in the right ventricle. The walls of the left ventricle work harder and therefore are thicker and generate a higher pressure to overcome the high pressure of the aorta. Although the pressures in the aorta and the pulmonary trunk are different, the rate of the pressure change is roughly equal and blood is ejected into the systemic and the pulmonary circulations at roughly the same time.

Diastole, the time of ventricular relaxation, has three phases; the period of isovolumetric relaxation, the period of passive filling, and the period of active filling (Figure 6.12). Once the period of ejection is over, the ventricles begin to relax and the pressure in the ventricles begins to fall. The blood that was being pushed into the

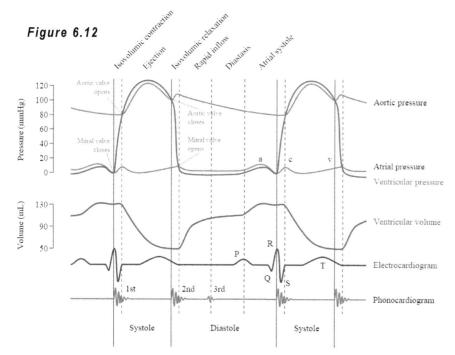

Figure 6.12

aorta and pulmonary trunk stops flowing and the blood in those spaces begins to move backward toward the heart, closing the semilunar valves. At this point, the AV valves are still closed, the semilunar valves become closed and the ventricles continue to relax causing a decrease in ventricular pressure. This is the period of isovolumetric relaxation; the ventricles are relaxing with no change in ventricular volume. During the entire systolic period, blood was still returning back to the atria from the body and lungs causing a slight increase in atrial pressure. Once the pressure in the atria exceeds the pressure in the ventricles (the pressure in the ventricles is falling due to relaxing muscles), then the atrioventricular valves will open. This completes the period of isovolumetric relaxation and the period of passive filling begins. Blood moves from the atria into the ventricles down a pressure gradient and will fill the ventricles (~70% of filling occurs during this period). Depolarization of the SA node and atria followed by contraction of the atria start the period of active filling and blood will be pushed into the ventricles by the contracting atrial muscles.

The spread of action potentials throughout the heart and the subsequent contraction of the muscle maximizes the flow of blood throughout the heart. The SA node depolarizes first and spreads across the atria causing the atrial muscle to contract starting from the top of the atria toward the ventricles pushing blood through the atrioventricular valves into the ventricles. The action potential spreads through the interventricular septum to the apex of the heart which then spreads upward toward the base. The contraction of the muscle follows the spread of the action potential and directs the blood flow in the ventricle from the apex upward toward the base and the opening of the semilunar valves.

Heart Sounds

During the cardiac cycle, the heart generates normal sounds that can be heard on the surface of the body using a stethoscope. These traditional sounds are described as "lub, dub, lub, dub." The first sound, "lub," is generated at the start of systole by a collection of events that cause sound in a short time span (refer back to Figure 6.12). The atrioventricular valves close but this does not cause any sounds that can be heard directly, rather the vibration of the valves and surrounding tissues cause the major noise that can be heard. In addition, turbulent blood flow also vibrates the tissues and are the main source of the sound. The first heart sound is rather low in pitch and relatively long. The second sound is generated at the start of diastole. In this case the semilunar valves close rapidly. The bulging semilunar valves and move back and forth due to elastic recoil in the valves and create vibrations in the vessel walls. The second heart sound, "dub," is higher in pitch and a shorter in length. By placing the stethoscope in different regions on the chest, a clinician can listen and determine how well the valves are functioning, or rather if they are not functioning properly (See Figure 6.3).

A heart murmur refers to any abnormal heart sound. There are many types and causes of heart murmurs. Most heart murmurs result in an increased work for the heart muscle. A stenosis, or the narrowing of blood vessel, causes turbulent blood flow around the constriction and creates a change in the "normal" heart sounds. The stenosis can occur in any of the large vessels arising from the heart; for example an aortic stenosis or a pulmonary stenosis. This might be congenital and the person may be born with the narrowed vessel, or the murmur might be acquired. For example, build-up of plaque could also cause a narrowing of the inside of the vessel creating the turbulent blood flow and the heart murmur. Another common source of heart murmurs result from leaky heart valves. As people age, the valve edges become roughened and stiff and do not close as firmly, allowing a small amount of blood to move backwards and cause changes in heart sounds. Ruptured chordae tendinae will also allow some blood to be pushed between the valves and blood will flow backward causing abnormal sounds.

Any abnormal openings in the heart chambers and large vessels will cause changes in blood flow and thus abnormal sounds. During development, there are two openings that allow blood to bypass the pulmonary circulation. Some of the blood bypasses the lungs because the fetus exchanges gases, nutrients and wastes at the placenta and not the lungs. There is a small opening in the interatrial septum called the foramen ovale. Blood can pass directly from the right atrium to the left atrium without passing into the pulmonary circulation. At birth, the foramen ovale usually closes completely. If it remains partially open, blood can pass between the atria resulting in a heart murmur. Another opening that is present during development is a small vessel between the pulmonary trunk and the aorta called the ductus arteriosus. If this vessel remains open after birth, blood will flow from the aorta into the pulmonary trunk. Recall that the systemic circulation is high (~120 mmHg) whereas the pulmonary circulation is relatively low (~25 mmHg) and blood will flow down the pressure gradient. Finally, if there are any abnormalities in the development of the heart walls these can result in large openings and thus abnormal heart sounds. These are usually extremely serious and result in significant changes in blood flow and oxygenation of the newborn and require immediate surgery.

Cardiac Regulation

The total amount of blood that leaves the heart per unit time is called the cardiac output. In mammals, cardiac output (CO) is calculated by taking the heart rate multiplied by the stroke volume (average volume per beat from one ventricle). Using average values cardiac output can be calculated as:

$$CO = HR \; x \; SV$$
$$CO = 72 beats/min \; x \; 70ml$$
$$CO = 5040 \; mls/min$$

Therefore, in normal resting human hearts CO is approximately 5,000 ml/min. CO can be altered by changing either heart rate and/or stroke volume. Heart rate can be changed by altering the frequency of the pacemaker activity. Stroke volume is measured by taking the end-diastolic volume minus the end-systolic volume. Stroke volume can be altered changing either the end-diastolic volume or the end-systolic volume. The end-diastolic volume can be altered by changing 1) the venous filling pressure, 2) the atrial pressure generated during active filling, 3) the distensibility of the ventricle and 4) the time available for filling. The end-systolic volume can be altered by changing 1) the ventricular ejection pressure and 2) the pressure or the resistance of the outflow vessels (aorta or pulmonary trunk). Both the heart rate and the stroke volume are under several control mechanisms. These are either intrinsically or extrinsically regulated.

Intrinsic Regulation

CO can be regulated by mechanisms which are intrinsic to the heart muscle or processes that are unique to the muscle cells themselves without any outside influences. The Frank-Starling mechanism is the primary intrinsic regulatory mechanism of the heart. As the ventricles fill with blood, the muscle cells and intracellular sarcomeres are stretched. This is referred to as pre-load or the load that is put on the muscle before it contracts. Essentially, any increase in load or ventricular volume will result in increase in the force of muscle contraction. This is due to the lengthening of the muscle fibers and is referred to as the Frank-Starling mechanism. Otto Frank (1895) first described frog cardiac muscle in terms of length and tension; similar to the way that scientists viewed skeletal muscle function. Frank showed that increases in length of the muscle cells resulted in a greater force of contraction. Muscle contraction increased up until a certain point after which any increases in length caused muscle force to decrease similar to what is observed in skeletal muscle. This is due to a decrease in actin-myosin overlap. In 1914, using an isolated heart-lung preparation from dogs, Ernest H. Starling further described the relationships between ventricular filling (which increases muscle cell length), pressure and cardiac output. Both scientists have been given credit for their work describing this intrinsic mechanism which is now called the Frank-Starling mechanism.

Increases or decreases in venous return will change the amount of blood that enters the ventricles and affect muscle length. Changes in venous return are common occurrences and can change on a beat to beat moment. Sympathetic stimulation (during exercise or stress) will cause constriction of veins and increase the amount of blood returning to the heart. Inhaling deeply causes a negative pressure in the thoracic cavity which draws blood into the heart and increases venous return. And even simply moving body parts will squeeze veins and force more blood out of the veins toward the heart. Increases in venous return cause a subsequent increase in the force of contraction of the heart. Decreases in venous return occur during resting conditions when sympathetic activity is reduced. When a person stands still, blood pools in the lower limbs due to gravity and less blood returns to the heart. During strong exhalations, pressure in the thoracic cavity increases and causes less blood to enter the heart. Any decrease in venous return causes a decrease in the force of contraction of the heart.

Simple physiological changes such as body position, breathing and exercise alter the amount of blood returning to the heart. When more blood enters the ventricles, the sarcomeres are stretched and the amount of available actin-myosin cross-bridge interactions increases. This ensures that blood that enters the heart will be pumped out of the heart and prevents overfilling of the ventricles.

The second intrinsic mechanism is referred to as the afterload or the load that the cardiac muscle has to exert force against. This can also be thought of as the resistance of the systemic and pulmonary circulations. An increase in afterload causes a compensatory increase in the force of contraction. This mechanism plays only a minor role in altering the force of contraction.

Extrinsic Regulation

Extrinsic regulation refers to the regulation of cardiac function from sources outside of the heart. These include both neural and hormonal influences. The neural components include innervation by sympathetic and parasympathetic fibers of the autonomic nervous system. The distribution of the pattern of innervation by each division of the autonomic nervous system is not equal, however. Parasympathetic fibers innervate primarily the SA node and therefore influence the frequency of the pacemaker activity or the heart rate. Sympathetic fibers are more widespread and project to the SA node and throughout the atrial and ventricular cardiac myocardium. Therefore, the sympathetic fibers not only influence the frequency of pacemaker activity, but also influence the force of contraction of the cardiac myocytes and can alter stroke volume.

Changes in heart rate occur by altering the frequency of SA nodal cell depolarization (Figure 6.13). At rest, the normal heart is under parasympathetic dominance, i.e., there is a weak parasympathetic stimulation which decreases the basal pacemaker rate. Therefore, if all autonomic activity is removed, the heart rate, set by pacemaker activity alone, would be faster than normal (~100 beats/min).

Parasympathetic neurons travel through the vagus nerve to innervate the heart. Pre-ganglionic fibers exit the medulla oblongata and travel through the neck region close to the carotid artery. They pass through the mediastinum and synapse with neurons positioned in ganglia which are located primarily in the adipose tissue associated with the epicardium surrounding the atria. The right vagus nerve mainly innervates the SA node and influences heart rate, whereas the left vagus nerve primarily innervates

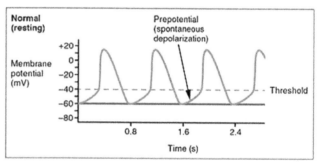

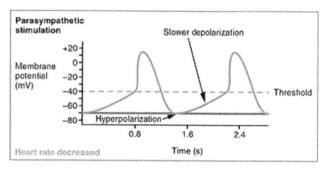

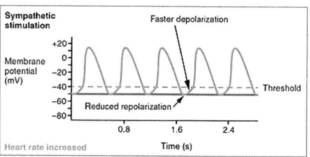

Figure 6.13

the AV node and influences AV conduction. The parasympathetic fibers release ACh which acts on muscarinic (M2) receptors (G-protein coupled receptors) (See Figure 6.14). The G-protein of the M2 receptor directly activates an ACh-regulated K^+ channel and results in cellular hyperpolarization. In addition, intracellular paths result in a decrease in the permeability of the F-type Na^+ channel and increases the permeability of the inward-rectifiying K^+ channel. Together, these changes cause a decrease in the slope of the pacemaker potential in the SA node cells and slow down heart rate.

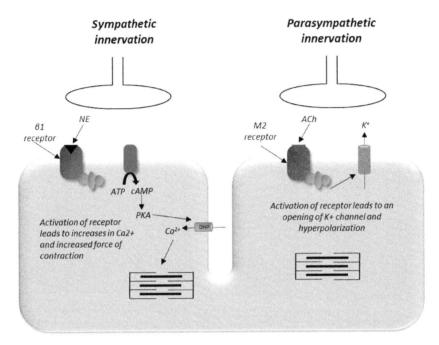

Figure 6.14

Sympathetic neurons that innervate the heart arise from the lower cervical and upper thoracic regions of the spinal cord and enter the chain ganglia. Post-ganglionic fibers pass through sympathetic nerves and travel through the mediastinum and travel bundled together with parasympathetic fibers. They then travel throughout the epicardium and enter the myocardium, usually traveling with the coronary vessels. Sympathetic stimulation causes heart rate and stroke volume to increase. On cardiac myocytes, sympathetic neurons release norepinephrine which binds to β1 adrenergic receptors (Figure 6.14). This is a Gs-coupled receptor and stimulates the production of cAMP from adenylyl cyclase. cAMP activates protein kinase A (PKA) which phosphorylates several proteins resulting in an increase in the speed of the contraction phase as well as the relaxation phase. Phosphorylation of L-type Ca^{2+} channels increases Ca^{2+} entry into the cell and increases the speed of contraction. PKA also phosphorylates phospholamban which is found associated with SERCA2 on the sarcoplasmic reticulum. Under resting conditions, phospholamban inhibits SERCA2 activity and slows the reuptake of Ca^{2+}. Phosphorylation of phosholamban reduces its activity and therefore Ca^{2+} is pumped more readily into the sarcoplasmic reticulum which increases the speed of the relaxation period. The relaxation period is also increased by the phosphorylation of troponin I, which decreases the binding affinity of Ca^{2+}

to troponin C. This quickly prevents actin-myosin binding and increases the relaxation period.

Cardiac function is also directly regulated by several hormones. During sympathetic dominance, the adrenal medulla releases norepinephrine and epinephrine into the general circulation. These hormones can bind directly to the β1 adrenergic receptor located on cardiac myocytes and increase heart rate and stroke volume. Thyroid hormones also influence cardiac contractility. Long-term increases in thyroid hormone can result in increased protein synthesis in muscle cells and lead to cardiac hypertrophy. Many other hormones can affect the cardiovascular system in general and may play roles in influencing cardiac function, such as insulin, glucagon and others like growth hormone.

CHAPTER 6, SECTION 1 – SUMMARY

➢ The mammalian heart contains 4 chambers which separate the flow of blood into a pulmonary and a systemic circulation.

➢ The heart contains a conduction system of modified cardiac muscle cells which direct the spread of the action potentials in a specific, coordinated direction throughout the heart. Action potentials start in a region called the SA node. Action potentials propagate throughout the atrial myocardium and to the AV node through gap junctions found between cells. The speed of the action potential slows through AV node and passes through the bundle of His to enter the right and left bundle branches which spread down throughout the interventricular septum. The bundle branches are connected to the Purkinje fibers and spread up the ventricular myocardium as a wave from the apex to the base of the heart.

➢ Action potentials in the conducting nodal cells are due to pacemaker potentials. The cells slowly depolarize due to the activation of the F-type Na^+ channels and the subsequent opening of the T-type Ca^{2+} channels. This depolarizing current is enough to bring the cell to threshold and opens up the L-type Ca^{2+} channels. A K^+ channel opens and results in cellular repolarization.

➢ Rapid depolarization of cardiac myocytes is due to the opening of voltage-gated Na^+ channels followed by rapid inactivation. A slow opening of the L-type Ca^{2+} channels also occurs and results in a long plateau phase. The closing of the Ca^{2+} channels and the opening of voltage gated K^+ channels lead to cellular repolarization.

➢ The ECG is a measure of the sum of electrical activity that arises from the heart and is measured by electrodes placed on the surface of the skin. The P wave corresponds to the atrial depolarization, the QRS complex to the ventricles depolarizing and the T wave is due to the repolarization of the ventricles.

➢ Cardiac muscle cell contraction is very similar to skeletal muscle contraction. Action potentials spread across the sarcolemma and down a T-tubule system. Activation of the DHP receptor however, leads to the activation of many RyRs on the sarcoplasmic reticulum. This so called calcium-induced-calcium-release is found only in cardiac muscle. Actin and myosin filaments are organized into sarcomeres and function like skeletal muscle.

➢ Systole is defined as the time of ventricular contraction. When the ventricles begin to contract, the blood forces the AV valves to close and the period of isovolumetric contraction occurs. When the pressure in the ventricles exceed the pressure in the arteries, the semilunar valves open and the period of ejection occurs.

➢ Diastole is the time of ventricular relaxation. As the ventricles begin to relax, blood flow causes the semilunar valves to close and the period of isovolumetric relaxation occurs. When the pressure in the atria exceed the pressure in the ventricles, the AV valves open and blood passively flows into the ventricles, the period of passive filling. When the SA node depolarizes and causes the contraction of the atria, this causes blood to be actively pushed into the ventricles and is referred to as the period of active filling.

➢ The total amount of blood that leaves the heart per unit time is called the cardiac output. Cardiac output is equal to the heart rate times the stroke volume (the volume of blood that leaves one ventricle).

➢ The Frank-Starling mechanism describes the intrinsic regulation of the heart. Changes in venous return alters the amount of blood that enters the heart and thus will influence the force of contraction. As the pre-load increases, the muscle cells stretch and the amount of available overlap between the actin and myosin increases. This allows the muscle to contract with a greater force.

➢ The parasympathetic nervous system innervates primarily the SA node. When ACh is released it binds to muscarinic receptors (M2) and results in a decrease in heart rate.

➢ The sympathetic nervous system innervates the SA node, but also innervates the myocardium as well. Norepinephrine binds the $\beta 1$ adrenergic receptors which leads to the opening of L-type Ca^{2+} channels and an increase in heart rate and an increase in the force of contraction.

Section 2 – The Vascular System

Peak systolic blood pressure is achieved by the muscular pumping action of the heart. Blood is then transported throughout the body under the regulatory control of the blood vessels. The primary functions of the peripheral circulation are 1) to carry and direct blood flow throughout the organs of the body to aid in the transport of nutrients, waste products, gases and hormones, and 2) to help regulate blood pressure. Blood vessels that carry blood away from the heart are called arteries and those vessels that carry blood back to the heart are called veins. The arterial system is also called the pressure reservoir which aids in the regulation of blood pressure and the preservation of a pressure gradient to maintain blood flow. The arterial system contains a series of blood vessels that start out as large conduit arteries and simply carry blood to the various organs and gradually decrease in diameter at every bifurcation. As the blood vessels decrease in diameter, the walls of the vessel change. The arteries begin with more elastic tissue (elastic arteries) and gradually become more muscular (arterioles). Arterioles of decreasing size give rise to capillary beds which are the site of fluid and solute exchange with the tissues. The blood collects from the capillaries into the venous system which contains venules and veins of increasing sizes. The venous system is called the blood reservoir and aids in the storage of blood during resting conditions. This is due to a very compliant blood vessel that easily stretches as fluid pools in these veins. Approximately 60% of the blood is in the veins and venules of the systemic circulation. This blood reservoir can then be utilized when needed. For example, during exercise, total blood volume can move from the blood reservoir to the working muscle tissues that need increased blood flow.

The entire cardiovascular system is lined with a simple squamous epithelium called the endothelium. The endothelium plays an extremely important role in the cardiovascular system and is involved in many functions. It serves as a lining of the blood vessels for the arteries, veins and heart chambers to prevent blood cells from adhering to the walls of the blood vessels under normal conditions, but they also play a role in the platelet aggregation and clotting to prevent bleeding when the wall becomes damaged. Endothelial cells secrete various

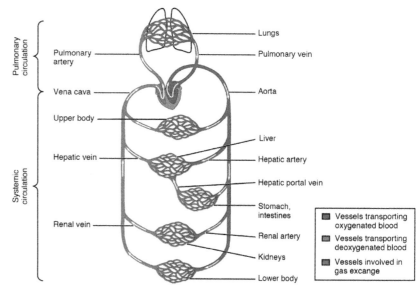

Figure 6.15

agents that act on the underlying smooth muscle to cause vasodilation or vasoconstriction as needed. During normal development and growth, they play a role in angiogenesis and the development of new vessels. They also play an important role in vascular remodeling and repair during adult stages. Finally, they produce growth factors and help to activate or degrade hormones and other substances that are found circulating in blood.

As described earlier, the heart plays a role in generating a high blood pressure and routing the blood into systemic and pulmonary circulations (Figure 6.15). The blood is then pumped to all the tissues of the body through the vascular system and plays a primary role in homeostasis. Blood flows through blood vessels down a pressure gradient through a particular resistance which is created in blood vessels in order to maintain flow. Thus total mean arterial blood pressure (MAP) is a combination of factors that are derived from both the actions of the heart, (cardiac output, CO) and the vascular system (total peripheral resistance, TPR).

$$MAP = CO \; x \; TPR$$
$$MAP = HR \; x \; SV \; x \; TPR$$

Typically, mean arterial blood pressure is measured using a sphygmomanometer attached to an inflatable cuff and a stethoscope. The cuff is wrapped around the upper arm and inflated to interrupt and stop blood flow to the arm. The stethoscope is placed in the antecubital space to listen to blood flow as it passes through the brachial artery. When the cuff is inflated, there are no sounds to hear since blood is not flowing through the artery. As the cuff

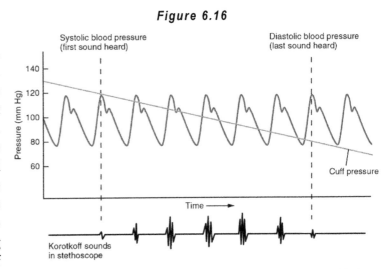

Figure 6.16

pressure is slowly released, a sound will eventually be heard in the stethoscope called Korotkoff sounds (Figure 6.16). This is the point at which the peak blood pressure during systole exceeds the cuff pressure and blood is pushed past the restriction. The sound corresponds to the blood being pushed through the restriction of the cuff causing turbulent blood flow. As the cuff pressure continues to fall, the sounds will change and eventually disappear. When the cuff pressure is below the diastolic pressure, blood flow becomes laminar or streamlined and no sounds will be heard. As the heart continues to beat, there is still a pulse pressure that you can feel with your fingers, but there are no sounds associated with the pulse pressure. Only the sounds of turbulent blood flow are heard with the stethoscope over an artery.

Maintenance of a "high" blood pressure is critical for normal blood flow. High blood pressure ensures that blood will move through the blood vessels from high pressure to low pressure and allow adequate tissue perfusion to occur at the capillaries. Clinicians strive to maintain a blood pressure above 70mmHg in critically ill patients to ensure adequate perfusion of oxygen and nutrients to all tissues in the body. Anything less than 70mmHg may indicate that some tissues are not receiving enough blood supply for normal organ function. The pressure at which blood vessels collapse and blood stops flowing is called the critical closing pressure. If this happens, blood flow can stop in critical organs and result in organ failure and even death.

Hemodynamics

Hemodynamics refer to the physical properties and mechanisms that control blood flow throughout the body. In terms of the cardiovascular system this refers to the ability of the heart to pump blood and the ability of the blood vessels to circulate the blood. The two most common hemodynamic disorders are systemic hypertension and congestive heart failure. In order to maintain adequate tissue perfusion, blood needs to flow through tissues. The relationships between flow, resistance and pressure can be described by laws of physical science and will be reviewed here.

Relationship between flow, pressure and resistance

The resistance to flow of any liquid through a tube is dependent upon three factors, the viscosity of the fluid (v), the length of the tube (l) and the diameter or radius of the tube (r).

$$R = \frac{8vl}{\pi r^4}$$

In regards to the cardiovascular system, the length of blood vessels and the viscosity of blood remains relatively constant under normal conditions. Therefore, in normal humans viscosity does not play a large role in regulating the resistance of blood vessels. During certain conditions and pathologies, however, the viscosity can be altered. Blood is comprised mostly of water and during severe dehydration or under conditions when red blood cell synthesis is enhanced (e.g. at high altitudes) blood may become more viscous and can greatly alter the resistance and affect blood flow through vessels.

During normal conditions, the one factor that is most physiologically relevant in terms of altering the resistance of blood vessels is the radius of the tube. Arterioles are surrounded with a large layer of smooth muscle which is under autonomic control. More or less sympathetic activity constricts or relaxes the smooth muscle and alters the radius of the arteriole, thus altering resistance. Very small changes in radius affect the resistance of blood flow since radius is expressed to the 4th power.

The inverse relationship between flow and resistance was first described in the mid 1800's independently by Jean Poiseuille and Gotthilf Hagen. As the resistance of the vessel increases, the flow of fluid through the vessel decreases and vice versa. The rate of flow through any tube is also dependent upon a pressure gradient and is expressed as the volume of fluid that passes a specific point per unit time. In the cardiovascular system, the blood that flows out of the heart at the aorta is approximately 5L/min. Flow is determined by a pressure (P) difference divided by the resistance (r) of the tube. This relationship between flow, pressure and resistance is referred to as the Hagen-Poiseuille's equation or commonly, Poiseuille's Law.

$$Flow = \frac{P_1 - P_2}{R}$$

Maintaining a pressure gradient is vital to sustain flow. Flow is dependent upon the difference between two pressures, NOT the absolute pressures. Blood flow can remain the same in two separate tubes, assuming a constant resistance. Rearrangement and substitution of the resistance equation leads to the following equation.

$$Flow = \frac{(P_1 - P_2)\pi r^4}{8vl}$$

This equation shows the relationships between the individual factors that underlie resistance and flow as they pertain to the cardiovascular system. In the body, blood vessels are not straight or of uniform length, blood flow is not always steady or laminar, and blood is a colloid suspension of cells, solutes and fluid, therefore the equation does not work exactly. Even so, the Hagen-Poiseuille equation works well to describe blood flow throughout the cardiovascular system.

As blood flows throughout the arterial system, it first passes through the large, conducting vessels (Figure 6.21). As a single blood vessel bifurcates and splits into two smaller vessels, the total pressure exerted on the walls does not change much and there is very little fall in total blood pressure. This is the reason that MAP can be measured at the brachial artery; an artery several branches away from the heart. These conduit vessels simply direct blood to the various organs. The regulation of blood flow occurs throughout the arterioles. Within an organ,

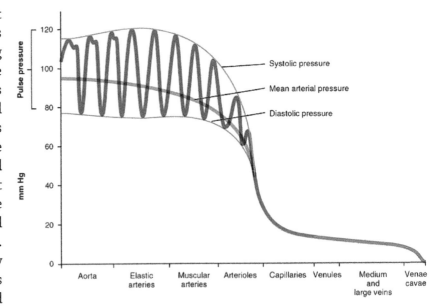

Figure 6.17

vasoconstriction of the arterioles will reduce blood flow to that organ. Alternatively, vasodilation of the arterioles will increase blood flow to an organ. Thus, the blood flow through any organ is dependent on the pressure gradient between the pressure of the blood flowing into an organ (MAP) and the pressure of the blood flowing out of the organ (venous pressure) divided by the resistance of the arterioles within that organ.

$$Flow_{organ} = \frac{(MAP - venous\ pressure)}{resistance_{organ}}$$

Since the venous pressure is close to zero and is virtually the same across all organs, this equation can be simplified.

$$Flow_{organ} = \frac{MAP}{resistance_{organ}}$$

Blood flow to the various organs are controlled by large conduit arteries that supply each organ. Each organ is under different control mechanisms. In general, the amount of blood flow to each organ is dependent upon the resistance of the arterioles of each organ. During different conditions such as exercise, the resistance of the arterioles can change to allow more or less blood flow to each organ based on the physiological needs of the tissues.

Once blood passes the arterioles, it moves into the capillary beds. Blood flow through capillaries is regulated not only by the total amount of blood coming from the arterioles, but also the placement of pre-capillary sphincters which direct blood flow away from capillary beds. Pre-capillary sphincters are controlled by local tissue factors that affect the smooth muscle of the sphincter. Increases in tissue CO_2 cause a local vasodilation of the pre-capillary sphincter and result in an increased flow through that particular capillary bed. When cells increase their metabolism, CO_2 is a by-product. If cells increase their activity, an increase in blood flow would be helpful to supply the tissue with adequate O_2 and nutrients and remove wastes like CO_2. Likewise, decreases in cellular activity result in a decrease in CO_2 levels and subsequent vasoconstriction of pre-capillary sphincters and reduced blood flow to areas that do not need it.

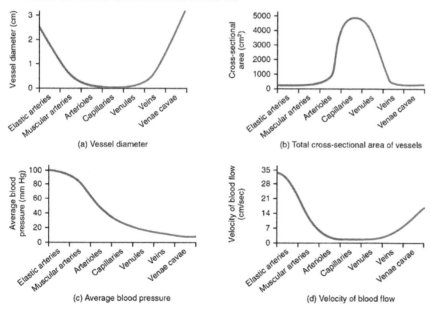

(a) Vessel diameter

(b) Total cross-sectional area of vessels

(c) Average blood pressure

(d) Velocity of blood flow

Figure 6.18

The sheer numbers of capillary beds create the greatest cross-sectional area of all the blood vessels (See Figure 6.23, on the next page). Each capillary is extremely small (approximately the size of a red blood cell) but there are many, many capillaries in the body. Throughout most tissues, every cell is, on average, only 3 cell lengths away from a capillary. As blood moves from the arterioles to the capillaries to the veins, pressure drops. Throughout this system a gradient of high to low pressure is maintained to ensure the flow of blood. Since the cross-sectional area increases over the capillary bed, the rate of flow or the velocity of blood flow also decreases (Figure 6.23). This is important to allow for adequate exchange of materials with the tissues. As blood moves from the capillaries into the venous system (down a pressure gradient), the rate of flow or the speed that the blood is traveling increases. The velocity of the blood flow is dependent on the total volume of blood within the vessels (size and number of blood vessels).

As blood flows into the venous system, it is still driven by a pressure gradient. Veins contain less smooth muscle, but they are still under autonomic control which helps increase venous return to the heart. In addition, the action of skeletal muscles helps pump or move blood toward the heart. Since muscles squeeze the veins, the directional flow is achieved by the presence of valves which ensure blood moves in only one direction, toward the heart. Without the valves, the muscles would press the blood in both directions.

Vascular compliance is a measure of how stretchy a blood vessel is; i.e., it measures the elasticity of vessels. Compliance is measured by the dividing a change in volume by the change in pressure.

$$compliance = \frac{\Delta V}{\Delta P}$$

Veins have a larger compliance than arteries. They stretch more and therefore hold more blood, thus the veins are considered a blood reservoir. Arteries are also compliant, however. As blood is pushed into the arteries during systole, the arteries stretch under the increased pressure. As the blood continues to move through the vessel during diastole, the elastic walls of the arteries recoil and help move blood by increasing the pressure (a decrease in the radius of the vessel).

Pulse pressure is the difference in pressures generated between systole and diastole. Since the pressure wave is not uniform in size, the mean arterial pressure can be estimated by taking 1/3 of the pulse pressure added to the diastolic pressure. The pulse pressure increases as stroke volume increases and when compliance decreases. Compliance of arteries decreases as we age; our arteries become more stiff and non-compliant. This results in a compensatory increase in in pulse pressure and total systemic blood pressure to ensure blood flow through the entire system. The most frequent site used to measure pulse pressure is at the radial artery (in the wrist) and can be used to determine heart rate.

As blood circulates throughout the blood vessels, they exert a hydrostatic force against the wall of the blood vessel. The forces that act on the wall are proportional to the diameter (D) of the vessel and the blood pressure (P).

$$Force = D \, X \, P$$

Therefore, if the diameter of a blood vessel increases and there are no changes in pressure, the forces exerted on the wall of the blood vessel increase. This is important when considering weakened blood vessels. When an artery weakens and forms a bulge on the side of a vessel, this forms what is called an aneurysm. These are particularly dangerous in arteries, where the pressures are high, and the forces applied to the thinning wall increase. This can cause a rupture and result in death.

Mechanisms controlling vasoconstriction and vasodilation

Blood flow through the circulation is controlled by multiple mechanisms including local controls and extrinsic factors (nervous activity, total blood volume, and hormonal controls). Smooth muscle cells surrounding arterioles show a certain degree of intrinsic or basal tone. The level of tone of arteriolar smooth muscle can be modified in order to change the diameter of arterioles. Vasoconstriction decreases the diameter whereas vasodilation increases the diameter of blood vessels.

Local controls

Some arterioles in the body are under strong local control mechanisms including active hyperemia, flow autoregulation, reactive hyperemia and local responses to injury. The term hyperemia simply means an increased blood flow. Active hyperemia is a mechanism which increases blood flow to a tissue or organ in direct response to an increase in metabolic activity. When cells increase their metabolic activity, tissue O_2 levels decrease, CO_2 levels increase and various metabolites are released into the interstitial fluid, such as H^+ ions, K^+ ions, adenosine, and bradykinin. The increased CO_2 and other metabolites exert a strong vasodilatory effect on smooth muscle. Vasodilation of arterioles supplying the tissue will reduce the resistance of blood vessels and increase blood flow. This will bring more oxygenated blood and nutrients to the working tissue and take away the waste products of metabolism. This mechanism is highly developed in blood vessels that supply skeletal muscle, cardiac muscle and glandular tissues.

Flow autoregulation is another local control mechanism found in tissues such as the brain and kidney. In these tissues, the primary emphasis is on supplying a constant and uninterrupted flow of blood to the tissue. The downstream mechanisms are similar to active hyperemia, however the initiation of the flow autoregulation mechanism is different. Flow autoregulation is activated not by an increase in tissue metabolism, but rather a drop in arterial pressure to the organ. If this happens, similar changes are observed in the tissue; O_2 levels decrease, CO_2 levels increase and various metabolites are released into the interstitial fluid. These substances (especially CO_2 and metabolites) will exert a strong vasodilation in the blood vessels in an attempt to restore blood flow back to normal.

Reactive hyperemia is an extreme form of autoregulation and occurs when blood flow to a tissue is blocked for a short period of time and then is quickly restored. This can happen when a blood clot stops blood flow to a particular tissue and then quickly passes and blood flow is restored. During the time of the blockage, blood vessels are exposed to extreme reductions in O_2, increases in CO_2 and other metabolites. This causes a profound vasodilation. When blood flow is restored, the 'reaction' is an extreme transient increase in blood flow to the tissue.

Finally many local factors play an important role during an inflammatory response and aid in immune and repair processes. During an injury to a tissue or the invasion by foreign material, many local substances are released in order to initiate and maintain an inflammatory response. In order to help initiate the immune response, local factors induce vasodilation of local blood vessels and enhance permeability of capillaries which increases blood flow to the injured tissue. Local factors also attract white blood cells to the area to aid in the local response to an injury or infection.

Extrinsic factors

Vasomotor tone is also controlled by extrinsic mechanisms which include autonomic nervous regulation and hormonal control. In general, most blood vessel diameter is controlled by the sympathetic division of the nervous system. Sympathetic stimulation causes global vasoconstriction of blood vessels. Sympathetic post-ganglionic neurons release norepinephrine which bind to $\alpha1$ adrenergic receptors to activate a G_q-protein signaling cascade. This leads to an increased influx of Ca^{2+} from external and internal stores which lead to smooth muscle contraction and subsequent vasoconstriction. Decreased activity of sympathetic neurons leads to less permeability of Ca^{2+} and subsequent vasodilation. There is very little to no parasympathetic innervation of smooth muscle in most arterioles in the human body. However, a notable exception is in the penis of the male, where parasympathetic innervation of arterioles, leads to vasodilation and erection (Chapter 10). Another class of autonomic neurons release nitric oxide and are called the noncholinergic, nonadrenergic neurons and influence blood flow in some arterioles. These are prominent in arterioles of the digestive system in which nitric oxide causes significant vasodilation of arterioles.

Hormones also control blood vessel diameter. Epinephrine and norepinephrine are released from the adrenal medulla in response to stress and exercise (sympathetic dominance). Circulating epinephrine and norepinephrine can bind to adrenergic receptors in all tissues and in blood vessel smooth muscle can result in vasoconstriction. In the arterioles of skeletal muscles, however, the smooth muscle cells contain $\alpha1$-adrenergic receptors at sympathetic synapses, but there are numerous $\beta2$-adrenergic receptors also found on smooth muscles. When these get activated, they can cause smooth muscle vasodilation. This, along with local factors, overrides the sympathetic influences and results in vasodilation of arterioles in skeletal muscles that are actively working during exercise.

There are other hormones and substances that play a significant role in arteriole function. Angiotensin II is a potent vasoconstrictor of blood vessels and are involved in blood pressure regulation. Vasopressin is also a potent vasoconstrictor when released in large amounts. Atrial natriuretic hormone is a strong vasodilator and decreases blood pressure. Other influences include substances released from endothelial cells. Nitric oxide is continuously released in small amounts to play a role in maintaining an open blood vessel. And endothelin-1 is released in response to mechanical damage or chemical stress and acts as a potent vasoconstrictor to restrict blood flow.

CHAPTER 6, SECTION 2 – SUMMARY

➤ Blood pressure is due to the muscular actions of the heart in addition to the regulatory mechanisms controlling the blood vessels. Therefore, mean arterial pressure is equal to cardiac output times the total peripheral resistance.

➤ The resistance to blood flow is dependent upon the viscosity of the fluid, the length of the tube and the diameter or radius of the tube: $R = 8vl/\pi r^4$. In terms of normal physiology, sympathetic control of the radius of the blood vessels, specifically the arterioles, contribute to changes in resistance.

➤ Blood flow through a tube is dependent not only on the resistance, but also a pressure gradient: Flow = $P_1 - P_2$ / R. Therefore, maintenance of a pressure gradient is critical to sustain blood flow.

➤ Arterioles are controlled by a variety of extrinsic and local control mechanism.

➤ Arterioles are innervated by sympathetic neurons and when activated result in vasoconstriction. Less sympathetic activity causes vasodilation.

➤ Local control mechanisms include active hyperemia, flow autoregulation, reactive hyperemia and local inflammatory responses.

➤ Blood vessel resistance is also determined by a variety of hormones, including epinephrine, angiotensin II, nitric oxide, and endothelin-1.

Section 3 – Integrated Regulatory Control Mechanisms

Regulation of mean arterial blood pressure involves many systems that work together. Remember that mean arterial pressure (MAP) is dependent on the function of the heart, both the HR and the SV as well as the total peripheral resistance of all vessels in the body (TPR).

$$MAP = HR \; x \; SV \; x \; TPR$$

Any changes in CO or TPR can cause a change in blood pressure. There are many mechanisms that help control blood pressure; some of these mechanisms occur on a short time scale and help maintain pressure on a moment to moment basis, whereas other mechanisms occur over a longer time scale and take hours to days to ensure long lasting effects.

The central neural control mechanisms that help coordinate and integrate incoming and outgoing information regarding the control of systemic blood pressure arise from specific nuclei within the brain. Most incoming sensory afferents that can influence blood pressure project to the nucleus of the tractus solitarius (NTS) located in the brainstem. From the NTS, neurons project to multiple brain regions including the hypothalamus, the rostral ventrolateral medulla (RVLM) and the caudal ventrolateral medulla (CVLM). Most outgoing motor efferent information arise from the RVLM and project down to spinal pre-ganglionic sympathetic neurons which ultimately innervate the heart and blood vessel and influence blood pressure.

Short term blood pressure mechanisms

Blood pressure can be regulated on a very short term basis; essentially on a beat to beat basis. The most important mechanism regarding daily blood pressure control is the baroreceptor reflex and is important in regulating blood pressure every moment throughout the day as you change body position. The chemoreceptor reflex also influences blood pressure quickly. However, this reflex is very important in the control of blood gases and ventilation (Chapter 7). The adrenal medullary reflex is important in the control blood pressure during times of increased stress and during exercise. The last mechanism that will be covered is the CNS ischemic response which is only activated in extreme, life-threatening conditions in an attempt to quickly alter blood pressure.

Baroreceptor reflex

The baroreceptor reflex is a short term regulatory mechanism that maintains a constant blood pressure on a moment-to-moment basis (See Figure 6.19). Special sensory receptors are found within the walls of the large vessels near the heart; the aorta, aortic arch and the base of the internal carotid artery. These receptors are sensitive to stretch. If blood pressure rises in the vicinity of the receptors, the walls of the vessels expand and the receptors are stretched and activated. The frequency of the action potentials arising from these special baroreceptors increases. This information projects into the NTS within the medulla. The NTS stimulates neurons in the CVLM which in turn inhibit neurons within the RVLM. This integration of neural inputs (along with other information) results in a decrease in sympathetic outflow from the RVLM to the heart, arterioles and veins. As sympathetic

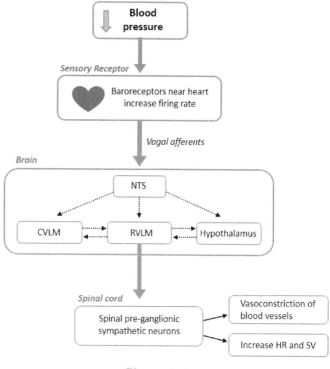

Figure 6.19

activity decreases, the outflow of parasympathetic activity increases. The combined actions autonomic activity will cause a decrease in MAP; HR and CO decrease in addition to a decrease in TPR.

The baroreceptor reflex also works with changes in blood pressure in the opposite direction. If blood pressure falls, the baroreceptors are not stretched as much. The frequency of the action potentials that project to the NTS decreases. This will stimulate neurons in the RVLM and induce a reflex to increase sympathetic output and decrease parasympathetic output which ultimately increases blood pressure. This is a classic example of a negative feedback mechanism.

With every heartbeat, the pulse pressure creates a pressure wave in the blood vessels and there is an increase in stretch during systole and decreased stretch during diastole. The baroreceptors are constantly firing in phase with the pulse pressure; an increased frequency during systole and reduced firing during diastole. This constant input into integrative centers of the brainstem "inform the brain" of the resting pulse pressure. In conditions where blood pressure changes, for example, during systemic hypertension, the baroreceptors increase their firing rates and try to initiate the negative feedback loop. If they are unable to initiate a response (because of other underlying pathology) then the baroreceptor reflex has the ability to reset or adapt to a new "normal." Adaptation is necessary since the baroreceptor helps to control fluctuations in blood pressure with changes in body position (getting up from bed).

Chemoreceptor reflex

Special chemoreceptors sensitive to changes in blood O_2, CO_2 and pH are found in carotid bodies, aortic bodies and in the brainstem (Figure 6.20). This reflex is primarily activated during certain lung or metabolic conditions or when individuals are subjected to high altitudes. The carotid bodies are a small organ located at the bifurcation of the common carotid artery. They contain glomus cells which are sensitive to changes in blood gases and get stimulated when arterial P_{O2} decreases, P_{CO2} increases or pH decreases. The glomus cells stimulate sensory afferents of the glossopharyngeal nerve (IX) which project into the NTS of the brainstem. Chemoreceptors are also localized within the aortic wall and these are called aortic bodies. Similarly, aortic bodies respond to changes in blood gases and nervous impulses are carried via the vagus nerve (X) to the NTS of the brainstem. Central chemoreceptors are located on the surface of the ventral medulla and are neurons that are sensitive the changes in gases in the CSF. They also project to the NTS. The neurons of the NTS project to the RVLM and stimulate pre-ganglionic sympathetic neurons to cause vasoconstriction and an increase in blood pressure. The chemoreceptor reflex plays a role in altering blood pressure, however, it is instrumental in causing changes in ventilation and will be covered in Chapter 7.

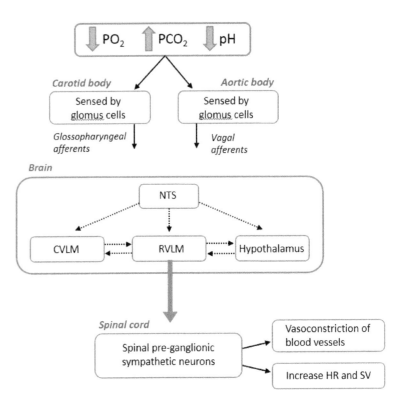

Figure 6.20

Adrenal medullary mechanism

The adrenal medullary mechanism is triggered during times of sympathetic dominance; stress and physical activity. When sympathetic outflow increases, sympathetic stimulation of the adrenal medulla also occurs. Recall that the adrenal medulla contains modified post-ganglionic cell bodies. Sympathetic pre-ganglionic neurons release ACh and stimulate the glomus cells of the adrenal medulla which release norepinephrine and epinephrine. These neurohormones are released into the interstitial fluid and move into the capillary bed supplying the adrenal medulla. Epinephrine and norepinephrine move throughout the general circulation and can act on α- and β-adrenergic receptors everywhere in the body. Their general response is to cause an increase in heart rate, an increase in stroke volume, and vasoconstriction of blood vessels in general (primarily skin and viscera) which together result in an increase in blood pressure.

Central nervous system ischemic response

The central nervous system ischemic response is not a regulatory mechanism that controls blood pressure on a day to day basis. This response only occurs during extreme life-threatening situations. It is the body's last system of defense against a drastic reduction in blood flow. During a severe hemorrhage in which the loss of blood is large and blood flow to the brain is severely restricted and blood flow to the tissue can slow or even stop (ischemia). Neurons within the medulla that are sensitive to increased CO_2 and decreased pH become excited when blood flow decreases. These neurons project to centers controlling sympathetic activity and dramatically increase sympathetic activation to increase heart rate, stroke volume and vasoconstriction in an effort to restore blood flow back to the brain. If blood flow is not restored within a few minutes, the neurons will stop functioning due to the lack of oxygen, there will be a sudden vasodilation and blood pressure will drop and death will ensue.

Long term blood pressure mechanisms

Several mechanisms control blood pressure over longer periods of time. Most of these mechanisms activate a series of events which occur throughout the body to initiate long term changes. For example, the renin-angiotensin-aldosterone system activates events in the kidney, the blood and the adrenal gland to initiate changes in the amount of Na^+ reabsorption in the kidney tubule which in turn affect the amount of fluid absorbed by the kidney and therefore increases blood pressure. Whereas the atrial natriuretic peptide increases Na^+ excretion by the kidney and therefore decreases blood pressure. The anti-diuretic hormone mechanism alters the amount of H_2O absorption by the kidney and the fluid shift mechanism controls the movement of fluid from the various compartments in the body. All of these mechanisms initiate changes which last hours to days.

Renin-angiotensin-aldosterone system

The renin-angiotensin-aldosterone system controls blood pressure over long periods of time and once events are initiated can lasts for hours to days (Figure 6.21). This mechanism essentially controls blood volume by changing the amount of Na^+ (and therefore H_2O) that is reabsorbed by the kidney. Within the kidney, afferent arterioles supply blood to a structure called the renal corpuscle where filtration occurs. Blood is filtered across a capillary bed into

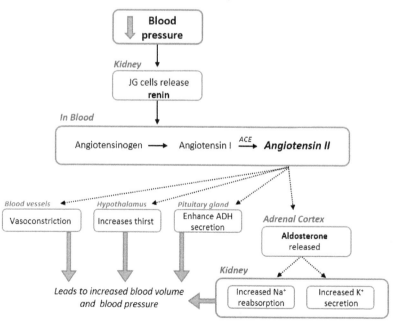

Figure 6.21

the renal tubules where ions, amino acids, glucose, and H_2O are reabsorbed across the epithelium of the tubule. Anything to be excreted in urine is left behind in the kidney tubule and becomes urine.

When systemic blood pressure decreases over ex tended periods of time, a special baroreceptor, the juxtaglomerular cells (JG cells) located in the afferent arteriole of the kidney sense the falling blood pressure. These cells lie next to (juxta) the glomerulus which is the name of the capillary that filters blood in the kidney. The JG cells are sensitive to stretch and therefore as blood pressure falls, the amount of stretch applied to the JG cells decreases causing them to enhance renin secretion into the blood. Renin is an enzyme that cleaves angiotensinogen, a circulating blood protein and produces angiotensin I. As angiotensin I continues to circulate throughout the blood, eventually it will pass through the pulmonary circulation. Angiotensin converting enzyme (ACE) is found on the endothelium of pulmonary blood vessels and will convert angiotensin I to angiotensin II.

Angiotensin II has multiple effects in the body.

14) Angiotensin II is a potent vasoconstrictor. Vasoconstriction increases blood pressure and restores blood pressure back towards normal.
15) Angiotensin II acts on the brain to enhance the feeling of thirst in order to increase water intake.
16) Angiotensin II also acts on the brain to increase the appetite for Na^+ intake (which in turn increases H_2O absorption).
17) Angiotensin II also stimulates the release of anti-diuretic hormone (ADH) from the posterior pituitary which increases H_2O absorption in the kidney (see next section).
18) Angiotensin II also has a high affinity for receptors located on cells of the zona glomerulosa of the adrenal cortex. These cells release aldosterone.

Aldosterone is a steroid hormone that act on intracellular receptors in cells of the distal convoluted tubule and collecting ducts of the kidney nephron. Activation of the receptors initiate gene transcription of proteins involved in Na^+ transport (see Chapter 8; Na^+/K^+ ATPase, Na^+/H^+ exchanger and the Na^+/K^+ exchanger) which will enhance Na^+ reabsorption in the kidney. Increased Na^+ reabsorption increases the osmolarity of the interstitial space and therefore more H_2O will be absorbed. The mechanism takes effect within hours and will last for many hours to restore blood pressure back towards normal.

Vasopressin or anti-diuretic hormone (ADH) mechanism

Vasopressin (or arginine vasopressin, AVP) is a hormone that is released in response to increased blood osmolarity (See Figure 6.22). Osmoreceptors located in the hypothalamus sense the osmolarity of blood. During dehydration, the osmolarity of blood increases and the osmoreceptors increase the firing frequency of action potentials. Osmoreceptors stimulate neurons located in the paraventricular and supraoptic nuclei of the hypothalamus. These neurons project down the infundibular stalk to release the neurohormone, AVP, from the posterior pituitary. AVP diffuses into the interstitial space and into the capillaries. As AVP circulates throughout the body, it comes into contact with its target tissue, the cells lining the distal convoluted tubule and collecting ducts of the kidney tubule. AVP acts on membrane bound, G_s-protein coupled receptors which activates adenylyl cyclase and downstream signaling cascade. This leads to an increase in the number of aquaporin-2 H_2O channels on the apical surface of the kidney tubules (Chapter 8). This enhances H_2O reabsorption and in turn increases blood volume and therefore blood pressure. During times when the body is hydrated, the amount of AVP secreted from the hypothalamus decreases. This will lead to less aquaporin-2 channels embedded in the membrane of kidney tubules and less water reabsorption.

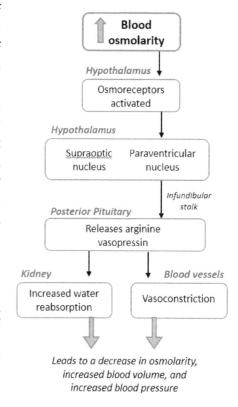

Figure 6.22

During conditions of significant blood loss, hemorrhage, AVP is released in large quantities. When this happens, AVP acts on smooth muscle of blood vessels to cause vasoconstriction and increase vasomotor tone. This is the mechanism that led to the term vasopressin. Under normal conditions, low levels of AVP that help regulate osmolarity of blood do not have a significant effect on vasomotor tone.

Atrial natriuretic peptide (ANP)

Atrial cardiac myocytes are also involved in regulating blood pressure. The muscle cells of the atria have secretory vesicles which contain the hormone, atrial natriuretic peptide (ANP). When blood volume increases, increased stretch is applied to the walls of the atria and cause increased release of ANP into the circulation. Like other hormones, ANP has multiple effects and helps control blood pressure and regulate H_2O and Na^+ homeostasis. In general, ANP acts on smooth muscle cells of blood vessels resulting in a strong vasodilation and a subsequent decrease in blood pressure. ANP also acts on kidney tubules to enhance Na^+ and H_2O excretion decreasing blood volume.

ANP binds to guanylyl cyclase-A or guanylyl cyclase-B receptors on target tissues. These receptors contain guanylyl cyclase activity on its internal structure and once ANP binds to the receptor it activates guanylyl cyclase activity. GTP is converted to cGMP which activates cGMP-dependent protein kinases (PKG) which phosphorylate various proteins in cells. In blood vessels, increases in intracellular cGMP lead to smooth muscle relaxation. This happens globally in the body. It also acts on the blood vessels that surround the glomerulus in the kidney. ANP causes a strong vasodilation in the afferent arteriole and a vasoconstriction in the efferent arteriole. This enhances filtration of blood and decreases blood volume by increasing urine output. In the kidney, ANP also acts directly on cells lining the distal convoluted tubule. cGMP inhibits the Na^+/Cl^- transporter and decreases reabsorption of Na^+. In the collecting ducts, PKG phosphorylates a Na^+ channel and decreases the reabsorption of Na^+. Decreases in Na^+ reabsorption lead to a decrease in H_2O reabsorption and therefore more fluid is excreted and blood volume goes down.

Fluid shift mechanism

Capillaries are the smallest blood vessels in the body and their primary function is to allow for exchange of gases, nutrients and wastes between the circulation and the tissues. Different types of capillaries are found in various locations in the body and depend on the function of the capillary in that particular tissue (Figure 6.23). In general, capillaries consist of a simple squamous epithelium sitting on a basement membrane (in most cases). Capillary types include continuous, fenestrated, or sinusoidal capillaries. Continuous capillaries do NOT have gaps between cells and are generally less permeable than most capillaries. They may even have tight junctions between cells like the pulmonary circulation or in the brain. Fenestrated capillaries have pores in the endothelial cells. The fenestrae (or windows) are areas of the cell in which there may be a complete pore or there may be a small diaphragm which contains the cell membrane with no cytoplasm. These capillaries tend to be leaky and are designed for exchange of fluid and small molecules between the capillary and the interstitial fluid. These are commonly found in many tissues, such as skin, the intestines, and kidneys. Sinusoidal capillaries are extremely leaky and have very large fenestrae, less basement membrane and sometimes large gaps between cells. Sinusoidal capillaries are common in endocrine organs, the liver, spleen and bone marrow.

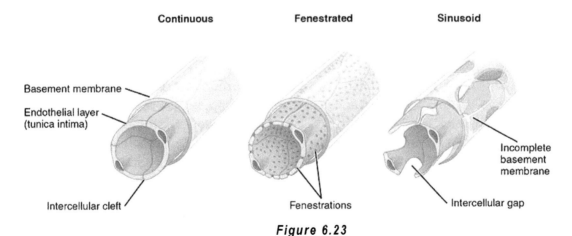

Figure 6.23

Each capillary is extremely small and is approximately the size of an individual red blood cell. However, there are millions of capillaries; approximately 25,000 miles of capillary length. Therefore, the capillary bed contains the greatest cross-sectional area of all the blood vessels. So as blood travels from the aorta to the arteries to the capillary bed, the pressure drops but so does the velocity of blood flow. As blood continues to move throughout the venous circulation, there is a continual drop in pressure, but the speed of the blood flow actually increases. This is due to a decrease in the number of vessels, as blood moves from the capillary beds to a smaller number of veins and finally into the atria. In the capillaries, the slow rate of blood flow aids in the exchange of material between the blood and the tissues; O_2 can be picked up in the lungs, glucose can be delivered to the interstitial space and waste such as CO_2 can be picked up.

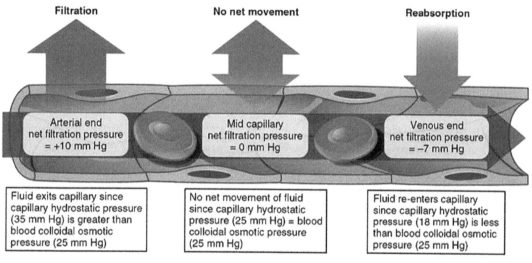

Filtration   **No net movement**   **Reabsorption**

Arterial end net filtration pressure = +10 mm Hg

Mid capillary net filtration pressure = 0 mm Hg

Venous end net filtration pressure = −7 mm Hg

Fluid exits capillary since capillary hydrostatic pressure (35 mm Hg) is greater than blood colloidal osmotic pressure (25 mm Hg)

No net movement of fluid since capillary hydrostatic pressure (25 mm Hg) = blood colloidal osmotic pressure (25 mm Hg)

Fluid re-enters capillary since capillary hydrostatic pressure (18 mm Hg) is less than blood colloidal osmotic pressure (25 mm Hg)

Figure 6.24

Exchange of material at the capillary occurs primarily due to simple diffusion; molecules move from high concentration to low concentration. Filtration is the movement of fluid out of the capillary whereas reabsorption is the movement of fluid into the capillary. In general, filtration occurs on the arterial side of the capillary bed and reabsorption occurs on the venous side (Figure 6.24). The net force responsible for moving fluid across the capillary wall is called the net filtration pressure (NFP). The NFP is dependent on two pressures, the net hydrostatic pressure and the net osmotic pressure.

$$NFP = hydrostatic\ pressure - osmotic\ pressure$$

The hydrostatic forces are the physical pressures that are applied by the fluid to the sides of the capillary wall; the blood pressing on the inside of the vessel (blood pressure or BP) and the interstitial fluid pressing on the outside of the vessel (interstitial fluid pressure (IF). The net hydrostatic pressure is calculated by subtracting the interstitial fluid pressure from the blood pressure. The osmotic pressures are due to the number of solute particles (primarily large, non-diffusible solutes) that do not pass freely across the capillary wall. The solutes in blood exert a blood colloid osmotic pressure (BCOP) and the solutes in the interstitial space exert an interstitial fluid colloid osmotic pressure (ICOP). The net osmotic pressure is calculated by subtracting the ICOP from the BCOP. The total net filtration pressure changes as the fluid moves through the capillary bed, such that a positive net filtration pressure favors movement out of the blood vessel on the arterial end and a negative net filtration pressure favors movement into the blood vessel on the venous end of the capillary.

$$NFP = (BP - IFP) - (BCOP - ICOP)$$

As blood enters the capillary from the arterial end, the blood pressure is relatively high and exerts a strong positive net hydrostatic pressure. The BCOP is relatively high and therefore the osmotic pressure favors the movement of blood into the capillary. However the total net filtration pressure (net hydrostatic minus the net osmotic pressures) favors the movement of fluid out of the capillary. As blood continues to move through the capillary, the net hydrostatic pressure falls due to a loss of fluid such that by the end of the capillary the osmotic forces outweigh the hydrostatic forces and fluid moves from the interstitial space into the capillary. Only 9/10s of the fluid returns to the capillary. The remaining fluid drains into lymphatic vessels and eventually lymphatic vessels empty into the venous circulation.

Blood pressure, the permeability of the capillary and osmotic pressure can all influence the movement of fluid from the capillary to the tissues and vice versa. If capillaries become more permeable, proteins and larger molecules can enter the interstitial space increasing the ICOP. This will draw more fluid into tissues resulting in edema. Edema can be caused by inflammatory mediators which increase fluid entry into tissues to draw more white blood cells to infected tissues to help mediate an immune response. Edema can also be caused by a variety of other illnesses and conditions. For example, liver disease or some kidney diseases or protein starvation can all lead to decreased numbers of proteins found in blood. This decreases the BCOP and thus more fluid enters tissues (essentially less solutes to "hold" fluid in the capillary). Edema can also be caused by removal of lymph nodes and lymphatic vessels. Recall that 1/10 of the volume that comes from capillaries returns to the blood by way of the lymphatic vessels. If this route is blocked or removed then more fluid is retained in the tissues resulting in edema.

CHAPTER 6, SECTION 3 – SUMMARY

➢ The regulation of blood pressure is a coordinated effort by multiple organ systems which function together to achieve changes in CO, TPR and blood volume. There are both short term regulatory mechanisms that work in a matter of seconds to minutes to restore or alter blood pressure and there are long term regulatory mechanisms that work over minutes to hours to days to help control blood pressure.

➢ The baroreceptor reflex responds very quickly to alterations in blood pressure to help maintain blood pressure constant. Special mechanoreceptors located in the large vessels that leave the heart detect decreases in blood pressure. The body responds with an increase in sympathetic outflow which increases HR, SV, and TPR.

➢ The chemoreceptor reflex is sensitive to changes in arterial O2, CO2 and pH. Decreases in O2 or pH, or an increase in CO2 are detected by chemoreceptors located in the carotid and aortic bodies. Impulses are sent into the brainstem and respond by increases in sympathetic outflow.

➢ The adrenal medulla is stimulated whenever sympathetic activity increases. Pre-ganglionic neurons stimulate the adrenal medullary chromaffin cells to release epinephrine and norepinephrine into the general circulation. These neurohormones can activate adrenergic receptors everywhere in the body and increase blood pressure by increasing HR, SV and TPR.

➢ The CNS ischemic response is a last effort by the CNS to reestablish blood pressure when blood flow is severely restricted in the brainstem. Increased sympathetic output increases HR, SV, and TPR in an effort to restore blood flow to the brain.

➢ Long term mechanisms of blood pressure regulation includes the renin-angiotensin-aldosterone system. Cells in the kidney detect decreases in blood pressure and release renin into the general circulation. Renin cleaves angiotensinogen into angiotensin I which gets converted to angiotensin II in the pulmonary circulation. Angiotensin II is a potent vasoconstrictor and it acts on receptors in the adrenal cortex to release aldosterone. Aldosterone acts on the kidney tubule to increase Na^+ reabsorption which helps retain more water and increases blood volume and thus blood pressure.

➢ Anti-diuretic hormone or vasopressin regulates blood volume by increasing water reabsorption in the kidney. Osmoreceptors in the hypothalamus detect increases in blood osmolarity and stimulate neurons to release ADH or vasopressin from the posterior pituitary. Circulating ADH acts on kidney tubules to increase water reabsorption and thus increases blood volume and blood pressure.

➢ During conditions of high blood pressure, the atrial cells of the heart release the hormone ANP. ANP acts on the kidney tubules to decrease Na+ reabsorption and thus more Na+ and water are excreted from the kidney.

➢ The fluid shift mechanism moves fluid from the extracellular and intracellular compartments. Capillary movement is influenced by hydrostatic and osmotic forces and results in a net filtration at the arteriolar ends of capillaries and a net absorption of fluid at the venous end of the capillary.

Section 4 – Blood

General components of blood

Blood is composed of plasma (55%) and formed elements (cells and platelets). Plasma is approximately 90% water and contains dissolved proteins and solute particles. The major proteins of blood are albumin, globulins and fibrinogen. The primary role of albumin is to help regulate osmosis and osmotic pressure which influences the movement of fluid across capillaries and cells. Globulins are a component of the immune system and help fight off foreign substances and fibrinogen is a protein involved with blood clotting (see below). Plasma also contains other dissolved solute particles such as ions (Na^+, K^+, Ca^{2+}, Mg^{2+}, etc...), nutrients (glucose, amino acids, etc...) and waste products (urea) and other regulatory substances like clotting factors or hormones.

There are three main categories of formed elements in blood, erythrocytes (red blood cells), leukocytes (white blood cells) and thrombocytes (platelets). The production of any and all of the formed elements is called hematopoiesis. All blood cells are derived from a common stem cell, a pluripotent hematopoietic stem cell (HSC). The cell undergoes a series of cell divisions that give rise more HSCs and to several distinct lineages, 1) the myeloid lineage which gives rise to granulocytes, megakaryocytes and macrophages, 2) the lymphoid lineage which gives rise to the lymphocytes, the T-cells and B-cells, and 3) the erythroid lineage which gives rise to erythrocytes. Once a cell has differentiated into a distinct lineage it is fated to become a distinct cell. Approximately $10^{11} – 10^{12}$ new blood cells are produced daily.

During development, hematopoiesis occurs primarily in the liver, thymus, spleen and lymph nodes. After birth, hematopoiesis is largely confined to the red marrow of bones of the axial skeleton (the skull, ribs, sternum, vertebrae, pelvis and proximal femur and proximal humerous).

Erythrocytes

The most numerous type of formed element in blood is the red blood cell or erythrocyte. There are approximately 4.5-5.5 million erythrocytes in 1 µl of blood. Erythrocytes are biconcave discs which can bend and fold easily and contain large amounts of hemoglobin to aid in the transport of O_2 and CO_2. Hemoglobin is made of 4 protein chains or globin molecules each bound to one heme group containing an iron atom. In adult human hemoglobin, there are two α globin molecules and two β globin molecules in a single hemoglobin. During development (embryonic and fetal stages), there are different isoforms of the globin molecules which reflect the needs of the hemoglobin and change the binding affinity for O_2.

Production of red blood cells, or erythropoiesis takes approximately 4 days from stem cell to release of a mature cell into the circulatory system. The cell undergoes differentiation from a pro-erythroblast, to an early, intermediate, and late erythroblast stages. At the last stage, the nucleus is extruded (in mammals) and the cell becomes a reticulocyte. Reticulocytes can be released into the general systemic circulation and is simply an immature erythrocyte. The reticulocyte contains residual RNA and is slightly larger in size. The appearance of many reticulocytes in a blood sample indicates that erythrocyte turnover is enhanced.

Leukocytes

The white blood cells or leukocytes are involved with various aspects of the innate and adaptive immune response mechanisms. There are approximately 7000 leukocytes in 1 µl of blood in normal humans. Infections increase the number of circulating leukocytes and numbers greater than 10,000/µl are indicative of an active systemic infection. Less than 4,000/µl leukocytes are not enough to adequately protect an individual from infections. Physicians use the total numbers of leukocytes as well as differential cell counts (counting individual types of leukocytes) to help diagnose and treat individuals with infections. All circulating leukocytes have the ability to move from the blood and into tissues and are attracted to sites via chemotaxis. Chemical mediators released from leukocytes and other resident cells and tissues attract more leukocytes to a region of infection to help mount an immune response. Leukocytes display diapedesis and send out cytoplasmic extensions and squeeze out of the circulation between endothelial cells and into tissues. They move around tissues using an amoeboid-like movement.

There are 5 types of circulating leukocytes in blood. The most common type of leukocyte is the neutrophil. Approximately 40-75% of circulating leukocytes are neutrophils. Neutrophils are also called polymorphonuclear cells (PMNs) due to the unusual shape of the lobulated nucleus. The number of lobes of the nucleus can range from 3 up to 5 lobes and indicate the age of the neutrophil; the more lobules the older the cell. The primary role of neutrophils is the phagocytosis of bacteria and cellular debris. They have numerous granules that contain lysozymes that are used to destroy invading bacteria. They also contain specific proteins called phagocytins which are antibacterial. Neutrophils are the primary cell involved in the acute inflammatory reaction and they very rarely reenter the circulation after entering tissues. They often die at the site of inflammation and are the primary contributor of pus.

The second most common type of leukocyte in blood is the lymphocyte. About 20-40% of all circulating leukocytes are lymphocytes. They are also the smallest of the leukocytes and contain a large nucleus with relatively little cytoplasm. Lymphocytes are the primary cell involved with all adaptive immunological defense responses. Blood serves as the route by which lymphocytes travel between tissues. Lymphocytes are found in high numbers in lymphatic nodules, lymph nodes and the spleen. They are also found in higher concentrations in connective tissue under epithelia that line surfaces exposed to the outside environment, i.e., the gut, lungs and skin. The lymphocytes found in blood are usually relatively inactive. There are two categories of lymphocytes, T-lymphocytes and B-lymphocytes. In general, the B-lymphocytes are the cells responsible for creating antibodies and the T-lymphocytes are involved with other immune responses.

Monocytes are the largest of the circulating leukocytes. Monocytes comprise approximately 2-10% of all leukocytes. Monocytes contain a large kidney or moon shaped nucleus that takes up about half the size of the cell. Once monocytes enter tissues they become tissue resident macrophages. Their main function is in the clean-up of tissue debris. They last longer than neutrophils and contain the cellular machinery to continue normal cell function over long periods of time. Some macrophages are residents of certain tissues and become established during development.

There are a fairly low number of eosinophils circulating in blood (~1-5%). Eosinophils contain a large bi-lobed nucleus and many large, eosinophilic or red granules (when stained with the standard hematoxylin and eosin stain). In general, eosinophils are attracted to areas in which histamine was released from mast cells and basophils, and play a role in phagocytosis of antigen-antibody complexes. Increases in eosinophils are particularly common in conditions that activate mast cells such as parasitic infections and asthma.

Finally, the last type of leukocyte found circulating in blood is the basophil. Basophils are the rarest of all leukocytes and comprise less than1% of all circulating leukocytes. Basophils have a distinct bi-lobed nucleus and many large irregular-shaped dense granules. The granules contain histamine and other substances that act on blood vessels to increase permeability and promote fluid exudation into the tissue. Histamine also acts on local sensory nociceptors and enhance the sensation of pain. Heparin is also released by basophils and prevents blood clotting (see below) thereby increasing the number of leukocytes that can be attracted to a tissue. In tissues, another cell, the mast cell, performs similar functions as the basophil and is involved in many allergic reactions.

Thrombocytes

The thrombocytes or platelets are in fact NOT a cell, but rather a piece of a cell that has been pinched off of a larger cell, the megakaryocyte. In the bone marrow, megakaryocytes are large multinucleated cells that pinch off pieces of their cells and are called platelets. Platelets are involved with aggregation and clot formation and stop blood from flowing out of broken blood vessels (see below).

Hemostasis

When a blood vessel is damaged, the blood (plasma and formed elements) can seep out into the tissue. Hemostasis is the stoppage of blood flow or the arrest of bleeding. Hemostasis is typically broken down into three mechanisms. However, the events that occur in these three mechanisms is not distinct and is actually a series of events along a continuum. Damage to blood vessel, either cutting a major vessel or a simple rip along the endothelial lining is enough to start a series of events to try and minimize blood loss. The first two events that take place after a blood vessel is damaged is constriction of the blood vessel or blood vessel spasm along with platelet aggregation. Depending on the severity of the damage, this can lead to blood coagulation or the formation of a blood clot.

Blood vessel spasm

In undamaged blood vessels, the endothelial cells that line all blood vessels are continuously releasing low levels of substances that maintain an open or patent blood vessel. Nitric oxide (NO) is released from endothelial cells and acts on smooth muscle to vasodilate blood vessels. NO also inhibits platelet activation, platelet adhesion and platelet aggregation. Endothelial cells also release prostaglandin I2 which is a very potent inhibitor of platelet adhesion. Together these substances prevent platelets from sticking to the walls of blood vessels and creating clots when there is no need. Whenever the blood vessel is damaged, however, mechanisms are activated which prevent the exudation of fluid into the tissues. In the damaged site, the endothelial cells are either damaged or they die and are no longer secreting substances to inhibit platelet activation. Platelets stick to collagen fibers and to a substance called von Willibrand's factor found in the underlying tissue. Von Willibrand's factor is a substance that is produced and secreted by endothelial cells on their basal surface. The main function of von Willibrand's factor is to help platelets stick to the site of tissue damage and to one another. Once platelets stick to the connective tissue, they become activated and begin to secrete multiple substances including thromboxane A2 (TXA$_2$). TXA$_2$ acts on smooth muscle and causes a strong vasoconstriction which results in blood vessel constriction and spasm. This decreases the amount of blood flowing through the damaged blood vessel and the underlying tissues.

Platelet aggregation

Platelet aggregation is the collection and aggregation of platelets which seal openings or damaged regions of blood vessels. The first stage of platelet aggregation is when the platelets stick to the damaged blood vessel and von Willibrand's factor in the surrounding connective tissue. Once the platelet sticks, this causes activation. The platelets begin to secrete substances and express surface receptors on their plasma membrane. Platelets release TXA$_2$ which is involved with blood vessel spasm and they also release ADP. TXA$_2$ and ADP act on circulating platelets to activate more platelets. Activated platelets also release platelet factor III and coagulation factor V which are part of the clot formation (see below). Finally, the third stage of platelet aggregation is the expression of fibrinogen receptors on the surface of their membranes. The circulating protein fibrinogen binds to the surface receptor on one platelet and binds the surface receptor on another platelet acting as a bridge between cells. This causes the platelets to stick to one another and form an aggregate.

Blood coagulation or clotting

The last stage of hemostasis is the formation of a solid blood clot. Essentially when a platelet aggregation forms the clot has already started to form. The formation of a full blood clot is dependent upon the size of the tissue damage and the degree of platelet activation. Once platelets are activated they begin a cascade of events in which multiple plasma proteins are activated, in series, to form a clot. There are three pathways that all need to get activated in order to have a complete well-established clot (Figure 6.25).

Figure 6.25

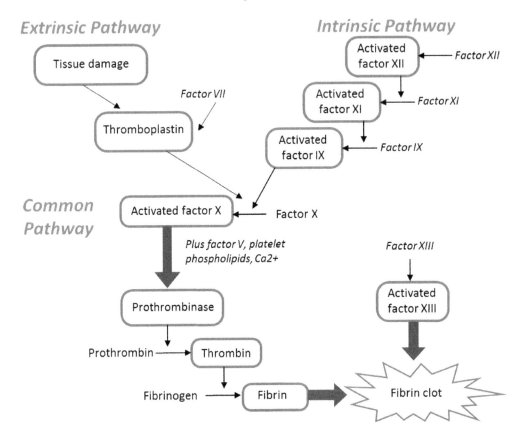

The extrinsic pathway starts clot formation. As the name implies, the pathway starts outside, or extrinsic, to the blood vessel. Once a blood vessel is damaged, the tissues outside of the vessel are exposed. As mentioned above, platelets release platelet factor III which is a glycoprotein and also a surface receptor to bind factor VIIa. This forms a structure called tissue factor which can activate another factor X. This is the start of the common pathway where the extrinsic and intrinsic pathways converge. Activated factor X (Xa) with the platelet, factor V (also released from activated platelets), Ca^{2+} and phospholipids on the membrane of the platelet form an enzyme called prothrominbinase. This enzyme can act on the blood protein prothrombin to form thrombin. Thrombin activates 3 key processes in the formation of the clot.

19) Thrombin acts as an enzyme to convert the blood protein fibrinogen into fibrin, an insoluble fiber.
20) Thrombin activates the intrinsic pathway which activates a series of additional factors (XII and XI) and together with factor VIII can also activate factor X and promote the formation of more thrombin (positive feedback mechanism) and therefore more fibrin.

21) Thrombin also activates factor XIII which is a necessary component for the stabilization of the fibrin clot.

The fibrin clot traps red blood cells and platelets together to form a barrier and prevents bleeding into through damaged vessel walls. If any one factor is missing, clots do not form. Another necessary ingredient in many of the steps mentioned above is Ca^{2+}, however, Ca^{2+} is always available in sufficient quantities.

The size of the blood clot is dependent on the balance of the factors that promote coagulation and the amount of factors that inhibit coagulation. There must also be ways to dissolve and remove the clot as the tissue repairs itself. The digestion of fibrin is called fibrinolysis. Plasminogen is a circulating blood protein that has an affinity for blot clots and gets caught up in the forming blood clot. Tissue plasminogen activator (t-PA) is an enzyme that activates plasminogen to form plasmin. Plasmin breaks down the fibrin clot into small pieces which are released into the bloodstream. Circulating fibrin pieces are removed by the kidney and the liver. t-PA is secreted slowly by damaged endothelial cells.

CHAPTER 6, SECTION 4 – SUMMARY

> Blood is composed of plasma and formed elements. Plasma contains mostly water with dissolved proteins and solute particles. The formed elements are the erythrocytes, the leukocytes and the thrombocytes.

> Erythrocytes are important in the transport of blood gases throughout the pulmonary and systemic circulations.

> Leukocytes play various roles in inflammatory and immune responses.

> Thrombocytes are critical components of hemostasis or the stoppage of blood flow.

> Hemostasis involves blood vessel spasm or constriction, platelet aggregation and blood coagulation or clotting.

> Blood clot formation starts outside of a blood vessel. Activation of platelets and various factors form an enzyme called prothrombinase. Prothrombinase converts prothrombin to thrombin in the blood. Thrombin activates 3 critical steps in the formation of a clot: 1) it converts fibrinogen to an insoluble fibrin thread, 2) thrombin activates an intrinsic pathway which positively feeds back to form more thrombin and 3) thrombin activates factor XIII which stabilizes the clot.

References and Suggested Readings

Baruscotti M, Bucci A, DiFrancesco D. 2005. Physiology and pharmacology of the cardiac pacemaker ("funny") current. *Pharmacology and Therapeutics* 107:59-79.

Bigatello LM, George E. 2002. Hemodynamic monitoring. *Minerva Anestesiologica* 68:219-225.

Desplantez T, Dupont E, Severs NJ, Weingart R. 2007. Gap junction channels and cardiac impulse propagation. *Journal of Membrane Biology* 218:13-28.

Dobrzynski H, Anderson RH, Atkinson A, Borbas Z, D'Souza A, Fraser JF, Inada S, Logantha SJRJ, Monfredi O, Morris GM, Moorman AFM, Nikolaidou T, Schneider H, Szuts V, Temple IP, Yanni J, Boyett MR. 2013. Structure, function and clinical relevance of the cardiac conduction system, including the atrioventricular ring and outflow tract tissues. *Pharmacology and Therapeutics* 139:260-288.

Garofalo F, Pellegrino D, Amelio D, Tota B. 2009. The Antarctic hemoglobinless icefish, fifty five years later: a unique cardiocirculatory interplay of disaptation and phenotypic plasticity. *Comparative Biochemistry and Physiology, Part A* 154:10-28.

Gordon AM, Regnier M, Homsher E. 2001. Skeletal and Cardiac muscle contractile activation: tropomyosin "rocks and rolls." *News in Physiological Sciences* 16:49-55.

Guyenet PG. 2006. The sympathetic control of blood pressure. *Nature Reviews Neuroscience* 7:335-346.

Jensen B, Boukens BJD, Postma AV, Gunst QD, van den Hoff MJB, Moorman AFM, Wang T, Christoffels VM. 2012. Identifying the evolutionary building blocks of the cardiac conduction system. *PLoS ONE* 7(9): e44231. doi:10.1371/journal.pone.0044231.

Jensen B, Wang T, Christoffels VM, Moorman AFM. 2013. Evolution and development of the building plan of the vertebrate heart. *Biochimica et Biophysica Acta* 1833:783-794.

Monahan-Earley R, Dvorak AM, Aird WC. 2013. Evolutionary origins of the blood vascular system and endothelium. *Journal of Thrombosis and Haemostasis* 11:46-66.

Patterson SW, Starling EH. 1914. On the mechanical factors which determine the output of the ventricles. *Journal of Physiology* 48(5):357-379.

Temple IP, Inada S, Dobrzynski H, Boyett. 2013. Connexins and the atrioventricular node. *Heart Rhythm* 10(2):297-304.

Zimmer HG. 2002. Who discovered the Frank-Starling mechanism? *News in Physiological Sciences* 17:181-184.

Chapter 7: Respiratory Physiology

In the animal kingdom, exchange of gases with the environment (water or air) occurs across skin, gills or lungs. Given the diversity of organisms, the apparatuses of gas exchange evolved in order to maximize the efficiency of gas exchange. In sedentary animals, like sponges, water moves in through a mouth structure and out pharyngeal slits and serves both digestive and respiratory functions. Gas exchange occurs by simple diffusion mechanisms alone. As animals evolved, the pharyngeal slits developed specialized cilia to actively move water across an epithelium where diffusion of gases could take place, but the epithelium still served digestive functions as well. Eventually, as animals became motile, gills evolved as a system of gas exchange separate from the digestive tract. Muscles of the mouth, or buccal pumps, and operculum were developed in fish to control water pressure and flow rates across gills to maximize gas exchange. As animals moved to land and became air breathers, buccal pumps push air into lungs and an aspiration pump evolved where air is drawn into lungs by muscles of the chest wall and abdomen. In mammals, the diaphragm evolved and became the major pump muscle required for changing lung volumes and creating pressure gradients in the lungs to generate air flow.

The lungs evolved to carry out gas exchange, however there are other functions of the respiratory system. The lungs have the ability to quickly alter blood pH by altering CO_2 levels and can alter pH on a breath by breath basis. The respiratory system is also involved in sound and voice production. Movement of air across the vocal folds in the larynx and across structures of the mouth produces vibration of tissues and produces the vocalizations of many animals and speech in humans. Movement of air across the nasal passages moves air across olfactory epithelium and is involved in the sense of olfaction or smell. And finally, the respiratory system also plays a role in the immune system and protects against entry of microorganisms into the body.

Section 1 – Lung Properties and Mechanics

Structure of the Respiratory System

Ventilation allows for respiration or gas exchange to take place in the alveoli. Ventilation is the mechanical processes that move air in and out of the lungs, whereas respiration refers to gas exchange. Gas exchange can take place between the outside of the body, the environment, and the lungs and is called external respiration. Internal respiration is referred to gas exchange which takes place between the blood and the tissues; i.e., inside the body. In mammals, air moves from the nasal cavity to the pharynx, into the trachea and down into the lungs (See Figure 7.1, on the next page). The respiratory system is traditionally divided into an upper and lower respiratory tract. The upper respiratory tract refers to the nasal cavity and the pharynx and their associated structures. The lower respiratory tract typically refers to the larynx, trachea, and all of the tubes within the lungs; bronchi, bronchioles and alveolar structures.

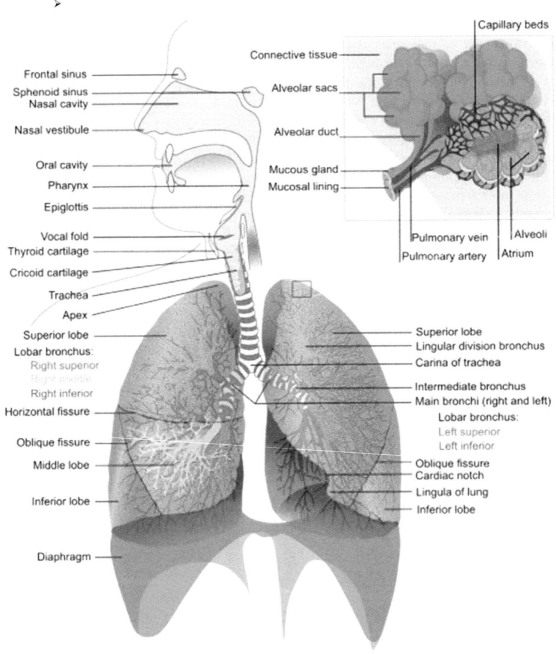

Figure 7.1

Air moves from the environment into the body through the nasal cavity. The nasal cavity plays several important roles in the respiratory system. It is lined with pseudostratified columnar epithelium and secretes mucus which is important in filtering and trapping large particles and debris and removing them from the air. The pseudostratified columnar epithelium also contains cilia which carries the mucus and trapped debris toward the oropharynx initiating the swallowing reflex and removal of unwanted substances. The nasal cavity also contains a large supply of blood which is involved with rapidly humidifying and warming the air. Finally, the nasal cavity also contains the olfactory epithelium and is involved with the sense of smell. In humans, the olfactory epithelium is limited to the most superior portions of the nasal cavity, however, animals with a good sense of smell contain a nasal cavity with a large portion of the chamber lined with olfactory epithelium.

The nasal cavity connects to the pharynx which is a common opening for the respiratory and digestive systems. The pharynx has three regions, the nasopharynx, the oropharynx and the laryngopharynx. Air travels through each of these regions before passing into the larynx. The larynx contains the epiglottis and vestibular folds which prevent swallowed material from passing into the trachea and is also the primary source of sound production. The

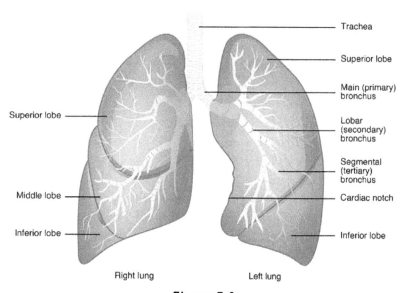

Figure 7.2

laryngeal cartilages maintain an open airway during the high pressures generated during inspiration and expiration. The larynx is continuous with the trachea which travels down the mediastinum and bifurcates into a right and left primary bronchi. Each primary bronchus supplies the right and left lungs. The primary bronchi split into secondary bronchi before entering each lobe of the lung; the right lung has 3 lobes and the left lung has 2 lobes (Figure 7.2). The tertiary bronchi each supply a bronchopulmonary segment which is distinctly separated from each other by connective tissue septa. The bronchi continue to branch into smaller vessels, slowly decreasing the amount of cartilaginous plaques. Once the cartilaginous plaques disappear, the airway is then called a bronchiole. Bronchioles contain a large amount of smooth muscle and is the vessel responsible for generating airway resistance. The bronchioles branch numerous times to terminate at the respiratory portions or respiratory zone of the lungs; the respiratory bronchioles, alveolar ducts and alveoli and their main function is gas exchange. The conducting zone of the respiratory system, however, includes the trachea, bronchi and bronchioles and their main purpose is to carry and clean the air before it reaches the respiratory portions of the lungs. The bronchi and some of the more proximal bronchioles are lined with pseudostratified columnar epithelium. The cilia moves in an upward direction in these airways to carry mucous, serous fluid and collected debris to the esophagus for swallowing. The trachea and bronchi also contain glands which secrete a seromucus secretion to aid in catching debris from the air.

The bronchioles terminate at blind-ended alveolar sacs which are interconnected to one another via pores of Kohn (Figure 7.3). The walls or septa of the alveoli consist of simple squamous epithelial cells, a small amount of interstitial space and capillaries. The interstitial space contains lots of elastic fibers which contribute to the recoil properties of the lungs and aid in expiration. Most of the alveolar surface is lined with a simple squamous epithelium

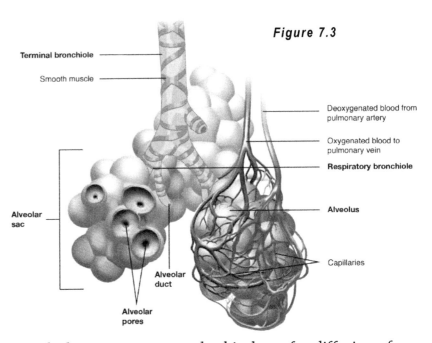

Figure 7.3

consisting of Type 1 pneumocytes which create an extremely thin layer for diffusion of gases. Occasionally, a simple cuboidal cell, the Type II pneumocyte is situated between alveoli and secretes surfactant, which creates a thin lipid layer covering the surface of the alveoli and reduces surface tension. Gas exchange takes place by diffusion across the alveolar membrane, and thus takes place at the thinnest sections of the alveolar membrane consisting of the type I cell, the endothelial cell of a capillary and a shared basement membrane; i.e., no interstitial space. There are approximately 300 million alveoli in the human lung and the surface area is extremely large, about the size of a tennis court. This allows for adequate exchange of gases with the environment. Humans are born with far fewer alveoli and many alveoli develop after birth until approximately age 8.

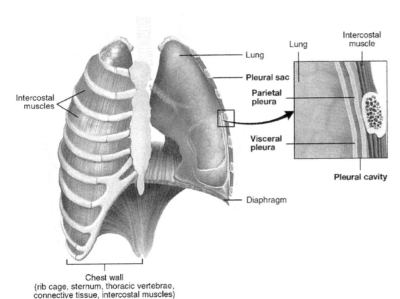

In mammals, the lungs are found in the thoracic cavity and are protected by the ribs, vertebrae and sternum, and separated from the abdominal cavity via the diaphragm. Each lung sits inside a separate pleural cavity which is lined with a simple squamous epithelium and secretes a thin layer of serous fluid (Figure 7.4). This fluid lubricates the two surfaces and prevents abrasion as the two surfaces pass one another during

Figure 7.4

each respiratory cycle; inspiration followed by expiration. The epithelial layer that is attached to the lungs is called the visceral pleura and the thoracic wall is lined with the parietal pleura. Between the lungs and thoracic wall is the intrapleural space which is under negative pressure which aids in lung expansion.

Ventilation

Total ventilation is the amount of air moved in and out of the lungs. Total ventilation is calculated by measuring the frequency of breaths (f) (breaths/min) times the average breath volume or tidal volume (V_T) (ml/breath).

$$\dot{V}e = f \: X \: V_T$$

Different terms can be used to describe breathing under different conditions. Normal resting breathing is referred to as eupnea or eupnic breathing. When breathing increases or decreases, such that ventilation does not match metabolic demands, this is referred to as hyperventilation (breathing more than is necessary for gas exchange) and hypoventilation (not breathing enough to meet metabolic demands). For example, when someone hyperventilates, you often hear someone say, "Breathe in a paper bag." Hyperventilation causes one to blow off or excrete more CO_2 compared to production levels and levels of CO_2 in the blood decrease below normal. "Breathing in a bag" causes you to rebreathe air that contains a higher amount of CO_2 (that you just exhaled) and restores blood gas levels of CO_2 back toward normal. This helps reduce anxiety and returns ventilation back to normal. Apnea is the term that refers to a pause in breathing or no breathing at all. This is word that is observed more frequently these days as obesity levels increase causing increased awareness of obstructive sleep apnea. Obstructive sleep apnea occurs when the upper airways collapse during sleep; usually due to a combination of extra weight in the neck region and a lower control of upper airway pressure during sleep. When this happens, an apnea occurs (breathing stops). When the patient wakes, upper airway tone and breathing is restored. The waking that occurs during sleep is not usually conscious but it does prevent the patient from receiving the restorative effects of deep sleep and therefore they are fatigued and tired throughout the day. Positive airway pressure applied during sleep opens the airways and remedies this disease. Finally, dyspnea is a term that refers to labored or uncomfortable breathing; a feeling of needing to breathe and not being satisfied with the breath. This is a common occurrence in patients with asthma.

Alveolar ventilation

As we ventilate, air first passes through the conducting portions of the lung; the trachea, bronchi and bronchioles. No gas exchange takes place in these spaces and, therefore, is called the anatomical dead space. This is approximately 150mls in an adult human. As air passes down into the alveoli, some of the air may travel to alveoli that are non-functional (e.g., no blood flow to those alveoli and therefore no gas exchange); this is referred to as physiological dead space. The amount of air that reaches the alveoli and participates in gas exchange is called the alveolar ventilation volume and can be calculated by subtracting the total dead space volume of one breath (V_D) from the tidal volume (V_T). Total alveolar ventilation (V_A) therefore is the alveolar ventilation volume times the frequency.

$$\dot{V}_A = (V_T - V_D) \, X \, f$$

What is the significance between total ventilation and alveolar ventilation? The pattern in which you breathe can greatly affect how much air moves in the alveoli and is available for gas exchange. For example, if three different scenarios were created (Table 7.1) in which the pattern of breathing changes (the frequency or tidal volume) but the total ventilation remains constant, you'll notice that the amount of alveolar ventilation and thus gas exchange can vary greatly. Subject #2 is breathing a "normal" frequency and V_T which creates 5700ml/min of alveolar ventilation. Subject #1 is breathing the same total ventilation, but each V_T is significantly reduced and the frequency is elevated. In this case, the amount of alveolar ventilation is zero and therefore no gas exchange takes place at all. Subject #3 changes the pattern of breathing such that alveolar ventilation increases. Specific changes in breathing pattern can greatly impact gas exchange at the alveolar surface. This is important to consider when examining only total ventilation.

Table 7.1. Changes in breathing pattern affect alveolar ventilation

Subject	Frequency (breaths/min)	Tidal Volume (ml)	Total Ventilation (mls/min)	Anatomic dead space ventilation (mls/min)	Alveolar ventilation (mls/min)
1	50	150	7500	150 X 50 = 7500	0
2	12	500	7500	150 X 12 = 1800	5700
3	5	1500	7500	150 X 5 = 750	6750

Pressure gradients in the respiratory system

Air moves in and out of the lungs by bulk flow and moves from areas of high pressure to areas of low pressure. The movement of airflow is derived from the following equation:

$$Flow = \frac{P_{alv} - P_{atm}}{R}$$

In order to generate airflow, a pressure gradient needs to be generated between the alveoli (P_{alv}) and the atmosphere (P_{atm}). Airflow is also dependent on the resistance of the airways; high resistance in the airways creates lower flow rates whereas low resistance creates higher flow rates. The pressures within the lungs are created by changing lung volume. This relationship can be explained by Boyle's Law where P is the pressure, V is the volume and k is a constant.

$$P = \frac{k}{V}$$

Boyle's law describes the inverse relationship between pressure and volume (Figure 7.5). As volume increases, the pressure decreases and vice versa. So in terms of lung function, when lung volume increases during the inspiratory phase, then the pressure inside the lung decreases. This decrease in lung pressure will cause a pressure gradient to occur between the outside environment and the inside of the lungs and air will move down this pressure gradient into the lungs.

The volume of the lungs (or the thoracic cavity) is controlled by the activation of skeletal muscles. Contraction of the diaphragm and external intercostal muscles results in an increase in lung volume (Figure 7.6). The change in lung volume decreases the alveolar pressure

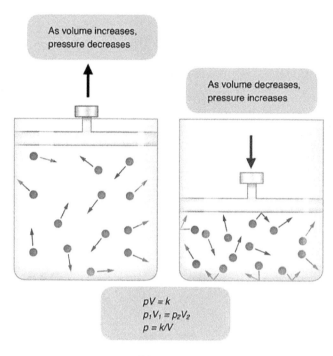

$$pV = k$$
$$p_1V_1 = p_2V_2$$
$$p = k/V$$

Figure 7.5

(P_{alv}) compared to atmospheric pressure (P_{atm}) and air will move down its pressure gradient and fill the lungs with air ($P_{atm} > P_{alv}$). At the end of inspiration, the diaphragm will stop changing length and the volume of the lungs will stop changing size. When this happens, there will be no change in volume and thus no change in pressure ($P_{atm} = P_{alv}$) and airflow will stop. As expiration begins, the muscles begin to relax and lung volume decreases (Figure 7.6). The decrease in volume will cause an increase in alveolar pressure (due to Boyle's law). This increase in pressure will cause a pressure gradient to occur between the lung and the environment and air will flow out of the lung down its pressure gradient ($P_{alv} > P_{atm}$). Finally at the end of expiration, the volume of the lungs stops changing and thus the pressure gradient between the atmosphere and the lungs becomes equal and airflow stops. This entire cycle repeats itself over with every breath that is taken.

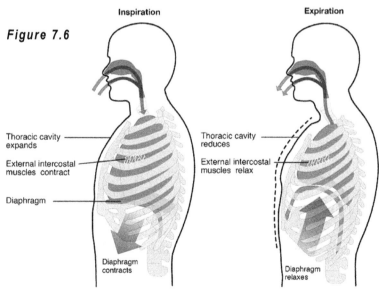

Figure 7.6

The lungs are not attached to the thoracic wall by muscles or connective tissue, they are simply sitting in pleural spaces within the thoracic cavity. So, how then, do the lungs increase in size as the thoracic wall and diaphragm muscles contract? The lungs are similar to balloons and changes in volume depend on two factors; the pressure difference between the inside and outside of the alveoli and how stretchable the walls of the lungs are. Transmural pressure refers to a pressure difference across a wall (Figure 7.7). There are two important transmural pressures within the respiratory system; 1) the transpulmonary pressure (P_{tp}) which is the difference between the pressure inside the alveoli (P_{alv}) and the intrapleural space (P_{ip}) and 2) the chest wall pressure (P_{cw}) which is the difference between the intrapleural space (P_{ip}) and the atmospheric pressure (P_{atm}). The intrapleural space is under negative pressure at rest (end-expiration) (-4cmH$_2$O).

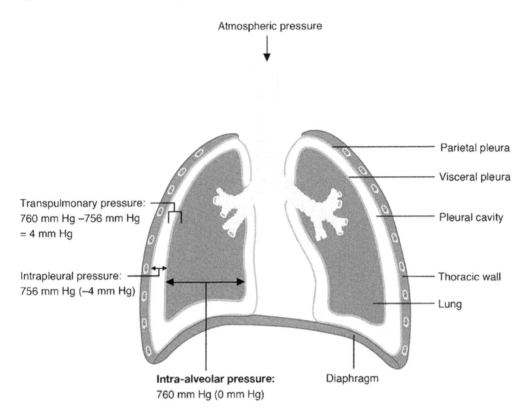

Atmospheric pressure

Parietal pleura

Visceral pleura

Transpulmonary pressure:
760 mm Hg −756 mm Hg
= 4 mm Hg

Pleural cavity

Intrapleural pressure:
756 mm Hg (−4 mm Hg)

Thoracic wall

Lung

Intra-alveolar pressure:
760 mm Hg (0 mm Hg)

Diaphragm

Figure 7.7

At rest (end-expiration), the elastic recoil of the lungs and the surface tension inside the lungs tend to pull the alveoli inward and the chest wall elastic recoil wants to pull the chest wall outward. Thus, at rest the transpulmonary pressure ($P_{tp} = P_{alv} − P_{ip}$) exactly opposes the chest wall pressure ($P_{cw} = P_{ip} - P_{atm}$) and maintains the airways open. During inspiration, as the diaphragm and external intercostal muscles contract, the intrapleural space also enlarges. As the volume increases, the pressure within the intrapleural space decreases and the pressure becomes even more negative. Remember that the intrapleural space has a negative pressure at rest. Since the intrapleural space is closed and not open to the atmosphere, the pressure inside the intrapleural space continues to decrease throughout entire inspiratory phase. The decreasing pressure along with the static forces of the intrapleural fluid within the intrapleural space aid in lung expansion. At end-inspiration, the transpulmonary and chest wall pressures again oppose each other and no change in volume or airflow occurs. During expiration, the muscles of the diaphragm and chest wall begin to relax, returning to their original state. This causes a decrease in the volume of intrapleural space; as volume decreases, the pressure increases (according to

Boyle's Law). The transpulmonary pressure increases and returns toward the pre-inspiration values. The elastic recoil of the lungs pull the alveoli inward and the P_{alv} becomes greater the P_{atm} and air flows outward. At end-expiration, again the forces opposing the inward elastic recoil of the lungs (P_{tp}) is equal to the forces opposing the outward elastic recoil of the chest wall (P_{cw}), the pressures in the alveoli become the same as the atmosphere and airflow stops.

Lung compliance

The change in lung volume for an increase in transpulmonary pressure is called the lung compliance. It essentially measures the amount of stretch within the lungs.

$$Compliance = \frac{\Delta V}{\Delta(P_{alv} - P_{ip})} = \frac{\Delta V}{\Delta P_{tp}} =$$

A decrease in compliance is caused by the lungs becoming less stretchy (or more rigid) and then for a given change in pressure the lungs will not change in volume very easily. An increase in compliance is when the lungs become more pliable and stretchy. The compliance or degree of stretch is dependent on two factors, the elasticity of the alveolar walls themselves and the forces caused by surface tension properties on the alveolar surfaces. The elasticity of the alveoli is due to the amount of elastin and collagen fibers found within the walls of the alveoli. As lungs expand, the elastic fibers stretch, similar to rubber bands, and increase the amount of elastic force generated. During expiration, the elastic fibers return toward their original length. Many diseases affect lung compliance and can interfere with ventilation and gas exchange. For example, pulmonary fibrosis or the deposition of collagen fibers in the alveolar walls decrease compliance and make it harder to ventilate.

Surface tension

The forces caused by surface tension of H_2O are complex. The lung contains alveoli of many different sizes. The relationship between pressure (P), surface tension (T) and the radius (r) of an alveolus can be described by the Law of Laplace.

$$P = \frac{2T}{r}$$

If surface tension was constant in every alveolus, then alveoli with small diameters would have higher pressures than large diameter alveoli. This pressure gradient would cause air to flow from areas of high pressure to low pressure and the small alveoli would collapse. Surfactant is produced by type II pneumocytes and is released into the alveolar spaces. Surfactant is a single layer of phospholipids held together by a protein network which reduces the surface tension properties in the alveoli and stabilizes or equalizes the pressures so that air does not flow between alveoli of different sizes. Surfactant is released by stretching the type II cells. One possible reason that we sigh (a large, deep breath) is to stimulate and spread surfactant across alveolar surfaces. During development, surfactant production does not occur until late in gestation. Infants that are born prematurely can have a low surfactant production which can cause alveolar collapse at birth. The infant inspires strenuously against large surface tension forces which may ultimately cause exhaustion, inability to breathe, lung collapse and death. Therapy for these infants with respiratory distress syndrome include mechanical ventilation and administration of natural or synthetic surfactant in the trachea.

Mechanics of Breathing

Quiet breathing during times of rest utilize few muscles and uses very little energy (~3% of total body energy). In mammals, the primary muscle of inspiration is the diaphragm which is aided by the intercostal muscles and upper neck and airway muscles. Expiration at rest is largely passive. During exercise or during strenuous breathing, muscles are recruited to assist during both the inspiratory and the expiratory phases of the respiratory cycle. Ventilation can be increased by more than 25X compared to rest, but yet the total energy costs of ventilation still remain relatively low (~4% of total body energy). The cost of breathing is not very expensive in terms of total energy expenditure.

Inspiration

During quiet restful breathing, inspiration is achieved largely by the contraction of the diaphragm. The diaphragm is a circular muscle which forms a dome shape and separates the thoracic and abdominal cavities. Contraction causes the muscle to flatten and thus moves the abdominal contents downward and increases the thoracic cavity. Excitation of external intercostal muscles aid in respiration and slightly raise the ribs and stabilizes the thoracic cavity (prevents the ribs from moving inward due to negative intrapleural pressures). These two motions generate an increased lung volume and generate a pressure gradient to initiate inspiration. Air flows into the lungs as the pressure inside the lungs is reduced compared to the atmospheric pressure. Inhalation must overcome several forces including 1) the surface tension of the water on the surface of the alveoli and 2) the elastic recoil of the lung tissue. Surfactant aids in overcoming the surface tension properties in the lungs. And the negative pressure and the fluid in the intrapleural space aid in overcoming the elastic recoil of the lung.

During strenuous inspiratory efforts, multiple muscle groups are recruited to aid and assist in generating a quick change in lung volume. Upper chest and neck muscles such as the pectoralis minor, the scalene muscles, and the sternocleidomastoid muscles are activated to assist in the inspiratory effort.

Expiration

During quiet breathing, expiration is largely passive and is due to the relaxation of the diaphragm and external intercostal muscles. These muscles return to their starting length and the volume in the thoracic cavity decreases and pressure inside the lungs exceeds the atmospheric pressure and air is expelled. The energy that aids in expiration comes from the

1) elastic recoil of the lungs which return the alveoli toward their original lengths and 2) the surface tension properties in the alveoli.

During labored breathing, extra muscles are recruited to aid in increasing the speed of expiration. The internal intercostal muscles actively move the ribcage in a downward motion to assist in expiration. Similarly, the abdominal muscles contract which aid in pushing the diaphragm upward and pulling the sternum downward. The actions of these muscles decrease the volume of the lungs and increase the speed of the expiratory phase.

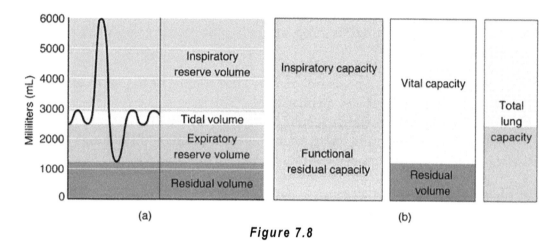

Figure 7.8

Lung volumes

During normal breathing, the volume of air that is inspired and expired is called the tidal volume (Figure 7.8). This volume can change based on the metabolic needs of the body. As the body increases the amount of work and produces more CO_2, then the tidal volume will increase (along with frequency). There are inspiratory and expiratory reserve volumes that can be recruited as necessary and can contribute to changing the tidal volume. The inspiratory reserve volume is the amount of air that can be actively inspired above a normal inspiratory effort. The expiratory reserve volume is the amount of air that can be actively exhaled beyond a normal exhalation. These three volumes (tidal volume, inspiratory reserve and expiratory reserve) together constitute the vital capacity or the total amount of lung volume that can be actively recruited to move air in and out of the lungs. It is measured by taking a maximal inspiratory effort followed by a maximal expiratory effort. Multiple factors affect vital capacity in humans. Body size, body position, strength of the respiratory muscles, how elastic the alveoli are. Many lung and cardiovascular diseases can affect the vital capacity of an individual. At the end of a full expiratory movement, there is still residual air remaining in the airways (the airways do NOT completely collapse removing all air). This is called the residual volume. This is important in the homeostasis of blood gases.

CHAPTER 7, SECTION 1 – SUMMARY

> The total amount of air that moves in and out of the lungs is called total ventilation. This is dependent upon the total volume of an average breath times the frequency of breaths.

> Alveolar ventilation is the total amount of air that is available for gas exchange. Breathing pattern, changes in frequency and tidal volume, can alter the amount of alveolar ventilation.

> Air flow into the lungs is proportional to a pressure gradient and inversely related to resistance.

> In order to generate a pressure gradient, the volume of the lungs is changed due to activation of muscles, primarily the diaphragm. During inspiration, lung volume is increased which results in a decrease in the alveolar pressure. This creates a pressure gradient between the atmosphere and the lungs and air flows into the lungs. The opposite occurs during exhalation.

> Lung compliance is a measure of the stretchiness of lung surfaces. It is measured as a change in volume over the change in pressure. Decreases in lung compliance decrease the efficiency of ventilation and thus affect gas exchange.

> The surface tension properties of the alveolar surfaces is high and favors alveolar collapse. Surfactant, a lipid-protein film, coats the inside of the alveolar surfaces and reduces surface tension and prevents alveolar collapse.

> Inspiration is due to the activation of the diaphragm and the external intercostal muscles. During labored breathing, additional muscles get recruited and aid in the inspiratory movements, such as the scalenes, the sternocleidomastoid and the internal pectoralis muscles. Inspiration must overcome the forces of elastic recoil and surface tension.

> Expiration is largely passive and is due the elastic recoil of alveolar septum and the surface tension properties in the lungs. The muscles return to their original length. During labored breathing, abdominal muscles and the internal intercostal muscles get recruited to aid in breathing movements.

Section 2 – Gas Transport Mechanisms

Principles of Gas Exchange

In animals, the hydrolysis of ATP into ADP and inorganic phosphate (P_i) is essential for normal cell function and life. Cells use the energy derived from this reaction to generate ionic concentrations across membranes, to synthesize proteins, nucleic acids and polysaccharides, for contraction of muscles, initiating cell movement, etc... Cells use O_2 to generate the majority of the ATP through a series of steps or a process called aerobic respiration:

$$C_6H_{12}O_6 + 6\,O_2 + 36\,P_i + 36\,ADP \xrightarrow{yields} 6\,CO_2 + 6\,H_2O + 36\,ATP$$

Thus, O_2 is critically important for normal cell function. Some tissues that are very active, like the brain and the heart require a constant source of O_2 in order to continue functioning and will die within minutes if O_2 is not supplied. Other tissues, such as the skin, can go for long lengths of time with reduced O_2. In order to supply O_2 to the tissues, the respiratory and the cardiovascular systems must be highly coordinated. Ventilation of the lungs must match the perfusion of blood through the lungs to maintain normal gas exchange.

Gas exchange takes place in two locations in the body. In the lungs, O_2 diffuses from the air through the epithelium of the alveoli into the blood of capillaries and CO_2 diffuses from the blood to the alveoli. In the tissues, however, O_2 moves from the blood into the tissues and CO_2 moves from the tissues to the blood. The diffusion of gases in both the lungs and tissues occurs due to concentration gradients. In the lungs, diffusion of gases across the alveolar membrane is dependent upon 4 factors.

22) *Membrane thickness* – the thicker the alveolar membrane the slower diffusion will take place or vice versa, the thinner the membrane the easier and faster diffusion will take place. Lungs are created with a very thin membrane to enhance diffusion rates. Diseases, like fibrosis, can increase the thickness of the membrane and impair gas exchange.

23) *Diffusion coefficient of gas* – CO_2 is 20 times more soluble in liquid compared to O_2 which is not very soluble in liquids. Therefore, many animals have developed proteins to bind O_2 and carry O_2 to the tissues; hemoglobin.

24) *Surface area* – In normal lungs, a large surface area ensures adequate gas exchange. Diseases like emphysema decrease surface area and reduce the available surface area for gas exchange.

25) *Partial pressure differences* – Gas moves from areas of high partial pressure to areas of low partial pressure.

Partial pressures of gas

As blood passes through the lungs, gas exchange takes place. In blood, the influence that O_2 and CO_2 have in a mixture of gas is expressed as a partial pressure of a gas (Pg). This can be expressed by Dalton's law which is equal to the fraction of the gas (Fg) times the barometric pressure (Pb).

$$P_g = F_g \; x \; P_b$$

Therefore, in dry air at sea level in which the O_2 concentration is 21%, we can calculate the P_{O2} to be:

$$P_{O_2} = 0.21 \; x \; 760 mmHg$$
$$P_{O_2} = 160 \; mmHg$$

As air passes through the nasal passages and the upper airways the air is warmed to 37°C and becomes saturated with water vapor. At 37°C, the water vapor dilutes the inspired gases by about 5-6% and exerts a partial pressure of 47mmHg. Thus, the P_{O2} of air that reaches the trachea can be calculated.

$$P_{O_2} = 0.21 \; x \; (760 - 47) mmHg$$
$$P_{O_2} = 150 mmHg$$

The P_{O2} of tracheal, inspired air is a constant, unless you change altitude, or administer supplemental O_2. Now, try to calculate the P_{O2} at Pikes Peak, CO and at the top of Mount Everest. Pikes Peak is just west of Colorado Springs, CO and is one of a few mountain peaks that rise above 14,000ft in the continental US. At increased elevations, the barometric pressure becomes reduced and the Pb is ~480mmHg. Mt Everest is known as the Earth's highest mountain rising above 29,000ft. The Pb is ~250mmHg. Answers can be found at the end of the chapter.

The air in the trachea moves along the bronchi and bronchioles and reaches the alveoli with little to no change in partial pressure; i.e., no gas exchange takes place along the conducting airways. In normal lungs, the alveolar membrane is extremely thin and has a large surface area to aid in gas exchange. Gas exchange across the alveolar capillaries is rapid due to a relatively large P_{O2} gradient. As the blood moves though the capillary, it only needs to travel ¼ of the distance in order to complete gas exchange. Gas transport in the blood is dependent on the binding properties of hemoglobin (see below). Provided normal blood and hemoglobin levels, O_2 is picked up in the lungs and the P_{O2} of blood is close to the P_{O2} of the alveolus. The P_{O2} is not exactly the same between the two compartments, however. A little blood that passes through the pulmonary circulation may not come into contact with an alveolar surface, or there may be areas of physiological dead space in cases of pathology. In these situations, no gas exchange takes place in a small amount of blood, thus the system is not perfect (but pretty close).

The blood is transported to the tissues via the systemic circulation where gas exchange can take place across the capillaries. Again, diffusion is dependent on P_{O_2} gradients, surface area and diffusion distances. At the same time, CO_2 gas exchange is also taking place but in the opposite directions; CO_2 is being picked up at the tissues and is lost across the alveolar surface. The O_2 and CO_2 are carried in blood using different gas transport mechanisms and can therefore be controlled separately.

Oxygen transport in blood

Recall that O_2 does not dissolve well in fluids. Therefore, only a small amount of O_2 is carried in blood as dissolved O_2 (~1.5%). Henry's law states that the concentration of a gas in a liquid is determined by its partial pressure and its solubility. CO_2 however, diffuses much more readily in liquids compared to O_2. Thus, in blood which is comprised mainly of water the amount of dissolved CO_2 is higher than O_2. In fact, without an O_2-binding protein, the blood cannot carry enough O_2 to meet the demands of the tissues in most animals. An interesting exception is the Antarctic icefish which lack hemoglobin. Cold temperature increases the solubility of O_2 in liquid. Therefore in the Antarctic icefish there is no need for binding proteins; there is adequate gas exchange due to the higher amounts of dissolved O_2 combined with the very low metabolic rate of the animal. In most vertebrates, including humans, the most common oxygen binding protein is hemoglobin and the majority of the oxygen is carried in blood bound to these proteins (~98.5%). Hemoglobin is found in erythrocytes and gives blood its characteristic red color; when O_2 is bound, the color of blood is a bright red and when O_2 is unbound the color is a darker, deeper mahogany color. In some animals, like insects and worms, the O_2-binding proteins are not hemoglobin, but other types of proteins that are different colors. Think back to a drive during a warm summer evening with bugs smashing on the windshield. The varying colors are due to the different binding proteins of the insects; yellow and green and blue colored "blood."

The primary function of hemoglobin is to transport O_2 and CO_2 in blood. Hemoglobin is made of 4 protein subunits each containing a heme group bound to a single iron atom. Each heme group is capable of binding a single O_2 molecule. The individual protein subunits of hemoglobin vary across the animal kingdom and across development within a single individual and change the affinity for O_2. For example, in the developing fetus, the binding affinity of hemoglobin for O_2 is stronger than the adult isoform. The stronger binding affinity helps in the transfer of O_2 from the mother to the fetus. In adult humans, hemoglobin contains two α and two β globin molecules. The binding affinity of hemoglobin for O_2 also varies at different partial pressures of O_2 and can be expressed in an O_2-hemoglobin dissociation curve (See Figure 7.9, on the next page).

In blood, the change in O_2 affinity is due to subunit cooperativity. Cooperativity is the process in which an O_2 molecule binds to one heme group and causes a conformational change in the protein which in turn increases the affinity for O_2 to adjacent heme groups. The rapid change in affinity as subsequent O_2 molecules bind is shown as the steep portion of the O_2-hemoglobin dissociation curve (Figure 7.9). When the partial pressure of O_2 is high in blood, O_2 binding affinity is high and O_2 binds fully and strongly to hemoglobin (See Figure 7.10). Alternatively, in the tissues where the partial pressure of O_2 is low, the O_2 binding affinity is low and therefore favors O_2 delivery to the tissues (See Figure 7.11). This changing O_2 affinity based on partial pressures and favors O_2 binding in the lungs and O_2 unbinding in the tissues.

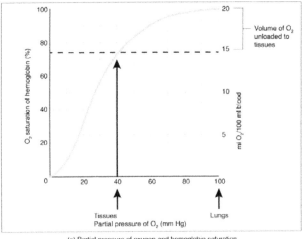

(a) Partial pressure of oxygen and hemoglobin saturation

The O_2-hemoglobin affinity is also influenced by other factors, including the pH, the partial pressure of CO_2, temperature, and organic phosphate ligands such as 2,3,-diphosphoglycerate (DPG) (Figure 7.9). Increases in H^+ ion concentration (or a decrease in pH) decreases the hemoglobin affinity for O_2. H^+ ions bind directly to hemoglobin decreasing the affinity for O_2; this is called the Bohr shift or the Bohr Effect. CO_2 also binds directly to amine ($-NH_2$) groups on hemoglobin and causes a decrease in the O_2 affinity. This is called the Haldane Effect. Increases in temperature also decreases the O_2 affinity for hemoglobin. All of these three factors, decrease in pH, increase in temperature and an increase in CO_2 occur in working muscles and thus favor the removal of O_2 from hemoglobin at the tissue when the need for O_2 is the highest.

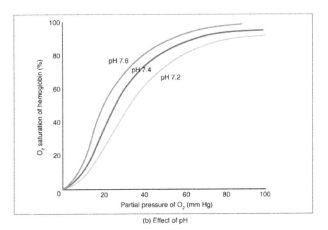

(b) Effect of pH

In addition to hemoglobin, erythrocytes also contain high levels of DPG. DPG binds to hemoglobin and decreases the affinity of O2 for hemoglobin. DPG levels rise when O_2

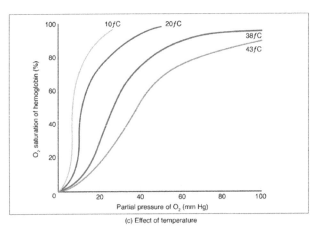

(c) Effect of temperature

Figure 7.9

levels fall or pH increases or there are reductions in blood hemoglobin. This also favors the removal of O_2 in tissues and enhances O_2 uptake in the lungs. But it can also create problems if one is exposed to high altitude. At high altitudes, where O_2 levels are low, DPG levels increase substantially. This favors removal at tissues but inadvertently decreases O_2 uptake in the lungs.

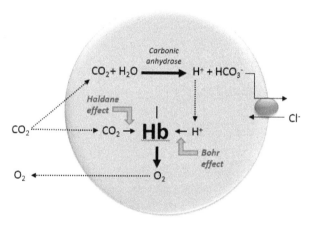

Figure 7.10

Carbon dioxide transport in blood

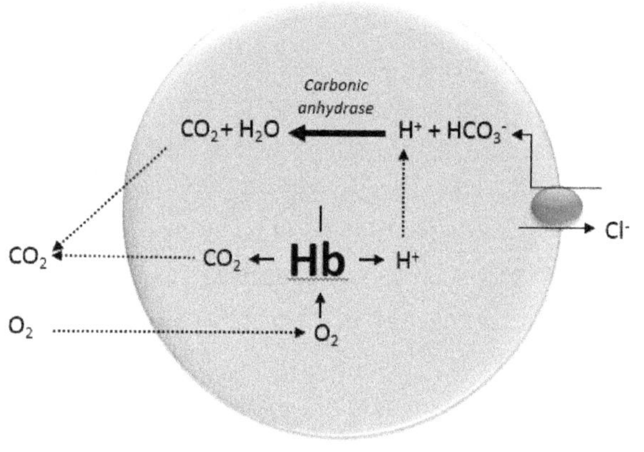

CO_2 is transported in the blood via three mechanisms. CO_2 is dissolved in plasma (~7%) at a higher concentration than O_2, CO_2 binds to hemoglobin and other blood proteins (~23%), but the majority of CO_2 is carried in blood as bicarbonate ions. In the tissues, CO_2 combines with water (which is freely available) to form carbonic acid (H_2CO_3). Carbonic acid dissociates into bicarbonate ions (HCO_3^-) and H^+ ions.

$$CO_2 + H_2O \xrightarrow{CA} H_2CO_3 \xrightarrow{yields} HCO_3^- + H^+$$

Carbonic anhydrase (CA) catalyzes this reaction in erythrocytes (Figure 7.11). When CO_2 levels are high such as in the tissues this reaction is favored. Inside the erythrocyte, the HCO_3^- ions are transported out of the cell through an HCO_3^-/Cl^- exchanger that transports one HCO_3^- for each Cl^- ion. This is known as the chloride shift mechanism. The H^+ ions that are formed can bind to hemoglobin and which contributes to the decreased affinity for O_2 (Bohr Effect) and O_2 unloading at the tissues. CO_2 can also bind directly to hemoglobin and cause a conformational

Figure 7.11

change in the hemoglobin to decrease its affinity for O_2. Again, this is referred to as the Haldane Effect. In the lungs, carbonic anhydrase assists in completing the above reaction in the opposite direction and results in the formation of CO_2 and H_2O (Figure 7.10). CO_2 can then easily diffuse out into the alveoli down its concentration gradient.

Blood pH can easily be altered with changes in PCO_2 in the arterial blood. If one holds their breath, P_{CO2} rises causing an increase in the number of H^+ ions produced. This is because carbonic anhydrase is not only found inside erythrocytes, but it can also be found associated with endothelial cells lining the lumen of blood vessels. This can lead to a decrease in the blood pH and is called a respiratory acidosis. Alternatively, if one "pants" and blows off CO_2, the amount of H^+ ions in the blood will decrease and cause the blood pH to rise. This is referred to as a respiratory alkalosis. Blood pH can also be controlled by the kidney and will be covered in more detail in Chapter 8.

Respiratory neural control

Ventilation is accomplished through the rhythmic movement of the thoracic cavity, moving air in and out of the lungs to allow gas exchange to occur at the alveolar surface. Ventilation requires a well-coordinated motor output to skeletal muscles to produce this smooth rhythmic movement. Breathing is divided into three phases; inspiration, post-inspiration (or inspiratory-braking) and expiration. These phases are controlled by motor neurons that control the pump muscles which move air in and out of the lungs as well as muscles that control airway resistance (upper airways). The motor neurons are under regulatory control mechanisms that arise from neural centers in the brainstem. These centers are responsible for the generation of the basic respiratory rhythm as well as the integration of sensory inputs and reflexes that control breathing patterns and affect ventilatory output.

Rhythm generation appears to involve complex interactions of specific membrane properties of a group of neurons which act as pacemakers, and the network interactions between neurons found in several nuclei of the brainstem. The regions involved in rhythm generation include the pre-Bötzinger complex and the parafacial respiratory group (pFRG) (Figure 7.12) and are found continuous with a column of neurons known as the ventral respiratory group (VRG). Neurons within these regions generate a basic rhythm which can then be modified to alter respiratory frequency and tidal volume. Electrical impulses are generated from the rhythm generator and sent via pre-motor neurons (found within the VRG and DRG) to motor neurons of the muscles that participate in ventilatory control. Inspiratory premotor neurons are located more rostrally in the column and expiratory premotor neurons are clustered together in more caudal regions and they project to the motor neurons which control activation of skeletal muscles involved with breathing.

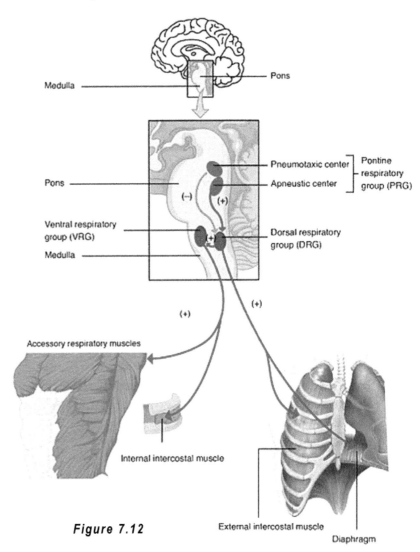

Figure 7.12

In mammals, including humans, the primary muscle for breathing is the diaphragm. Motor neurons arise from C3, C4 and C5 (in humans) and travel through the phrenic nerve to innervate the diaphragm. Other muscles involved in breathing include the external and internal intercostal nerves which arise from each intercostal space (T1-T11) to innervate the external and internal intercostal muscles at each respective costal space, abdominal muscles which are innervated from nerves that arise from T7-L1, and upper airway muscles which are innervated by cranial nerves. The various muscle groups are activated to increase or decrease the volume of the lungs and cause changes in airflow.

Inputs from mechanoreceptors, chemoreceptors and/or from higher brain centers alter ventilation to meet the metabolic demands of the body. Inputs from lung stretch receptors and peripheral chemoreceptors project to the nucleus of the tractus solitarius (NTS) in the medulla and comprises part of a region that is designated the dorsal respiratory group (DRG). The DRG projects to the VRG and modifies its rhythmic output to meet the changing needs of the body. In some species, the DRG also contains inspiratory premotor neurons which project down the spinal cord to innervate respiratory muscles. Finally, higher brain centers can also modify breathing via multiple pathways. Within the pons, several nuclei, including the pontine respiratory group (PRG), are also important in modifying respiratory motor output and plays a major role in switching the phases between inspiration and expiration. Other centers, such as hypothalamic and reticular neurons influence breathing during wake and sleep cycles, during changes in body temperature, and during emotional states. And centers involved with speech formation alter breathing patterns to generate the air flow needed for speech production.

The goal of ventilation is to maintain proper levels of arterial O_2, CO_2, and pH in blood and bodily fluids. In order to achieve this goal, there must be receptors to sense changes in these parameters and a mechanism in place to respond to any changes in O_2, CO_2, and pH. Sensory receptors are found in strategic locations in the body to detect changes in arterial O_2, CO_2, and pH. These receptors are found in aortic bodies, carotid bodies and in the brainstem. Mechanoreceptors in the lungs and chest wall detect stretch and help coordinate the length of the inspiratory phase. Sensory receptors send impulses to the DRG and brainstem regions integrate and process the inputs. An appropriate motor response is activated to change ventilation and restore gas levels back to normal values.

Chemoreceptors

Chemoreceptors are found in a couple of key locations to detect changes in arterial blood gas partial pressures and concentrations.

26) Central chemoreceptors are found on the ventral surface of the medulla and detect changes in CO_2 and pH of the cerebral spinal fluid surrounding the brain and spinal cord.
27) Carotid bodies are found at the bifurcation of the internal and external carotid arteries and sense changes in O_2, CO_2 and pH of the blood that is directly going to the brain.

28) Aortic bodies are found embedded in the walls of the aorta and some of the large vessels emerging from the aortic arch and also detect changes in O_2, CO_2 and pH of systemic blood.

In the blood vessels of the brain, CO_2 can readily diffuse across the blood-brain barrier (BBB), however, H^+ and HCO_3^- cannot. Once CO_2 diffuses across the BBB into the cerebral spinal fluid (CSF), however, the enzyme, CA converts CO_2 and H_2O to H^+ and HCO_3. The change in H^+ ion concentration can alter the pH of the CSF. Both increases in CO_2 and a decrease in pH will stimulate central chemoreceptors found on the ventral surface of the medulla. These chemoreceptors cause a compensatory increase in ventilation which results in more CO_2 being expelled from the lungs and attempts to restore the blood gases back to normal. Alternatively, if CO_2 levels decrease and the pH of the CSF increases, the firing rate of chemoreceptors decrease. There will be a subsequent decrease in total ventilation which restores CO_2 (and thus pH) back toward normal.

Peripheral chemoreceptors are located in the carotid bodies and aortic bodies. The carotid bodies are small organs situated at the bifurcation of the common carotid arteries. The carotid body contains sensory glomus cells which detect increases in CO_2, decreases in O_2, and a decrease in blood pH. If any of these changes are detected, the glomus cells increase the release of neurotransmitter which stimulates afferents of the glossopharyngeal nerve. These glossopharyngeal sensory afferents project to the DRG and will in turn influence the output of the VRG and alter ventilation. In this case, ventilation will increase in an attempt to return the blood gases back to normal. Again, this reflex works in the opposite direction. If CO_2 decreases, O_2 increases or pH increases, there will be reduced release of neurotransmitter and the glossopharyngeal afferents will have reduced action potential firing.

Aortic bodies function in a similar manner as the carotid bodies although their influence in breathing does not appear as pronounced and may be more involved with changes in gas concentrations and not partial pressures. Sensory inputs from aortic bodies arise from vagal afferents that also project to the DRG to influence ventilatory output.

At rest, ventilation in humans is regulated primarily due to changes in arterial P_{CO2} and not P_{O2}. At rest, arterial P_{O2} is completely saturated (refer to the O_2-hemoglobin dissociation curve, Figure 7.9). Arterial P_{O2} needs to fall below ~80% before there will be a substantial effect on ventilation. This is because hemoglobin remains saturated at these partial pressures, therefore ventilation is not affected substantially with small reductions in P_{O2}. Small changes in arterial P_{CO2}, however, causes a rapid and linear increase in total ventilation. Likewise, small changes in pH also cause a rapid, linear increase in ventilation.

Mechanoreceptors

In the lungs and chest wall, there are special mechanoreceptors that sense the stretch of the lungs and chest wall and therefore detect the "volume" of the lungs. During inspiration, the lungs and chest wall expand and stretch vagal afferent mechanoreceptors. The frequency of action potentials of the vagal afferents increase and project into the DRG. These sensory inputs are involved with inspiratory braking and stimulate an "off-switch" to help to stop the inspiratory phase. This reflex is called the Hering-Breuer Reflex. In newborns and infants this appears to be an important mechanism helping to control the respiratory pattern of breathing. In adults during quiet breathing, this does not appear to have a great influence on breathing and other regions of the brain such as the pons, appear to play more important roles in the activation of the "off-switch."

There are a multitude of vagal afferent sensory receptors that are found in the lungs that affect breathing. Irritant receptors are found in the trachea and bronchi and are important in initiating the cough reflex due to inhaled particles, dust, smoke, etc... Other receptors in the lungs detect stretch and may contribute to the feeling of dyspnea in patients with apnea and other lung disorders.

CHAPTER 7, SECTION 2 – SUMMARY

> ➢
> ➢ Gas exchange in the lungs is dependent upon 1) the thickness of the gas exchange membrane, 2) the diffusion coefficient of the gas, 3) the surface area of the gas exchange surface, and 4) the partial pressure gradient.

> ➢ In a gas mixture, each individual gas is expressed as a partial pressure of the total gas mixture.

> ➢ Oxygen does not dissolve well in liquid. Thus, most of the O_2 in blood is carried bound to hemoglobin, only ~1.5% of O_2 is freely dissolved in blood.

> ➢ Carbon dioxide is primarily carried as bicarbonate ions (~70%). CO_2 and H_2O combine to form H^+ and HCO_3^-. Some CO_2 binds to hemoglobin and other proteins (~23%), and some is dissolved freely in plasma (~7%), (more so than O_2).

> ➢ The Bohr Effect is the effect of pH on the affinity of O_2 for hemoglobin. As pH decreases, the affinity of hemoglobin for O_2 decreases. This is advantageous in the tissues where pH decreases the amount of available O_2 also goes down; O_2 delivery is enhanced. And in the lungs where pH increases, there is a stronger affinity for O_2 and O_2 is readily picked up in the lungs.

> ➢ The Haldane Effect is the effect that CO_2 has on the O_2 binding affinity for hemoglobin. As CO2 binds to hemoglobin, the affinity for O_2 decreases. Again, this is advantageous in the tissues where CO2 levels are high and P_{O2} is low. The reverse also happens in lungs, and as P_{CO2} decreases the O_2 affinity increases.

> ➢ Respiratory neural control is regulated by neurons located in multiple nuclei of the medulla. Neurons in the pre-Bötzinger complex and the parafacial respiratory group are involved with creating a basic respiratory rhythm and they

project to premotor neurons located in the VRG. Various sensory inputs and inputs from higher brain centers modify the basic respiratory rhythm.

➢ Chemoreceptors that are sensitive to arterial P_{O2}, P_{CO2} and pH are found in the medulla, the carotid bodies and the aortic bodies. As P_{O2} and pH decrease or the P_{CO2} increases, sensory inputs project to respiratory centers to modify and increase total ventilation.

➢ Mechanoreceptors respond to the stretch of the lungs and chest wall and thus detect the "volume" of breaths. The Hering-Breuer Reflex helps to switch between the inspiratory and expiratory phases. Stretch receptor feedback increases during the inspiratory phase and turns inspiration off.

Answers to problems in Chapter 7

For inspired, tracheal air at Pike's Peak:

$$P_{O_2} = 0.21 \, x \, (480mmHg - 47mmHg)$$
$$P_{O_2} = 90.9mmHg$$

For inspired, tracheal air at Mt. Everest:

$$P_{O_2} = 0.21 \, x \, (250mmHg - 47mmHg)$$
$$P_{O_2} = 42.6mmHg$$

There are extremely low levels of arterial PO_2 at the peak of Mt. Everest. Notice that the inspired tracheal air at Mt. Everest is close to the venous blood of a person at sea level.

References and Suggested Readings

Costa KM, Accorsi-Mendonça D, Moraes DJA, Machado BH. 2014. Evolution and physiology of neural oxygen sensing. *Frontiers in Physiology* 5:1-16.

Garcia AJ, Zanella S, Koch H, Doi A, Rameriz JM. 2011. Networks within networks: The neuronal control of breathing. *Progress in Brain Research* 188:31-50.

Lahiri S, Forster II RE. 2003. CO2/H+ sensing: peripheral and central chemoreception. *The International Journal of Biochemistry and Cell Biology* 35:1413-1435.

Milsom WK. 2010. Adaptive trends in respiratory control: a comparative perspective. *American Journal of Physiology: Regulatory, Integrative and Comparative Physiology* 299:R1-R10.

Perry SF, Similowski T, Klein W, Codd JR. 2010. The evolutionary origin of the mammalian diaphragm. *Respiratory Physiology and Neurobiology* 171:1-16.

Piskuric NA, Nurse CA. 2013. Expanding role of ATP as a versatile messenger at carotid and aortic body chemoreceptors. *Journal of Physiology* 591920:415-422.

Richter DW, Smith JC. 2014. Respiratory rhythm generation in vivo. *Physiology (Bethesda)* 29(1):58-71.

Chapter 8: Renal Physiology

Single celled and small multicellular organisms use mechanisms of simple diffusion to rid their bodies of waste and toxic substances. As animals enlarged, diffusion with the environment was no longer an option due to large distances. Animals began to evolve circulatory systems to transport substances throughout their bodies as well evolve excretory organs to remove waste products. In general, these excretory organs are called kidneys. In addition to waste removal, the kidneys also play important roles in osmoregulation and the homeostasis of the extracellular fluid compartment. In some animals, particularly aquatic fish, amphibians and invertebrates, other organs such as gills, skin and the intestines play major roles in osmoregulatory functions, whereas more terrestrial animals use other organs to merely assist in osmoregulation. Osmoregulation refers to the regulation of the osmotic pressure of the extracellular fluid compartment. In general, water and substances enter the body through the mouth and digestive tract, and water and substances leave the body through the digestive and excretory organs. The regulation of water balance and ionic composition of extracellular fluid is accomplished through a coordinated effort over multiple organ systems. The kidneys, however are the major organs involved in homeostasis of water and osmotic balance and the removal of toxic waste products.

In mammals, the urinary system includes two kidneys, each with a ureter that drain into a common bladder which then empties out of the body through a single urethra. The kidneys filter blood which allows them to function and 1) remove wastes, and 2) regulate water, ion and pH homeostasis. The kidneys also function to 3) help regulate blood pressure through renin production, and 4) regulate red blood cell synthesis by producing erythropoietin. The kidneys are the major excretory organ of the body, however, some waste products are also removed by the skin, lung, liver and intestine.

Anatomy of the mammalian kidney

Mammals typically contain two kidneys that sit retroperitoneal (posterior to the peritoneal cavity) and are protected by the floating ribs of the rib cage. A region called the hilum is on the medial aspect of the kidney and contains the major vessels running to and from the kidney; the renal artery, renal vein and ureter. The kidneys are covered with a tough, fibrous connective tissue capsule which aids in protection of the kidney tissue. The inside of the organ contains two layers; an inner medulla and outer cortex. Within mammals, the internal structures and organization of the cortical and medullary tissue can vary slightly between species. In humans, the outer cortical tissue periodically penetrates deep toward the center of the kidney and forms renal columns (See Figure 8.1, on the next page). The renal columns separate the medullary tissue into pyramidal-shaped structures. The tips or apex of the pyramids, the renal papilla, is the location where urine is collected into spaces called calyces. The minor and major calyces drain into a central renal pelvis and forms the opening to the ureter which exits at the hilum.

Blood enters the kidney through the renal artery and travels through a series of arteries and arterioles before entering the nephron where blood is filtered (See Figure 8.2). The renal artery branches into segmental arteries at the hilum region and divides into interlobar arteries which travel between the pyramids and renal columns. Branches that arc over the base of the pyramids, the arcuate arteries then give rise to interlobular arteries the course through the cortical tissue. Small branches off of the interlobular arteries, the afferent arterioles provide blood to each nephron.

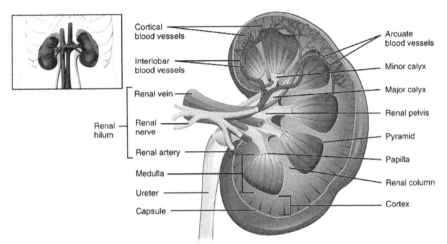

Figure 8.1

The nephron is the functional unit of the kidney and is the location where blood is filtered to begin urine formation (See Figure 8.3). Each nephron contains a renal corpuscle, a proximal convoluted tubule, a loop of Henle, and a distal convoluted tubule. The collecting ducts also play a role in forming urine, but developmentally arise from different tissues and are thus not considered part of the nephron. The renal corpuscle is comprised of a capillary bed which twists into a small ball called the glomerulus (See Figure 8.4). A single afferent arteriole supplies each glomerulus with blood and a

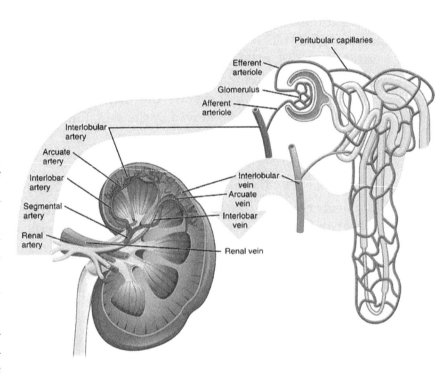

Figure 8.2

single efferent arteriole exits the glomerulus. The glomerulus is covered with an epithelium called Bowman's capsule. Bowman's capsule is made of two layers surrounding Bowman's space. The visceral layer of Bowman's capsule covers the glomerular capillary and the parietal layer of Bowman's capsule lines the wall of the renal corpuscle. Bowman's space is the space between the parietal and visceral layers of Bowman's capsule. The visceral layer is made of specialized cells called podocytes which are involved with the filtration of blood from the glomerulus into Bowman's space. The podocytes have a cell body which contains a nucleus and several primary extensions or processes extending away from the cell body which give rise to many secondary processes. The secondary processes rest on the basement membrane of the endothelium of the capillary and the secondary processes of one podocyte interdigitate with the secondary processes from another podocyte creating a filtration slit. The filtration slit helps determine what size particles can be filtered at the glomerulus.

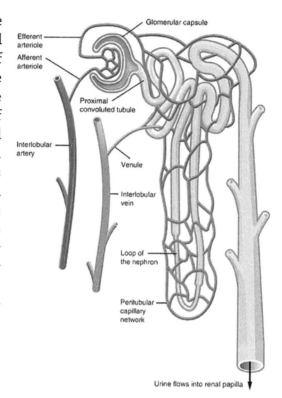

Figure 8.3

Fluid from Bowman's space enters a tube which sits opposite to the afferent arteriole and is called the proximal convoluted tubule (PCT). The PCT is lined with a simple cuboidal epithelium with many long microvilli on its apical surface. Absorption of many solutes and water occurs in this region and microvilli greatly increase the surface area of these active cells. Solutes and water move from the apical surface to the basal surface at such a high rate, that even the basal surface is convoluted in shape and thus increases the surface area of the basal side of the epithelial cells as well. The PCT winds in a torturous manner before descending and becoming the loop of Henle.

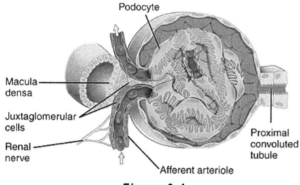

Figure 8.4

The loop of Henle is a straight tube that descends toward the center of the kidney, some of the tubules extend very deep into the medulla of the kidney and are involved with the concentration of urine. The descending loop of Henle then loops around and ascends in another straight line; the ascending limb of the loop of Henle. The loop of Henle starts as a simple cuboidal epithelium and is called the thick descending limb. The epithelium changes to a simple squamous epithelium, the thin descending limb and then ascends as the thin ascending limb before becoming a thick ascending limb of the Loop of Henle. The descending and ascending limbs are very straight tubes coursing through the center of the medulla. The ascending limb meets the distal convoluted tubule (DCT) and again, as the name implies, the tubule winds in twisting manner before meeting the collecting tubules. The reason for the name *distal* is not due to its anatomical location relative to the renal corpuscle, but rather to the length of distance that the filtrate had to flow through the tube to arrive in that location i.e., the fluid in this compartment is the farthest from where the filtrate was first formed. In fact, the distal convoluted tubule from one nephron will make an intimate contact with the renal corpuscle from which it arose forming the macula densa, one portion of the juxtaglomerular apparatus (refer back to Figure 8.4). The collecting tubules join collecting ducts which descend again, in a rather straight line through the medulla toward the tip of the renal papilla.

Urine formation

Urine is formed using three different processes.

> *Filtration*: filtering the blood through the glomerulus into Bowman's space.
> *Reabsorption*: solutes and water are reabsorbed (up to 99%) from the filtrate throughout the tubular network of the nephron, and
> *Secretion*: certain substances are actively secreted into the filtrate through the nephron tubule.

Urine is the fluid that remains in the collecting ducts after filtration, reabsorption and secretion have occurred. Urine drains from the kidney and is stored in the bladder before excretion from the body. Glomerular filtration filters blood by bulk flow and is only selective based on the size of particles. All components of blood are filtered except the larger molecules such as proteins. Water, ions, glucose, amino acids and urea are filtered freely across the glomerulus. Reabsorption of various ions, molecules and water occurs across the tubular walls of the nephron. Different areas of the nephron are specialized for reabsorption of specific ions and substances. Secretion of ions and various substances occurs in specific areas of the nephron. Together these processes form the final end-product, urine.

Glomerular filtration

The first stage of urine formation is glomerular filtration which occurs at the renal corpuscle (See Figure 8.5). Blood flows through an afferent arteriole into a glomerular capillary and is filtered past the endothelial cells and the podocytes into Bowman's space. The filtration membrane is composed of the fenestrated endothelial cells, the basement membrane of the glomerular capillary, and the filtration slits or gaps between the secondary processes of the podocytes which help to limit the size of the particles entering Bowman's capsule. Filtration at the renal corpuscle is dependent on five factors, 1) blood pressure, 2) changes in the diameter of the afferent and efferent arteriole, 3) Bowman's space pressure, 4) the osmotic pressure of the blood, and 5) the particle size relative to the filtration slit size.

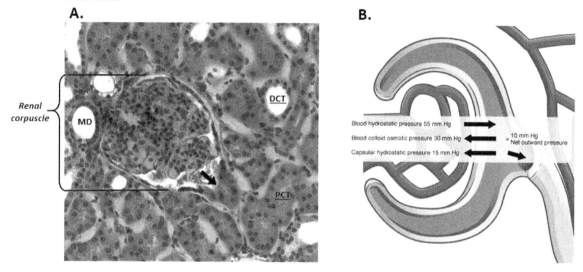

A.

Renal
corpuscle

MD

DCT

PCT

B.

Blood hydrostatic pressure 55 mm Hg

Blood colloid osmotic pressure 30 mm Hg

Capsular hydrostatic pressure 15 mm Hg

= 10 mm Hg
Net outward pressure

Figure 8.5

Simple changes in total blood pressure to the kidney will alter glomerular filtration rates (GFR). As blood pressure increases more filtrate is pushed across the filtration membrane and will increase GFR. Alternatively, any decreases in blood pressure will result in a reduction in GRF. In fact, in life-threatening conditions where blood pressure is extremely low, GFR can fall to zero and a patient can go into renal failure; i.e., no renal function.

The blood vessels entering and leaving the glomerulus are both arterioles and are regulated by sympathetic innervation and hormonal control which can alter GFR. If the afferent arteriole constricts, less blood will enter the glomerulus and GFR will decrease; alternatively if the afferent arteriole dilates, more blood will flow through the glomerulus and GFR rates will increase. If the outflow from the glomerulus is reduced by constricting the efferent arteriole, then GFR rates will rise (i.e., more plasma is pushed across the filtration membrane). On the other hand, if the efferent arteriole dilates, more blood will flow to an area of lower pressure in the efferent arteriole and less filtrate will pass the filtration membrane and total GFR will decrease.

Pressure in Bowman's space also influences how much filtrate is pushed through the filtration membrane; as pressure in Bowman's space increases, the total amount of filtrate that moves across the membrane will fall and GFR will decrease. The pressure within Bowman's capsule increases as the bladder fills up. Essentially, placing more fluid in the finite tubular system increases Bowman's pressure. Other pathological conditions, such as swelling of the kidney or a urinary obstruction can cause Bowman's capsule pressure to rise.

In addition to the hydrostatic forces on GFR, the osmotic pressure also influences movement of fluid across capillaries. The osmotic pressure in the capillary is much greater than in Bowman's space. Remember that proteins and cells do not cross the filtration membrane and remain behind in blood. As fluid crossed the filtration membrane, the osmotic pressure of the blood that remains behind increases. The increased osmolarity of the blood entering the efferent arteriole ensures that fluid remains in the capillary. Therefore, the blood that leaves the glomerulus and enters the efferent arteriole has a higher osmotic pressure compared to the blood entering the glomerulus. The efferent arteriole gives rise to the peritubular capillary which surrounds the same nephron from which it arose and will reabsorb much of the fluid that was filtered at the glomerulus.

Therefore, increases in blood pressure in the glomerulus (P_G) favors filtration, whereas, the fluid pressure in Bowman's space (P_{BS}) and the osmotic forces of blood in the glomerulus (π_G) oppose filtration. Thus, the net filtration pressure is equal to:

$$Net\ filtration\ pressure\ =\ P_G - P_{BS} - \pi_G$$

Other factors that influence filtration across the membrane have to do the size of the particles and the size of the filtration slits. The glomerular capillary has many fenestrae which allow fluid to pass through the membrane and they are surrounded by the podocyte secondary processes creating a filtration slit. The openings are approximately 40Å wide and small molecules such as water, amino acids, glucose, ions, etc... can freely pass through the slits. As particle size increases, the percentage of particles that filter through the membrane goes down. Things like hormones and small polypeptides can cross the filtration membrane, however, not as freely. Larger proteins, such as albumin and fibrinogen, and cells are too large to fit through the filtration slits and remain in blood.

Certain pathological conditions can alter the size of the filtration slits and allow larger substances to cross the filtration membrane. Some infections and toxins can cause swelling of the podocytes and cause a decrease in the filtration rate. Some diseases of blood or hemolytic diseases can cause massive hemolysis or the breakdown of red blood cells. The liver is unable to keep up with the removal of these red cell waste products and the hemoglobin can precipitate in blood. This precipitation creates needle-like crystals that can plug the filtration slits. Ethylene glycol or antifreeze poisoning results in a similar phenomenon and reduces filtration. The ethylene glycol molecule or hemoglobin crystals are just about the size of the slit and will get caught and cause obstruction and eventually decrease the kidneys ability to filter blood.

In some conditions, podocytes can be damaged and result in cell death. A reduction in the number and size of the podocyte processes can cause an increase in the filtration slit size and cause a great increase in GFR. In either case, renal function is greatly altered. In the first case, if GFR is greatly reduced, waste products can build up in plasma and cause cellular toxicity and eventual death. If filtration slit size increases, cells and large proteins can pass the filtration membrane and enter the nephron. If that happens there are no mechanisms to reabsorb any of these proteins or cells and they will be excreted with urine. Not only will essential components of blood be lost, but the increased number of solutes present in the filtrate will increase the osmotic forces and more water will be excreted causing dramatic decreases in blood volume and pressure resulting in cardiac insufficiency.

Proximal convoluted tubule (PCT)

As the filtrate flows through the nephron, reabsorption of solutes and water occurs. Substances move from the lumen of the tubule through the apical and basal surfaces of the epithelial cells and into the interstitial space using multiple transport mechanisms. Ultimately the reabsorbed solutes and water are collected by the peritubular capillary network. Up to 99% of the filtrate that was formed in Bowman's space can be reabsorbed by the tubules of the nephron.

The filtrate in Bowman's capsule moves down a pressure gradient to enter the PCT. The PCT is the location for the majority of solute reabsorption; up to 67% of the filtrate is reabsorbed in the PCT alone. The epithelial cells lining the PCT contain a number of transporters and carrier molecules located on their apical and basal surfaces which move substances across the epithelial cells and into the interstitial space (Figure 8.6). Most solute reabsorption is a secondary active transport mechanism and is linked to the active transport of Na^+ across the basal surface. Epithelial cells that line the PCT have numerous Na^+/K^+ pumps on the basal surface of their cells. Recall that 3 Na^+ ions are transported out of the cell for every 2 K^+ ions that are moved into the cell requiring 1 molecule of ATP. This creates a low Na^+ concentration in the cell's interior and a strong driving force for Na^+ reentry. The reabsorption in the 1st half of the PCT is devoted to the reabsorption of Na^+, glucose, amino acids and HCO_3^- and the 2nd half is devoted primarily to the reabsorption of ions, primarily Na^+ and Cl^- and is involved with pH regulation.

Lumen of Proximal Convoluted Tubule

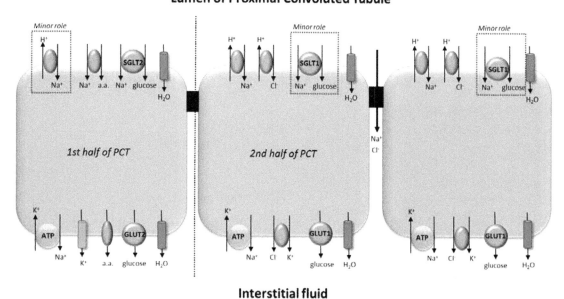

Interstitial fluid

Figure 8.6

In the 1st half of the PCT, the apical surface of the epithelial cells contain a large number of co-transport proteins which transport Na^+ with a variety of substances such as glucose and other sugars, amino acids, etc... (See Table 8.1, on the next page). The strong concentration gradient for Na$^+$ moves substances across the cell membrane via a co-transporter. These substances will continue to pass through the basal surface primarily through facilitated transport mechanisms. As the solute particles move from the lumen to the interstitial space, there is a net flow of water which follows the osmotic gradient. The molecules and ions that are reabsorbed from the PCT will move from the interstitial space to the peritubular capillary network. This capillary is highly permeable and contains a low blood pressure due to a lack of fluid (lost across the filtration membrane). The movement through the capillary is slow and the blood is hyperosmotic due to the large number of solutes (proteins) that were left behind in the capillary. The hyperosmotic forces draw water back into the peritubular capillary quickly.

Table 8.1. Some plasma membrane proteins used for the transport of substances across the apical and basal membranes of cells lining the nephron tubule.

Apical membrane	Basal Membrane
Proximal convoluted tubule	
Na+-Cl- co-transporter	Na+-K ATPase
Na+-K+ co-transporter	GLUT1 and GLUT2
Na+-Ca++ co-transporter	
Na+-Mg++ co-transporter	
Na+-glucose co-transporter (SGLUT1 and SGLUT2)	
Na+-amino acid co-transporter	
Na+-fructose co-transporter	
Na+-K co-transporter	
Na+-K co-transporter	
Na+-K co-transporter	
Na+-K co-transporter	
Na+-K co-transporter	
Na+/H+ antiporter	
Thick ascending loop of Henle	
Na+-Cl- K+ co-transporter	Na+-K ATPase
Na+/H+ antiporter	K+-Cl- co-transporter
Distal convoluted tubule	
Na+-Cl- co-transporter	Na+-K ATPase
Na+-K+ co-transporter	

Under normal conditions, all of the nutrients such as glucose and amino acids that are filtered are reabsorbed in the PCT. For example, the transport of glucose occurs primarily in the 1st half of the PCT and 1 glucose is co-transported with 2 Na$^+$ ions using a Na$^+$-glucose transporter (SGLUT2) across the apical surface of epithelial cells. Glucose moves down its concentration gradient and exits the cell across the basal surface through a facilitated transport mechanism using a glucose transporter (GLUT2). Most glucose reabsorption occurs in the 1st section of the PCT, however, there is a small amount of glucose reabsorption that can occur in the 2nd half of the PCT. The number of transporters are significantly reduced compared to the 1st half and they are a different type of tranporter. On the apical surface, the SGLUT1 cotransporter also transports 2 Na$^+$ ions and 1 glucose molecule into the cell and the glucose moves out of the basal surface via GLUT1.

The 2nd half of the PCT is primarily devoted to Cl- reabsorption (whereas the 1st half moved primarily Na$^+$ ions) and some pH regulation. Again the Na$^+$/K$^+$ ATPase pumps are located in the basal surface and create a low concentration of Na$^+$ in the interior of the cell. On the apical membrane, two antiporters, a Na$^+$/H$^+$ antiporter and a Cl$^-$/H$^+$ antiporter, transport H$^+$ ions into the lumen of the PCT and bring Na$^+$ and Cl$^-$ into the cells interior. The Na$^+$ leaves the basal surface via the Na$^+$/K$^+$ pump and Cl$^-$ leaves via a K$^+$/Cl$^-$ cotransporter. Most of the H$^+$ ions that are transported into the lumen are recycled at the plasma membrane. Specific anions (such as hydroxide, oxalate, and bicarbonate ions) are secreted into the lumen which bind to H$^+$ and are recycled back into the cell membrane through various mechanisms. In addition to transcellular transport of Na$^+$ and Cl$^-$, both of these ions can be transported paracellularly, or pass through the tight junctions between cells. Since Cl$^-$ ions are not taken up in the first half of the PCT, the concentration of Cl$^-$ rises in the filtrate toward the 2nd half of the PCT. The movement of negative ions creates an electrical gradient causing Na$^+$ to follow. The reabsorption of ions and molecules such as glucose and amino acids into the interstitial space creates an osmotic gradient. Water passes from the lumen to the interstitial space through various aquaporin channels found in both the apical and basal surface of epithelial cells of the PCT.

Some small polypeptides and hormones and occasionally a few proteins are filtered at the glomerulus. These proteins can be taken up into the PCT via endocytosis of full or partially degraded proteins. Inside the cells, proteins are fully degraded into single amino acids which pass through the basal surface through facilitated transport mechanisms. In addition, some proteolytic enzymes are found on the apical surface of the epithelial cells of the PCT and can degrade peptides to single amino acids for transport. In a normal, healthy kidney, all of the protein is reabsorbed and thus only a trace amount of protein is found in urine.

Loop of Henle

After the PCT, the filtrate flows down through the medullary tissue through the descending and ascending loops of Henle (Figure 8.7). As the loop of Henle descends it quickly changes from a simple cuboidal epithelium (thick) to a simple squamous epithelium (thin). Then as the loop of Henle ascends it remains thin for a short distance before becoming thick again. The thin section of the descending limb is highly permeable to water via the aquaporin 1 channel and is moderately permeable to ions such as Na^+, K^+ and Cl^- (Figure 8.8). The ascending limb of the loop of Henle, both thin and thick sections, are impermeable to water but permeable to solutes. The thin ascending section is involved with the reabsorption of Na^+ and Cl^- via passive mechanisms and the thick segment of the ascending limb of the loop of Henle has multiple transport mechanisms to move solutes out of the lumen and into the interstitial space.

The descending limb of the loop of Henle can extend deep into the medullary tissue. The osmotic pressure of the medulla changes from ~300mOsm in the cortical tissue to ~1200mOsm at the tips of the pyramids deep in the medullary tissue. The high osmotic force of the interstitial space draws water out of the tubule through the epithelial cells lining the descending limb via the aquaporin 1 channel. As the tubule extends deep into the medulla, it is exposed to higher osmotic forces drawing out more water. The high osmolarity is due primarily to the presence of Na^+, Cl^- and urea in the interstitial space. Due to the high solute concentration and the permeability of the descending limb, some solutes move from the interstitial space INTO the lumen of the loop of Henle. By the end of the descending limb of the loop of Henle, another 15% of the filtrate volume is reabsorbed and thus a total of 80% of the filtrate has been reabsorbed. The filtrate in the lumen is roughly the same osmolarity as the osmolarity of the interstitial space as the loop of Henle descends into the medulla.

Figure 8.7

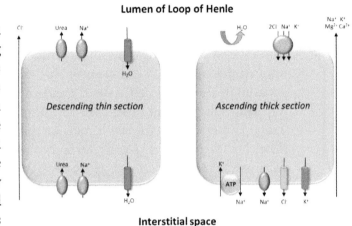

Lumen of Loop of Henle

Interstitial space

Figure 8.8

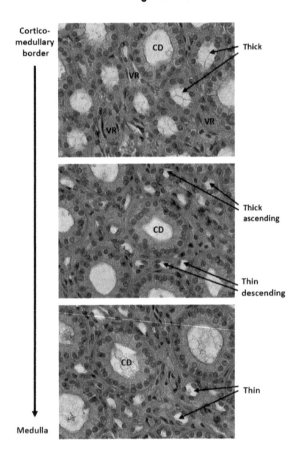

The ascending limb of the loop of Henle is NOT permeable to water (See Figure 8.8). The thin section is permeable to Na^+ and Cl^-, however, and thus, diffusion of Na^+ and Cl^- occurs passively as the limb ascends up toward the cortex. In the thick section of the loop of Henle, some solute particles move from the lumen to the interstitial space through transcellular mechanisms that utilize transporters (~50%) and through paracellular mechanisms that are passive (~50%). Like the PCT cells, there are numerous Na^+/K^+ ATPases on the basal surface of epithelial cells lining the thick section of the ascending limb of the loop of Henle. They pump Na^+ out of the cells into the interstitial space creating a strong driving force for Na^+ entry into the cells. On the apical surface, there are co-transporters which transport 1 Na^+, 1 K^+, and 2 Cl^- ions from the filtrate into the cells. The basal surface contains co-transporters which move K^+ and Cl^- out the basal surface (Na^+ leaves via the Na^+/K^+ pump). In addition, a Na^+/H^+ antiporter is present in the apical surface and plays a role in pH regulation.

Passive movement of ions also occurs between the cells lining the thick section of the ascending limb. Ion movement occurs due to a voltage gradient and Na^+, K^+, Ca^{2+}, and Mg^{2+} passively move between cells into the interstitial space due to the relative high positive charge inside the lumen. Since the descending thick section moves solutes out of the lumen without the movement of water, the filtrate in the lumen becomes hypoosmotic relative to the interstitial space of the cortex by the time it enters the DCT.

Distal convoluted tubule (DCT) and collecting ducts

The cells of the early DCT function the same as the ascending thick portions of the loop of Henle (Figure 8.9). The cells are also not permeable to water and continue to move solutes out of the lumen through transcellular mechanisms, thus continuing to dilute the filtrate. Again, the driving force for the movement of ions is due to a Na^+ gradient that is established by Na^+/K^+ ATPases found on the basal surface of cells. On the apical surface, Na^+/Cl^- co-transporters move Na^+ and Cl^- into cells and Cl^- moves out the basal surface through a Cl^- channel by simple diffusion mechanisms.

Figure 8.9

Lumen of Distal Convoluted Tubule

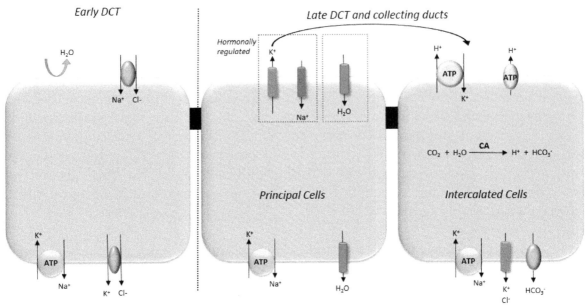

Interstitial fluid

The later portions of the DCT and the collecting ducts contain two different types of cells; intercalated cells and principal cells (Figure 8.9). The intercalated cells are involved with the regulation of pH homeostasis and contain H^+ pumps and H^+/K^+ antiporters in the apical membrane (see pH regulation below). The principal cells control ion movement of Na^+ and K^+ (which helps to recycle K^+ for use by the intercalated cell). The cells are under hormonal control which help regulate Na^+, Cl^- and water homeostasis. The principal cells contain Na^+/K^+ ATPases on their basal surfaces and a selective Na^+ channel on the apical surface. In general, aldosterone regulates Na^+ reabsorption and homeostasis, and ADH regulates water reabsorption and homeostasis. Both of these mechanisms help to regulate fluid balance and blood pressure.

Tubular secretion

Many substances enter the lumen of the nephron through glomerular filtration but some substances enter the lumen by tubular secretion. Tubular secretion is the process by which epithelial cells actively secrete substances into the lumen of the nephron. We have already learned that some ions, K^+ and H^+ are actively secreted into the lumen. Secretion of K^+ is involved with K^+ cycling and helps with the function of the intercalated cell in pH regulation. K^+ is also actively secreted when plasma K^+ levels rise above normal levels (see aldosterone regulation below). Secretion of H^+ is involved with pH regulation (see below). Other substances that are secreted are usually too large to fit through the glomerular filtration membrane. Some end-products of metabolism (organic anions and organic cations) and many drugs and toxic substances bound to plasma proteins are also secreted by tubular secretion. Some substances that are transported transcellularly are bile pigments, drugs like penicillin, atropine and morphine, and the sweetener saccharin. Multiple transporter mechanisms move substances across the epithelial cells of the PCT from the basal surface to the lumen for excretion. Most secretion occurs in the PCT, but secretion of K^+ and H^+ ions also occurs in the DCT.

Tubular excretion

Filtration, reabsorption, and secretion are the processes involved with urine formation. Everything that remains in the lumen of the collecting ducts then moves into the calyces and renal pelvis forming what is called urine. Urine moves from the renal pelvis into the ureters and finally into the urinary bladder for storage until urination or the excretion of liquid wastes.

Regulation of Ion and Water Homeostasis

The kidneys play important roles in the homeostasis of ions and water. The principal cells in the latter portions of the DCT and collecting ducts have receptors for two key hormones, aldosterone and vasopressin which help regulate the amount of water and ionic reabsorption.

Lumen of DCT and collecting ducts

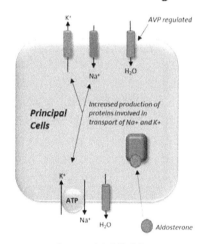

Interstitial fluid

Figure 8.10

Aldosterone

Aldosterone is steroid hormone that is released from the outermost region of the adrenal gland in response to low blood pressure (see Figure 6.21 in Chapter 6) or increased plasma K^+ concentrations. In the kidney, special cells responsive to stretch, the juxtaglomerular cells (JG cells) are found lining the walls of the afferent arteriole. The JG cells increase their secretion of renin in response to low blood pressure. Renin breaks down the circulating blood protein, angiotensinogen, into angiotensin I which is then converted to angiotensin II in the pulmonary circulation when it comes into contact with angiotensin converting enzyme (ACE). Receptors for angiotensin II are found on the cells of the zona glomerulosa of the adrenal cortex and aldosterone is released into the blood. Aldosterone acts primarily on the principal cells in the latter portion of the DCT and collecting ducts (Figure 8.10). Aldosterone acts on intracellular receptors of the principal cells and results in an increased synthesis and up-regulation of the Na^+/K^+ ATPase in the basal membrane, and Na^+ channels and K^+ channels in the apical membrane. This leads to an increase in Na^+ and Cl^- reabsorption in these regions of the kidney tubule. The movement of solutes into the interstitial space causes an increased osmotic gradient and water moves from the lumen into the interstitial space and then into the peritubular capillary network. This causes blood pressure to increase and return blood pressure back toward normal values.

The cells of the zona glomerulosa are also directly sensitive to increased plasma K^+ concentration. When K^+ levels increase in plasma, the zona glomerulosa cells release aldosterone which leads to an increased K^+ secretion and the loss of K^+ in urine. This causes a reduction in plasma K^+ concentration and restores plasma K^+ levels back to normal.

Vasopressin or Anti-Diuretic Hormone (ADH)

Lumen of DCT and collecting ducts

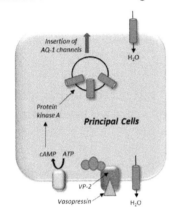

Interstitial space

Figure 8.11

Vasopressin (arginine vasopressin, AVP) also plays a role in blood pressure management. AVP however acts on kidney tubules to directly increase water absorption from the DCT and collecting ducts. On a normal basis, AVP is released from the posterior pituitary in response to an increase in plasma osmolarity. AVP can also be released in direct response to a large drop in blood pressure and in response to other factors and substances such as nausea, atrial natriuretic peptide (ANP) and angiotensin II.

The regulation of AVP release from the posterior pituitary is most tightly controlled by osmoreceptors and the detection of plasma osmolarity. As plasma osmolarity increases (i.e., as cells and tissues become dehydrated), osmoreceptors sense the change in osmolarity and begin to fire action potentials at a higher frequency. The osmoreceptors stimulate neurons located in the supraoptic and paraventricular nucleus of the hypothalamus. These neurons send axons down the infundibular stalk to release AVP into the blood. Circulating AVP acts on the vasopressin 2 receptor (V2) found on the principal cells of the DCT and the collecting ducts (See Figure 8.11). Stimulation of the V2 receptor located on the basal surface of principal cells activates a stimulatory G-protein (Gs) cascade. Gs activates adenylyl cyclase and produces cAMP which, in turn, activates protein kinase A (PKA). PKA induces the insertion of aquaporin 2 (AQP2) channels on the apical membranes of principal cells. On the basal membrane, principal cells contain AQP3 and AQP4 channels which regulate intracellular osmolarity of the principal cells. If AQP2 channels are present in the apical membrane, water can move down its concentration gradient from the lumen of the tubule through the cell and into the interstitial space. Recall that the filtrate that enters the DCT is hyposmotic and contains more water relative to the interstitial space of the cortical tissue and thus there is a gradient for water to move from the lumen of the DCT to the interstitial space and ultimately into the peritubular capillary network. This mechanism increases water reabsorption.

In conditions of continued dehydration, increased AVP release results in continued PKA activity (i.e., increased V2 receptor activation) and this leads to the synthesis of more AQP2 and AQP3 channels. The increase of AQP2 on apical membranes and AQP3 on the basal surface allows for even greater water reabsorption through cells. More V2 receptors are found on collecting ducts coursing deep through the medullary tissue where an even greater osmotic gradient allows for greater concentration of filtrate and therefore urine. Alternatively, if water levels increase and blood osmolarity decreases, less ADH is released from the posterior pituitary. AQP2 receptors are down-regulated or internalized so that less water is reabsorbed and more water is excreted with urine; i.e., urine becomes more dilute.

AVP is also released in large quantities in response to a large fall in blood pressure. In terms of blood pressure, greater than 5-10% change is needed to activate the release of. AVP releases in large amounts also has a vasoconstrictor response and can cause blood vessels to constrict causing a direct increase in blood pressure. Angiotensin II also stimulates AVP release during conditions of low blood pressure. Retention of water is an important mechanism to increase blood pressure.

Atrial Natriuretic Peptide (ANP)

ANP is a hormone that is released from the atria of the heart in response to an increase in blood pressure. Increased blood volume stretches the atrial cells of the heart and stimulates the release of ANP from cardiac myocytes. In general, ANP functions to increase water and Na^+ loss from the body; the exact opposite effect of aldosterone. ANP is a protein hormone which acts on natriuretic peptide receptors (NPR1 and NPR2) located in the kidney (Figure 8.12). ANP binds to receptors in the afferent arteriole to cause vasodilation and to receptors in the efferent arteriole to cause vasoconstriction. The combined effect is to increase glomerular filtration resulting in an increased urine output. In addition, ANP acts on NPR receptors located on the basal surface of cells lining the kidney DCT and collecting tubules. ANP binds to NPR receptors causing a conformational change in the

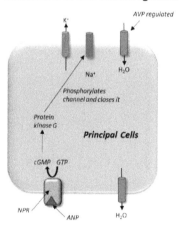

Lumen of DCT and collecting ducts

Interstitial fluid

Figure 8.12

receptor and the subsequent activation of guanylyl cyclase activity located directly on the intracellular region of the NPR receptor. Guanylyl cyclase activity increases the production of cGMP and activates PKG. In the principal cells of the kidney tubule, PKG phosphorylates the Na^+ channels, thus decreasing Na^+ reabsorption. The increased Na^+ concentration in the filtrate causes more Cl^- to remain due to an electrical gradient. When more Na^+ and Cl^- remain in the filtrate, the osmotic forces 'trap' water in the filtrate and more water is excreted by the kidney tubule. ANP also acts on the posterior pituitary to release less AVP which also decreases water absorption in the kidney tubule. Together, the effects are to increase water and Na^+ loss from the body by increasing urine output. This causes a reduction in blood volume and a fall in blood pressure.

Formation of concentrated or dilute urine

While the reabsorption of solutes is often tied to the reabsorption of water in some areas of the kidney tubule, the kidney regulates the excretion of solutes and water separately and allows the kidney to make concentrated or dilute urine in response to altered blood volume and blood pressure. Thus, the body can conserve great amounts of water or excrete any excess water from the body. The primary mechanism for the kidney's ability to concentrate urine is the countercurrent flow of fluid through the descending and ascending limbs of the loop of Henle in relationship to the flow of blood through the peritubular capillary network. The countercurrent nature of the parallel limbs and the selective permeability to water and solutes creates a hyperosmotic interstitial fluid which is important for generating the ability to concentrate urine.

The osmolarity of the interstitial fluid and the cells of cortical tissue is approximately 300 mOsm and is similar to other tissues in the body. As the medullary tissue moves away from the cortical tissue, there is a progressive increase in the osmolarity of the interstitial fluid from approximately 300 mOsm to 1200 mOsm. The primary solutes that comprise this increased osmotic pressure are Na^+, Cl^- and urea. This gradient is established primarily because the ascending limb of the loop of Henle is impermeable to water, but actively pumps solutes into the interstitial space.

In order to explain how this gradient can be established, examine Figure 8.13 in detail.

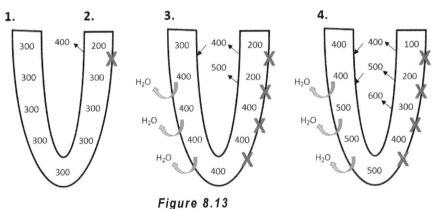

Figure 8.13

29) Assuming that the osmolarity of the interstitial fluid is 300 mOsm, then as the filtrate moves down the descending limb of the loop of Henle (which is permeable to both water and solutes), the net flow of water and solutes is zero and an equilibrium is established such that the amount of filtrate and the osmotic pressure of the filtrate inside the tube is equal to the interstitial fluid.

30) As the fluid starts to move upward into the thick section of the ascending limb of the loop of Henle, solutes are actively pumped out into the interstitial fluid which makes the filtrate inside the lumen hyposmotic and the interstitial fluid

becomes hyperosmotic. The ascending limb is impermeable to water reabsorption.

31) Now, as filtrate moves down the descending limb of the loop of Henle, water will be drawn out of the lumen toward the hyperosmotic interstitial space in order to reach a new equilibrium. Since the membrane of the descending limb is also permeable to solutes, some solutes will enter the lumen of the tubule and will further increase the osmolarity of the filtrate. Together, the loss of water and an increase in the number of solutes will contribute to the increased osmolarity of the filtrate.

32) Again, the filtrate enters the ascending limb of the loop of Henle and more solutes are pumped into the interstitial fluid which leads to an increase in the osmolarity of the interstitial space. This continues throughout the length of the renal papilla until a gradient is established from 300 mOsm to 1200 mOsm.

This creates a situation such that the fluid leaving the loop of Henle is relatively hyposmotic (~100 mOsm). As the filtrate passes through the DCT and collecting tubules located in the cortical region of the kidney, the filtrate can be concentrated to only 300 mOsm. The collecting ducts that descend through the medulla and the high osmolarity of the medulla allow for the concentration of urine. As ADH levels increase, more and more water can be reabsorbed from the filtrate into the interstitial space of the medulla. And thus urine can be concentrated to a final osmolarity of ~1200 mOsm.

The solutes that contribute to the high osmolarity of the medulla are due primarily to Na^+, Cl^- and urea. Urea is a waste product of protein metabolism and is filtered at the glomerulus. Two regions in the kidney tubule are permeable to urea, the descending limb of the loop of Henle and the collecting ducts. As the loop of Henle descends down into the medulla, the epithelial cells are permeable to urea and urea tends to move into the filtrate (down its concentration gradient), contributing to the high osmolarity of the filtrate by the time it reaches the end of the descending limb of the loop of Henle. At the end of the descending limb, the concentration of urea in the filtrate is higher than it was in the PCT. The urea moves with the filtrate though the DCT and collecting ducts in the cortical tissues and enters the collecting ducts of the medulla. As the collecting duct descends toward the renal papilla, the epithelium is also permeable to urea. Urea moves out of the collecting duct into the interstitial space down its concentration gradient. The movement of urea in the descending limb and the collecting ducts create an equilibrium with the interstitial space. Any excess urea that was filtered at the glomerulus is excreted in urine.

pH Regulation by Kidney

Most all cellular, tissue and organ functions are sensitive to pH. Any small change in pH can greatly alter many cellular and organ processes. The pH of normal extracellular fluid is regulated between 7.35 and 7.45. Intracellular pH is slightly lower than extracellular fluid but also highly regulated. Normal plasma pH can vary throughout the day due to ingestion of acidic or alkaline nutrients as well as the metabolic processes that occur in cells. For example, the breakdown of proteins yields acidic by-products, muscle function can lead to lactic acid release, cellular metabolism increases CO_2 production and an increase in H^+ production, etc... In general, those processes that lead to a net gain of H^+ in extracellular fluid are referred to as acidic and those processes that lead to a net loss of H^+ are called alkaline. Many normal functions can lead to alterations in extracellular pH. Regulation of plasma pH is carried out by both the respiratory system (see Chapter 8) and the renal system.

In the kidney, bicarbonate ions (HCO_3^-) are freely filtered at the glomerulus but the mechanism for reabsorption of the filtered HCO_3^- is not typical reabsorption via a membrane tranporter. As the filtrate moves through the nephron, there are NO transporters that reabsorb HCO_3^-, however there are mechanisms that allow the nephron to take back the HCO_3^- that was filtered at the glomerulus.

As stated earlier, the cells of the PCT and the DCT have the ability to secrete H^+ ions. The majority of pH regulation occurs within the PCT (~80%) (Figure 8.14). In the PCT, the enzyme, carbonic anhydrase (CA) located inside the epithelial cells converts CO_2 and H_2O and forms carbonic acid which then dissociates into H^+ and HCO_3^-. The H^+ is secreted into the lumen of the tubule using the H^+/Na^+ exchanger at the apical membrane. Within the lumen of the PCT, H^+ ions can combine with HCO_3^- in the filtrate to form H_2O and CO_2 with the aid of carbonic anhydrase located on the surface of epithelial cells.

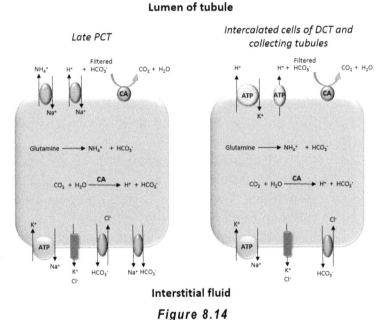

Figure 8.14

$$H^+ + HCO_3 \xrightarrow{\text{carbonic anhydrase}} H_2O + CO^2$$

On the basal surface, the HCO_3^- ions that are produced inside the cells are released into the interstitial space via a Na^+/HCO_3^- cotransporter and a $HCO_3^-/Cl-$ shift mechanism. Any excess H_2O or CO_2 simply moves due to concentration gradients. This allows the kidney to indirectly take back the HCO_3^- that was filtered.

A small amount of HCO_3^- is reabsorbed by a similar mechanism in the intercalated cells of the DCT and collecting tubules. In these cells, intracellular carbonic anhydrase combines H_2O and CO_2 to form H^+ and HCO_3^-. On the apical surface of cells, two mechanisms are employed to actively secrete H^+ into the filtrate. H^+ pumps secrete H^+ into the lumen using a single molecule of ATP and a H^+/K^+ ATPase exchanges 1 H^+ and 1 K^+

using ATP. The H^+ ions that are secreted into the lumen are free to combine with the filtered HCO_3^- to form H_2O and CO_2 which again diffuse freely across cells down concentration gradients.

A metabolic alkalosis is a condition in which the plasma pH is alkaline. The renal response to metabolic alkalosis is to decrease secretion of H^+. There is less H^+ to combine with HCO_3^- and some of the alkaline HCO_3^- is excreted in urine. This restores the metabolic acidosis back to normal values.

A metabolic acidosis is a condition in which the plasma pH is acidic. The renal response to metabolic acidosis is to increase secretion rates of H^+ such that all of the HCO_3^- that was filtered is "recaptured." During metabolic acidosis, excess H^+ is secreted into the filtrate so that it can bind to other non-bicarbonate buffers in the lumen such as HPO_4^{2-} and will be excreted from the kidney. This will result in a net loss of H^+ from the body. If plasma pH is still low, the cells lining the PCT have the ability to create new HCO_3^- ions from the metabolism of glutamine. In cells, glutamine is metabolized into ammonium ions (NH_4^+) and HCO_3^-. The HCO_3^- ions move down their concentration gradient into the interstitial space via the HCO_3^- transporters located on the basal surface and the NH_4^+ is exchanged for Na+ on the apical membrane. The NH_4^+ is a waste product and is excreted in urine. Increases in plasma HCO_3^-- will increase pH and compensate for the metabolic acidosis.

Juxtaglomerular (JG) apparatus

The JG apparatus contains three types of cells located in close proximity to each other next to the glomerulus and help in the homeostasis and regulation of blood pressure, red blood cell synthesis and Na^+ concentration. The three cells include the JG cells which help regulate blood pressure, the lacis cells which regulate red blood cell synthesis and the macula densa which helps regulate Na^+ levels.

JG cells are found lining the afferent arteriole and are sensitive to stretch. Decreases in blood pressure are sensed by JG cells which respond by increasing the release of renin into the circulation and initiating the renin angiotensin aldosterone system (RAAS). Renin is an enzyme that acts on circulating angiotensinogen and converts it to angiotensin I. As the blood passes through the respiratory circulation, it passes angiotensin converting enzyme (ACE) which converts angiotensin I to angiotensin II. Angiotensin II has multiple effects on the control of blood pressure, including vasoconstriction of blood vessels and the release of aldosterone from the adrenal cortex. Aldosterone acts on kidney DCT and collecting ducts to directly increase reabsorption of Na^+ (see above for detailed mechanisms).

Lacis cells are found sandwiched between the afferent and efferent arterioles. Lacis cells detect the O_2 levels of blood as they enter the kidney glomerulus. When blood O_2 levels decrease, lacis cells increase the secretion of erythropoietin into the blood. Erythropoietin is a protein hormone that stimulates red blood cell synthesis in bone marrow. Red blood cells contain hemoglobin which binds and carries more O_2. Increases in red blood cell numbers increases the blood's carrying capacity for O_2 (Figure 8.15).

The macula densa is a specialized region of the DCT which is sensitive to changes in the Na^+ concentration of the kidney filtrate. Na^+ concentrations may be reduced in the DCT due to several possible causes. 1) When the afferent arteriole constricts, less filtrate will form and this can result in reduced Na^+ concentrations in the DCT. 2) Reductions in blood volume may also lead to a reduced Na^+ concentration in the DCT, and 3) extreme changes in diet or pathological conditions may lead to reductions in plasma Na^+ concentration. The macula densa is a region of specialized cells lining a small portion of the DCT which winds up and passes between the afferent and efferent arteriole. The cells lining this region are specialized to sense Na^+ concentration of the filtrate. When less Na^+ is detected, the macula densa triggers vasodilation of the afferent arteriole which increases GFR. The cells also release prostaglandins which stimulate the JG cells to enhance the release of renin. Renin triggers the RAAS system which leads to increased Na^+ reabsorption and blood pressure.

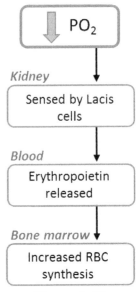

Figure 8.15

CHAPTER 8 SUMMARY

➢ The functional unit of the mammalian kidney is the nephron. The 1st portion of the nephron is the renal corpuscle which is involved in the filtration of blood across the glomerulus into Bowman's capsule. The filtrate flows through the proximal convoluted tubule, the descending and ascending loop of Henle, and the distal convoluted tubule. After the nephron, filtrate flows through a collecting tubule and ducts to empty into the calyces and renal pelvis.

➢ Urine is formed by the processes of filtration, reabsorption, and secretion.

➢ Glomerular filtration is dependent upon 1) blood pressure, 2) changes in the diameter of the afferent and efferent arterioles, 3) Bowman's space pressure, 4) osmotic pressure of the blood, and 5) the particle size relative to the filtration slit size.

➢ Many solutes are reabsorbed across the epithelium of the PCT. The 1st half of the PCT is involved with transport of many solutes such as amino acids and simple sugars. The 2nd half is more involved with the transport of ions and pH regulation. Specific mechanisms and transporters are found on the apical and basal membranes to help facilitate transport of various substances in the PCT.

➢ The loop of Henle is involved with setting up a large osmotic gradient in the medullary tissue which is important in the ability to concentrate urine. The descending limb is permeable to both water and solutes. The ascending limb is impermeable to water but is permeable to ions and actively transports ions out of the filtrate and into the interstitial space.

➢ The DCT and collecting ducts are responsible for pH regulation and the concentration of urine. Water and Na^+ reabsorption are under hormonal control mechanisms.

➢ Some substances are secreted into the lumen of the nephron, mostly into the PCT. H^+ ions are secreted in the regulation of pH, K^+ is secreted to help control K^+ homeostasis and other substances that are not readily available for filtration can be secreted for excretion in urine.

➢ Aldosterone is released by the adrenal cortex in response to a decrease in blood pressure or an increase in extracellular K^+ concentration. Aldosterone acts on the DCT and collecting ducts to increase the transport of Na^+ from the nephron tubule into the interstitial space and the secretion of K^+ into the tubule for excretion.

➢ Vasopressin (or anti-diuretic hormone) is released by the posterior pituitary in response to increases in blood osmolarity or decreases in blood pressure. Vasopressin acts on DCT and collecting ducts to increase water reabsorption.

➢ ANP is released in response to increased blood pressure. Cardiac myocytes in the atrium respond to high blood pressure and increase the release of ANP into the general circulation. ANP acts on the DCT and collecting ducts to increase Na^+ excretion and thus increase water excretion and urine formation.

➢ A metabolic alkalosis is defined as an alkaline plasma pH. The renal response to alkalosis is to decrease the secretion rate of H^+ which allows some of the freely filtered HCO_3^- to be excreted in urine.

➢ A metabolic acidosis is defined as an acidic plasma pH. The renal response to acidosis is to increase secretion of H^+. H^+ ions bind to HCO_3^-, excess H^+ bind to other non-bicarbonate buffers and the epithelial cells can also make new HCO_3^- to be released into the interstitial space.

➢ The JG apparatus contains three types of sensory cells located near the glomerulus. The JG cells sense blood pressure and release renin in response to a fall in blood pressure; this initiates the renin-angiotensin-aldosterone system. The lacis cells sense decreases in arterial P_{O2} and release erythropoietin to stimulate new erythrocyte production. The macula densa senses changes in the Na^+ concentration in the DCT and triggers vasodilation of the afferent arteriole to increase GFR.

References and Suggested Readings

Dantzler WH. 2005. Challenges and intriguing problems in comparative renal physiology. *The Journal of Experimental Biology* 208:587-594.

Harrison-Bernard LM. 2009. The renal renin-angiotensin system. *Advances in Physiological Education* 33:270-274.

Holz PH, Raidal SR. 2006. Comparative renal anatomy of exotic species. *Veterinary Clinics Exotic Animal Practice* 9:1-11.

Mount DB. 2014. Thick ascending limb of the loop of Henle. *Clinical Journal of the American Society of Nephrology* 9:1974-1986.

Chapter 9: Digestive Physiology

Obtaining nutrition is an essential requirement of all living organisms. Nutrients are needed for generating metabolic energy, cellular growth and repair, and maintenance of normal cellular physiology. Nutrients include carbohydrates, proteins, fats, water, ions, trace elements, and vitamins. In the animal kingdom, various strategies for obtaining nutrition, or feeding, have emerged and were influenced by both environmental and physiological constraints. Small organisms such as paramecium use simple cellular mechanisms such as endocytosis to engulf food particles. Endocytic vesicles then fuse with lysozymes to enzymatically digest the food particles releasing the nutrients into the cytosol of the cell. Some organisms such as parasitic tapeworms, flukes and crustaceans are able to absorb nutrients directly from their environment across the outer surface of their skin and had no need to develop organs to assist in feeding. Aquatic, non-motile (sessile) organisms utilized water currents to allow food to come to them and various strategies of filter feeding evolved. In general, a simple tubular structure runs down the center of the organism through which water moves. The movement of water through the tube is accomplished by a number of approaches in different organisms. Some organisms such as brachiopods orient their body in such a way to direct the flow of water into the tube. Other organisms like sponges have an anatomy which creates pressure gradients to direct water flow into the tube and out an upper spout similar to the wings on airplanes which create lift. Still other organisms use cilia or flagella to create a flow of water through the tube. Mucus is a common mechanism used to trap small particles in filter feeders and cells capture food by various cellular mechanisms including endocytosis. The filter feeding strategy is highly efficient and is even used by one of the largest mammals on earth, the baleen whale, which filters the water of millions of small crustaceans and is able to sustain such a massive life form on filter feeding alone.

Some motile animals, large and small, obtain their food by piercing and sucking strategies. Some nematodes, annelids, and arthropods, such as leeches and mosquitos, evolved methods to secrete enzymes through a specialized mouthpart to liquefy tissue or draw blood into their digestive organs. Jaws, teeth and beaks evolved to break seeds, chew tough vegetation, capture and kill prey, and rip, tear and grind food. Finally, some organisms evolved toxic substances to paralyze, subdue and kill their food sources. The feeding strategies that emerged were sufficient to obtain enough essential nutrients from the environment to maintain and support each type of life form.

Regardless of the types of feeding strategies that emerged, most animals evolved a digestive system which contains a simple tubular structure with 1) an opening or receiving end, 2) conducting and storage portions, 3) a digestive and absorption region, 4) a water absorbing region and 5) an exit or elimination region. In vertebrates, the opening end is the mouth or oral cavity and contains its associated structures (e.g. teeth). In general, food is mechanically digested and some enzymes are introduced to the food by salivary and other secretions which start the chemical digestion of food. Of course this is not always the case and some animals, like snakes and even alligators, eat their prey whole. The food is conducted usually to a storage compartment such as a stomach where some chemical and mechanical digestion takes place and converts food into chyme (a mixture of food and enzymatic juices). In some animals, true storage compartments exist such as the crop which store food for future metabolic needs. The chyme moves into the small intestine where digestion continues and absorption of essential nutrients takes place. The large intestine absorbs water and ions and the rectum stores feces for elimination through the anus.

General Anatomy of the Gastrointestinal System

In humans, the digestive system is comprised of a long, winding tube that extends from the oral cavity to the anus (Figure 9.1). This tube is called the gastrointestinal (GI) tract or the alimentary tract or canal. The digestive system also contains accessory organs, the liver, pancreas and gall bladder which secrete fluids such as water and enzymes into the GI tract which aid in digestion. The oral cavity or mouth is specialized in animals for obtaining appropriate nutritional food sources. In humans, teeth and the tongue are used to physically breakdown food into small pieces before swallowing. Food passes through the oropharynx, laryngopharynx, and the esophagus before emptying into the stomach at the cardiac sphincter. These structures pass through the neck and the mediastinum of the thoracic cavity and enter the peritoneal or abdominal cavity where the esophagus attaches to the stomach. The stomach produces a liquid chyme which empties through the pyloric sphincter into the small intestine and travels through the duodenum, the jejunum and ileum. The small intestine is connected to the large intestine or colon at the ileocecal junction. The cecum is a small outpocketing of the colon and is vestigial in humans. In some species, the cecum is a large organ important in the digestion of cellulose. Attached to the cecum is the appendix, another vestigial organ in humans. The colon is comprised of the ascending, transverse, descending and sigmoid colons and chyme is converted from a liquid form to a semisolid feces. The digestive tract ends at the rectum and anus where elimination or defecation occurs.

Figure 9.1

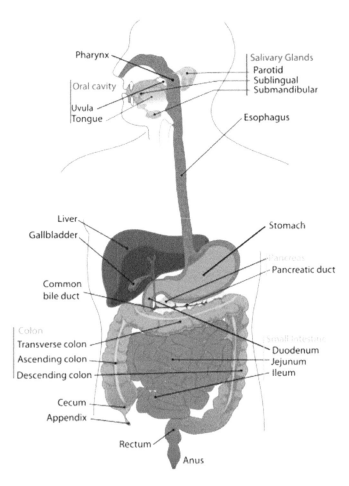

The entire abdominal or peritoneal cavity is lined with a thin, serous membrane (a simple squamous epithelium, the peritoneum) which secretes a watery fluid for lubrication into the peritoneal cavity. The parietal peritoneum covers the walls of the abdominal cavity and the visceral peritoneum covers the organs and mesenteries in the peritoneal cavity. The peritoneal cavity is clinically separated into 4 quadrants, the right upper, left upper, right lower and left lower quadrant. For example, the stomach is positioned in the left upper quadrant, the liver is found in the right upper quadrant of the peritoneal cavity and the appendix is situated in the lower right quadrant. Organs that sit behind the peritoneal cavity are referred to as retroperitoneal, e.g., the kidneys and adrenal glands and organs that are below the peritoneal cavity are located anteperitoneal, such as the bladder.

Digestive organs that can be found within the peritoneal cavity include the stomach, the small and large intestine, the liver, pancreas and gall bladder. The GI tract is loosely held in place in the peritoneal cavity by connective tissue sheets called mesenteries. The mesenteries are also a route for blood vessels, lymphatic vessels and nerves to travel to and from the GI tract. The mesentery proper attaches the small intestines to the dorsal peritoneal wall. Some specific mesenteries include 1) the lesser omentum which connects the lesser curvature of the stomach and duodenum to the liver and diaphragm. 2) The greater omentum connects the greater curvature of the stomach to the transverse colon. This attachment creates a large fold called the omental bursa which provides a protective cushion for the abdominal contents. 3) The transverse mesocolon connects the transverse colon to the dorsal peritoneal wall and 4) the sigmoid mesocolon attaches the sigmoid colon to the peritoneal cavity in a curved fashion, thus creating the sigmoid colon.

Histology of GI tract

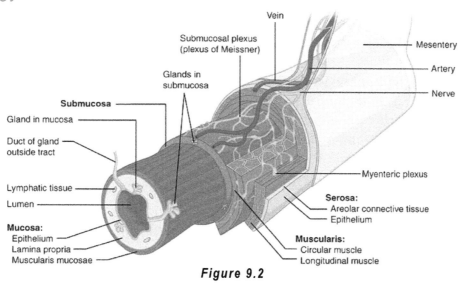

Figure 9.2

In mammals, the entire GI tract, from the esophagus to the anus, is comprised of several similar layers (Figure 9.2). The lumen of the entire gut is continuous with the external environment and is considered outside of the body. The entire lumen is lined with an epithelium which rests on a basement membrane. A layer of areolar connective tissue called the lamina propria separates the basement membrane from a thin layer of smooth muscle, the muscularis mucosa. The epithelium, lamina propria and muscularis mucosa together comprise the mucosa. The submucosa is a thicker layer of dense, irregular connective tissue under the mucosa. Surrounding the outer edge of the tube is a muscularis externa which usually contains two layers of smooth muscle (an inner circular and outer longitudinal muscle layer). The smooth muscle is used for mixing and propulsion of the chyme throughout the tube. Finally, on the outermost edge of the tube is a serosa or an adventitia. A serosa is found on the parts of the GI tract that are located within the abdominal cavity and is made of a simple squamous epithelium that secretes the peritoneal fluid. This layer is also called the visceral peritoneum. An adventitia is a layer of areolar connective tissue that directly connects the tube to other tissues (i.e., not sitting in a space). For example, the esophagus in the neck region is attached to the trachea via the connective tissue of the adventitia. These basic layers are found in all regions of the GI tract and contain specializations in specific regions that confer variations in function.

The esophagus is lined with a stratified squamous epithelium which provides a thick protective barrier for partially masticated food particles as they make their way to the stomach. The esophagus has special glands which secrete a thick seromucus secretion to help lubricate the lining and move the bolus of food from the oral cavity to the stomach. In humans, the upper 1/3 of the esophagus is skeletal muscle and the lower 2/3 is smooth muscle, but the entire esophageal phase of swallowing is under complete autonomic control.

The opening to the stomach is a tight sphincter, the lower esophageal sphincter (or cardiac sphincter) that helps keep the acidic contents of the stomach away from the esophageal lumen. The main function of the stomach is to start proteolytic digestion and make chyme, a liquid mixture of food particles and stomach secretions. Thus, the mucosa contains gastric pits and glands which secrete acid and enzymes used for the digestion of proteins. The stomach contains an extra thick layer of mucus on the surface which protects the simple columnar epithelium from autodigestion. The stomach also contains an extra layer of smooth muscle on the inside of the circular muscle called the inner oblique muscle and aids in producing strong mixing waves for mechanical digestion of food particles. The chyme moves from the stomach into the small intestine through another sphincter, the pyloric sphincter.

The entire small intestine is lined with a simple columnar epithelium that is specialized for digestion and absorption of nutrients. The simple columnar cells contain microvilli which increase the surface area of each cell and contains membrane associated enzymes and transporters involved in the absorption of nutrients. The mucosal lining creates finger-like projections that stick out into the lumen, villi, and also increase total surface area of the intestine. At the base of the villi, mucosal glands called the crypts of Lieberkühn secrete mucus into the lumen. The first portion of the small intestine, the duodenum, contains special glands in the submucosa which secrete a bicarbonate-rich, alkaline secretion to help neutralize the acidic chyme that entered from the stomach. The jejunum is the next portion of the small intestine, followed by the ileum. The ileum contains lymphatic nodules called Peyer's patches in the submucosa and mucosa and are involved in immune defense mechanisms. These specialized immune structures of the gut are also called the gut-associated lymphatic tissue (GALT). The entire small intestine is specialized for digestion and absorption of essential nutrients.

Chyme enters the large intestine at the ileocecal junction. The chyme enters as a liquid form and is converted into a semisolid feces by the time it reaches the end of the colon. The large intestine or colon is specialized for water absorption and the movement of semisolid feces. The mucosa contains simple tubular glands with many goblet cells that secrete mucus. The cells on the surface of the colon are specialized for the absorption of water. The muscularis externa is thick which aid in propulsion of an increasingly more solid feces. Feces are stored in the rectum immediately prior to elimination.

Neuronal innervation of the GI tract

The GI tract is innervated by the enteric nervous system which is often considered a separate entity from the CNS and PNS and contains more neurons than the entire spinal cord. The enteric nervous system contains all of the components of a neural circuitry necessary for reflex actions; sensory neurons, interneurons and motor neurons (Figure 9.3). The enteric nervous system can function independently of external inputs. The neurons of each area of the GI tract are connected and communicate through synapses. The neurons travel through the mesenteries to connect neurons in one area of the digestive tract to another area of the digestive tract. For example, when eating a large meal, activation of sensory neurons in the stomach synapse through interneurons to connect to motor neurons of the large intestine and initiate large mass movements and clear space in the colon for incoming food.

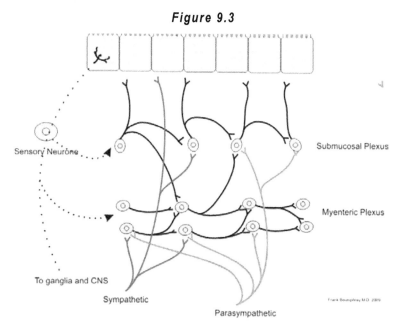

Figure 9.3

Sensory Neurone

To ganglia and CNS

Sympathetic

Parasympathetic

Submucosal Plexus

Myenteric Plexus

Enteric sensory neurons are involved with sensing chemical and mechanical alterations throughout the GI tract. For example, chemoreceptors can sense the chemical composition of the digestive tract and can sense acid and lipids which can initiate a reflex to secrete bicarbonate-rich secretions for neutralization or enzymes for digestion. There are also many mechanoreceptors that are sensitive to stretch as food or chyme moves into a region of the tube. These sensory neurons initiate reflexes which are involved in propulsion or mixing which occurs in the GI tract. Enteric motor neurons project to the muscularis mucosa, the muscularis externa and to secretory gland cells. Thus, motor neurons mediate peristalsis and mixing waves in the esophagus, stomach, small and large intestine. Motor neurons also project to glands and secretory cells to regulate secretions in the digestive tract. Interneurons connect sensory and motor neurons and mediate the reflex activity throughout the entire GI tract.

Within the submucosa, small ganglia (via vagal efferents) are found scattered throughout the GI tract and are collectively called the submucosal (or Meissner's) plexus. Post-ganglionic parasympathetic vagal fibers in the submucosa project to the muscularis mucosa and glandular cells. Sandwiched between the inner circular and outer longitudinal is another collection of small ganglia, the myenteric (or Auerbach's) plexus. Parasympathetic fibers in the myenteric plexus project primarily to the muscularis externa and help control mixing and peristalsis.

Physiological functions of the GI tract

Ingested food particles are broken down by the GI tract using mechanical and enzymatic digestion in order to aid in absorption of nutrients. All organisms need nutrients in order to generate the energy needed to power many reactions within cells and to supply the resources needed for growth and repair of cells and tissues. As food makes its way down through the various tubes and organs of the GI tract, specific processes occur that aid in the digestion and absorption of nutrients (Figure 9.4). Any leftover waste products are removed from the body through elimination.

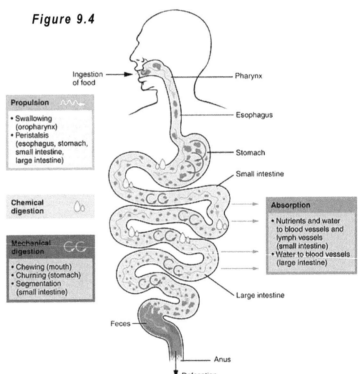

Figure 9.4

Oral cavity

Within the oral cavity or mouth, food is physically broken down into smaller pieces and mixed with digestive enzymes and secretions from saliva. The process of mastication is accomplished via the skeletal muscles of the jaw and head (temporalis, masseter, lateral and medial pterygoid muscles) which are activated by the trigeminal nerve to move the mouth and teeth in a grinding motion and rip and tear the food particles into small pieces. In the mouth, the presence of food stimulates various sensory receptors and can activate a simple mastication reflex. Inputs from sensory receptors cause a reflex inhibition of the skeletal muscles of mastication and they relax. As the muscles relax, they stretch due to gravity and initiate a reflexive contraction. This mastication reflex is normally overridden by higher brain centers and chewing is largely a conscious activity activated by impulses that originate in the primary motor cortex. The reflex however, is used clinically to determine the level of brainstem function in patients in a coma.

Surrounding the oral cavity, there are three pairs of salivary glands that secrete a seromucus solution into the cavity. The sublingual glands are the smallest of the salivary glands and are found lying inferior and lateral to the tongue. The sublingual secretions, both serous and mucous secretions, enter the oral cavity through 10-12 small ducts lying under the tongue. The submandibular gland sits under the jaw, just inferior and medial to the mandibular ramus and also contains a mixed serous and mucous type of secretion. The submandibular gland secretes saliva through a single submandibular duct which enters the oral cavity under the tongue next to the lingual frenulum. The parotid glands are located on the sides of the jaw and extend from the ear to the base of the jaw. They secrete a mostly serous type of secretion through a single parotid duct which empties into the superior oral cavity next to the upper second molar. Salivary secretions are under control of the parasympathetic nervous system. The parotid gland, submandibular gland, and sublingual gland secrete a solution containing water, lysozyme, immunoglobulin A, mucin (a proteoglycan) and salivary amylase. The salivary glands are stimulated by tactile reflexes initiated by food in the mouth, taste receptors, olfactory receptors, sensation of hunger, and thoughts of food that originate in the cerebral cortex. The tactile stimulation reflex is quite strong, as anyone with a new pair of braces or a mouthguard knows firsthand. Sensory inputs are integrated in brainstem nuclei and salivary secretions are initiated by parasympathetic fibers of the facial (VII) and glossopharyngeal (IX) nerves. The components of saliva function to moisten the food (water and fluids), initiate the chemical digestion of starches (amylase), lubricate the food (mucin) as it moves through the pharynx and esophagus, and kill and mark bacteria for destruction (lysozyme and IgA).

Just posterior to the oral cavity is the oropharynx. The oropharynx (and nasopharynx) contains lymphatic nodules, the tonsils, which are part of the immune system and are involved with detection and destruction of foreign material. No matter how well you clean or prepare your food, the food that we ingest is full of additional microorganisms and bacteria. The tonsils are resident collections of lymphatic cells that reside in the connective tissue just under the epithelium lining the pharynx. The palatine tonsils are found located on each side of the oropharynx and can be visualized (when enlarged) by looking into the oral cavity. The pharyngeal tonsils or adenoids are found in the roof of the nasopharynx and the lingual tonsils are found at the base of the tongue deep in the throat. When exposed to foreign material, the immune cells of the tonsils initiate an immune response and result in the swelling or enlargement of the tonsils. Foreign substances can originate in food, but more often originate from the air we breathe. Air also passes through the same upper regions of the nasal and oral cavities and breathing uses the same pharyngeal structures.

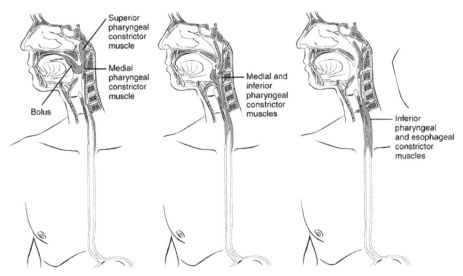

Figure 9.5

Swallowing

Swallowing or deglutition is comprised of three distinct phases, a voluntary phase, pharyngeal phase and esophageal phase (Figure 9.5). The voluntary phase of deglutition is under voluntary control and utilizes somatic motor neurons to control the muscles used during this phase. In the mouth, the genioglossus muscle of the tongue pushes a bolus of food up and back toward the upper palate and oropharynx. The food brushes against the tissue covering the hard palate, the soft palate, and the uvula which activates sensory afferents of the trigeminal (V) and glossopharyngeal (IX) nerves. Activation of the tactile sensory receptors initiates the pharyngeal phase of deglutition. The sensory afferents project to nuclei located in the brainstem and cause the reflex activation of motor efferents of the trigeminal (V), glossopharyngeal (IX), vagus (X), and the accessory (XI) nerves. The muscles lining the pharyngeal cavities and the upper 1/3 portion of the esophagus are all skeletal muscle, but the activity of the muscles are under autonomic control. During the pharyngeal phase of deglutition, the soft palate and uvula are elevated and the pharyngeal muscles surrounding the nasopharynx are constricted which prevent food from entering the nasal cavity. The epiglottis gets pushed downward by the movement of the bolus of food and blocks the entrance to the larynx. The glottal constrictor muscles which surround the vocal folds contract and help prevent food from entering trachea. The pharyngeal constrictors get activated first in the nasopharynx and constrict in a downward direction causing the food to get pushed downward. The peristaltic wave progresses through the oropharynx and the laryngopharynx and down to the esophagus. The propulsion wave includes a wave of relaxation which proceeds the constriction such that the upper esophageal sphincter relaxes and allows food to pass into the esophagus and starts the esophageal phase. The bolus of food activates tactile receptors of the trigeminal (V) nerve lining the esophagus as the food brushes the esophageal lining. Sensory inputs project to brainstem nuclei which activate motor efferents of the trigeminal nerve (V) which continue to control the peristaltic wave that pushes the bolus of food down the esophagus and into the stomach; the esophageal phase of deglutition.

Stomach

A bolus of food enters the stomach through the lower esophageal sphincter (or cardiac sphincter) and mixes with various substances that are secreted into the stomach lumen, creating a liquid called chyme. The function of the stomach is to store and mix food to create chyme as well as start the chemical digestion of proteins. In humans, the stomach is divided into three primary regions that differ in the types of cells and amounts of gastric secretions that arise from these regions (Figure

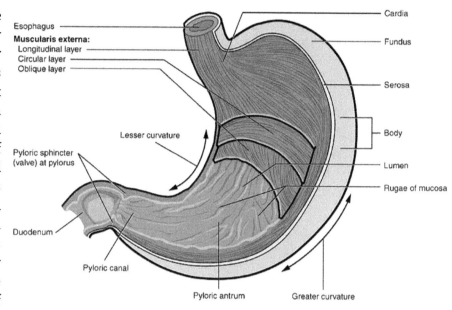

Figure 9.6

9.6). The fundus is the superior portion of the stomach, the body is main portion of the stomach and is the greatest site of gastric secretions, and the pyloric region is the inferior portion of the stomach and surrounds the pyloric sphincter and the opening to the small intestine. The muscularis externa of the stomach contains an extra layer of smooth muscle, the inner oblique muscle which aids in creating the strong mixing waves that occur in the stomach in response to food present in the stomach.

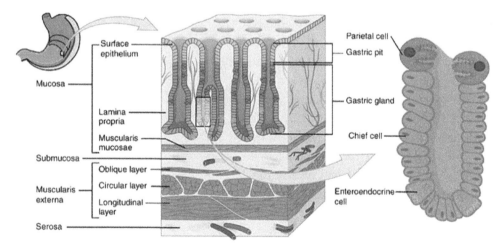

Figure 9.7

The stomach mucosa contains gastric pits and glands (Figure 9.7). The entire surface of the stomach and the gastric pits, or small depressions in the surface of the stomach, are covered with simple columnar, mucus cells. The mucus cells secrete a very thick, viscous mucus that covers the entire surface of the stomach and prevents autodigestion of the cells lining the stomach. Within the depths of the pits are openings to the gastric glands (Figure

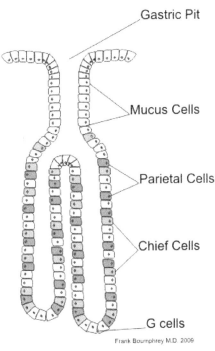

Figure 9.8

9.8). The glands are simple tubular or branched tubular glands that descend the length of the mucosa. The glands contain the cells responsible for secreting the substances used for proteolytic digestion, the parietal and chief cells as well as neuroendocrine cells that help to regulate these secretions.

Parietal cells contain the enzyme carbonic anhydrase which combines water and CO_2 to form carbonic acid which then dissociates into H^+ and HCO_3^- (Figure 9.9).

$$H_2O + CO_2 \xrightarrow{yields} H_2CO_3 \xrightarrow{yields} H^+ + HCO_3^-$$

HCO_3^- is shuttled out the basal surface of cells via a chloride shift mechanism and H^+ ions are transported into the stomach lumen using proton pumps to generate a highly acidic environment. The proton pump uses a single ATP molecule to exchanges 1 H^+ ion for 1 K^+ ion. Cl^- ions move down an electrical gradient into the stomach lumen through channels located on the apical surface and combine with the H^+ ions to form hydrochloric acid (HCl). In the stomach lumen, HCl decreases the pH and denatures or unfolds proteins.

Parietal cells also secrete a substance called intrinsic factor. Intrinsic factor binds to vitamin B12 in the lumen of the stomach and is responsible for the absorption of vitamin B12 in the lower portion of the small intestine. Cells in the lower regions of the ileum have special receptors that bind intrinsic factor bound to vitamin B12 and initiate endocytosis. Vitamin B12 is required for normal cell turnover. A reduction or loss of vitamin B12 can result in a form of anemia, pernicious anemia, due to a reduced rate of red blood cell synthesis.

Figure 9.9   **Lumen of Stomach**

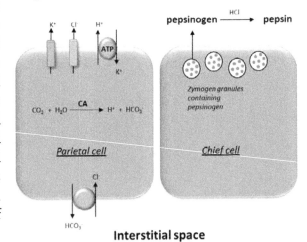

Chief cells are also found lining the gastric glands (See Figure 9.9). Chief cells secrete pepsinogen, an inactive form of the enzyme pepsin. The pepsinogen moves into the lumen of the stomach and is converted into pepsin by HCl. Once activated, pepsin molecules enzymatically break peptide bonds of large unfolded proteins into small polypeptides. Pepsin can also convert inactive pepsinogen to the active form of pepsin.

Different types of neuroendocrine cells are also found lining the gastric glands and release various hormones that play a role in regulating the secretions from parietal and gastric cells.

Regulation of gastric secretions

The secretions of the stomach are regulated through both neuronal and hormonal control mechanisms. The regulation of these secretions can be separated into three distinct phases, the cephalic phase, the gastric phase and the intestinal phase. Thoughts of eating, smells associated with eating, sights of food, and tactile stimulation of food in the mouth integrate within the medulla oblongata and initiate the cephalic phase of gastric secretions. Preganglionic neurons of the vagus nerve (X) project to postganglionic neurons located in the enteric nervous system and ultimately project to the muscles and epithelial cells lining the stomach. Several cells in the gastric glands are directly stimulated by vagal efferents releasing ACh which activate muscarinic receptors located on the basal surface of the cells (Figure 9.10). ACh stimulates parietal cells to produce and release HCl and intrinsic factor, and ACh stimulates Chief cells to release pepsinogen into the lumen of the stomach. ACh activates a specific type of neuroendocrine cells which releases gastrin. Gastrin is a hormone that is released into the interstitial space and influences nearby cells. Another type of neuroendocrine cell has a high number of receptors for gastrin and gastrin stimulates the release of histamine. Histamine receptors (as well as gastrin receptors) can also be found on parietal cells and stimulate the release of HCl as well as on Chief cells to release pepsinogen. The cephalic phase initiates low amounts of gastric secretions in anticipation of food.

Figure 9.10

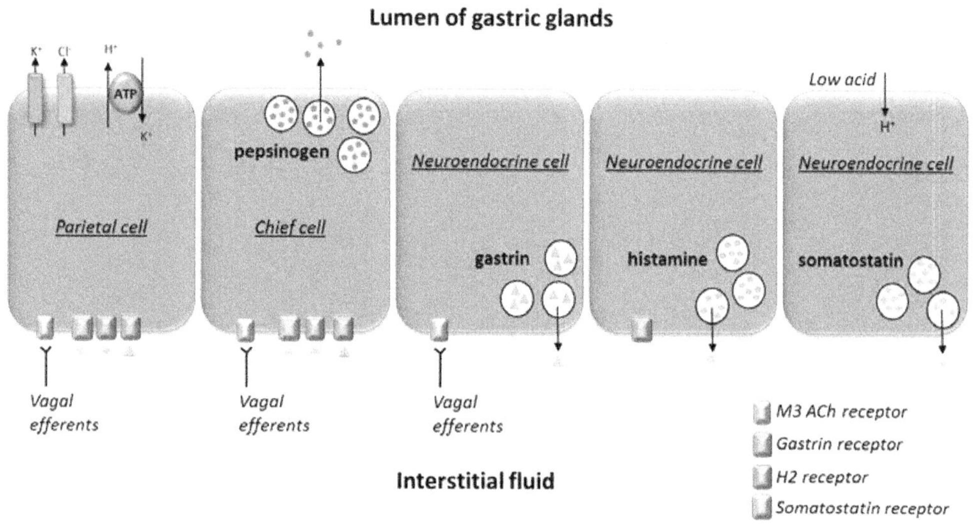

The gastric phase begins when a bolus of food enters the stomach. The wall of the stomach becomes distended and stretch receptors are activated which initiates reflexes within the enteric nervous system and lead to increased gastric secretions. Mechanoreceptors (sensory neurons) activate motor neurons (via interneurons) to stimulate parietal cells, Chief cells and neuroendocrine cells and the amount of gastric secretions increase. In particular, gastrin levels rise and cause increased amounts of histamine to be released. Histamine binds to H2 receptors on parietal cells and greatly enhance the secretion of HCl. H2 receptor activation leads to the insertion of more H^+/K^+ ATPases into the luminal plasma membrane enhancing acid secretion. As the pH falls to low levels (pH <2) negative feedback mechanisms are activated. Low pH directly causes gastrin secretion to be reduced which, in turn, decreases histamine and acid secretion. Low pH is also sensed by another neuroendocrine cell which releases somatostatin into the interstitial space. Somatostatin binds to receptors on parietal cells and directly decreases the acid secretion by causing an uptake of the H^+/K^+ ATPase from the plasma membrane.

The intestinal phase begins when chyme passes the pyloric sphincter and enters the duodenum. Distension of the duodenal wall, low pH, amino acids, and fatty acids are sensed by various mechanoreceptors and chemoreceptors which cause reflexes to inhibit gastric secretions. In general, acids and low pH tend to stimulate the release of the hormone secretin and dietary lipids stimulate the release of cholesystokinin (CCK). Secretin and CCK are released into the interstitial space from neuroendocrine cells lining the crypts of Lieberkühn in the duodenum. These two hormones inhibit the parietal, Chief cells, and the gastrin neuroendocrine cells and the gastric secretion rate decreases.

The intestinal phase also initiates neuronal reflexes and inhibit gastric secretions through the inhibition by nervous innervation. A short neural reflex intrinsic to the enteric nervous system sense distention of the duodenum and inhibit gastric secretions. In addition, distention of the duodenum activates vagal sensory afferents which feed back to the brainstem and inhibit the vagal motor efferents that are projecting to the stomach via a long neural reflex. This results in less activation of gastric secretion.

As chyme passes into the duodenum, another neural reflex is initiated that prevents over-filling of the duodenum. Stretching of the wall of the duodenum activates a reflex that causes the pyloric sphincter to constrict which will limit the amount of chyme that enters the duodenum at one time. This helps to regulate the amount of food emptying from the stomach.

Small intestine

The small intestine is comprised of the duodenum (~12 inches in length), the jejunum (~8 feet) and the ileum (~11 feet in length). The small intestine is the principal site for digestion and absorption of essential nutrients and therefore must contain a large surface area. There are three approaches that the small intestine takes to increase surface area, circular folds (or plica circularis), villi and microvilli (See Figure 9.11). The circular folds are large folds in the submucosa (8-10 millimeters high), visible to the naked eye which extend ½ to 2/3 the circumference of the tube and increase the total surface area ~3-fold. Large mammals and humans have circular folds which extend from the duodenum to half way through the ileum; small mammals do not have circular folds. The villi are microscopic folds in the mucosal layer. Between the villi are depressions that extend deep into the mucosa and form the crypts of Lierberkühn. The simple columnar epithelial cells that line the crypts of Lierberkühn are continuous with the cells lining the villus. Mitosis of the stem cells located deep in the crypts produces the simple columnar epithelial cells which migrate upward toward the tips of the villi and are released into the lumen taking approximately 48 hours to complete one cycle.

Figure 9.11

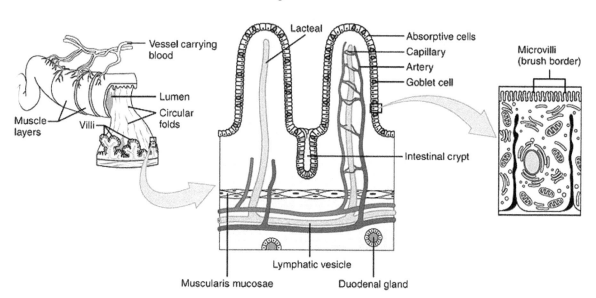

Cell turnover in the small intestine is extremely high and ~17 billion cells per day are released into the lumen. Four types of cells can be found lining the lumen of the small intestine and are called the enterocytes (the simple columnar epithelial cells), goblet cells, Paneth cells and neuroendocrine cells. The enterocytes contain microvilli on their apical surface and significantly increase the surface area of the lining of the small intestine (~20-fold). The microvilli contain enzymes bound to the plasma membrane along with various transporters to help digest and absorb essential nutrients (Table 9.1). The goblet cells watery fluid into the lumen comprised of water, electrolytes and mucus. The mucus helps to protect against digestive enzymes and stomach acids and the water and electrolytes help to absorb various nutrients across the plasma membrane of the enterocytes. The Paneth cells are found deep in the crypts of Lierberkühn but instead of migrating upward they migrate downward and stay deep in the crypts. The Paneth cells contain granules which contain antibacterial agents such as defensins. These proteins insert into the plasma membrane of bacteria and form large pores which disrupt cell volume and kills cells. The location and function of the Paneth cells appear to indicate a protective role of the stem cell population located deep in the cypts. Some of the neuroendocrine cells were mentioned earlier and secrete secretin and CCK. These hormones inhibit gastric secretions, but they also promote or stimulate secretions of various substances into the lumen of the small intestine.

Table 9.1. Some common enzymes of the digestive tract and their actions.

Enzyme	Site of Secretion	Site of Action	Substrate	Product formed
Carbohydrates				
Salivary amylase	Mouth	Mouth	starch	maltose
Pancreatic amylase	Pancreas	Small intestine	starch	maltose
Disaccharides				
Lactase*	Small intestine	Small intestine	lactose	glucose and galactose
Sucrase*	Small intestine	Small intestine	sucrose	glucose and fructose
Maltase*	Small intestine	Small intestine	maltose	glucose and glucose
Isomaltase*	Small intestine	Small intestine	saccharides	maltose
Proteins				
Pepsinogen – pepsin	Stomach			
Trypsinogen – trypsin	Pancreas	Small intestine	Proteins chymotrypsinogen	Polypeptides chymotrypsin
Chymotrypsinogen – chymotrypsin	Pancreas	Small intestine	Proteins	Polypeptides
Enterokinase*	Small intestine	Small intestine	trypsinogen	trypsin
Peptidases	Pancreas, Small intestine	Small intestine	carboxyl terminal of peptides	amino acids
Carboxypeptidases*	Small intestine	Small intestine	amino terminal of peptides	amino acids
Aminopeptidases*	Small intestine	Small intestine	RNA	nucleotides
		Small intestine	RNA	nucleotides
Ribonuclease	Pancreas			
Deoxyribonuclease	Pancreas	Small intestine	DNA	nucleotides
Lipids				
Pancreatic lipase	Small intestine	Small intestine	triglycerides	glycerol and fatty acids

* refers to enzymes bound to microvilli of the enterocytes of the small intestine

The entire small intestine has the same overall pattern of organization with some specific specializations in various regions. The primary organization is the appearance of villi with crypts of Lierberkühn and two layers of smooth muscle that aid in mixing and propulsion of chyme throughout the small intestine. Specializations of the duodenum include the appearance of submucosal glands called Brünner's glands. Brünner's glands secrete a bicarbonate-rich, alkaline secretion that neutralizes the acidic chyme from the stomach. During the intestinal phase of gastric secretions, as chyme is leaving the stomach and entering the duodenum, the hormone secretin is released which inhibits gastric secretions. Secretin also stimulates duodenal glands to increase their bicarbonate, alkaline secretions. Brünner's glands are under parasympathetic control and vagal efferents directly stimulate secretions. Finally, tactile stimulation of the duodenal mucosa stimulates secretion of duodenal glands through a neural reflex.

The jejunum has no specific specializations that are unique to the regions. Digestion and absorption of nutrients continues in the jejunum. The ileum, however, contains lymphatic nodules located in the interstitial space of the submucosa and mucosal layers. The lymphatic nodules, or Peyer's patches, are similar to tonsils and involved with immune defense against microorganisms both residing in the normal gut biota and newly introduced microorganisms that accompany the ingested of food.

Within the small intestine, chyme is mixed via segmental contractions and moved down the tube via propulsion waves. Peristalsis is under control of the enteric nervous system and is initiated in part due to tactile and chemoreceptor sensory inputs. In the small intestine, waves of peristalsis occur over short distances and propels the chyme toward the large intestine, or colon. The opening to the colon is regulated by an ileocecal sphincter. As a peristaltic wave moves toward the ileocecal sphincter, the preceding wave of relaxation, dilates the sphincter and chyme moves into the cecum. As the cecum fills up and distends, stretch receptors lining the cecum wall, initiate a reflex which tightly constricts the ileocecal valve. This prevents chyme from entering the cecum and increases the time for digestion and absorption to continue in the small intestine. This also prevents backflow from the colon into the small intestine.

Large Intestine

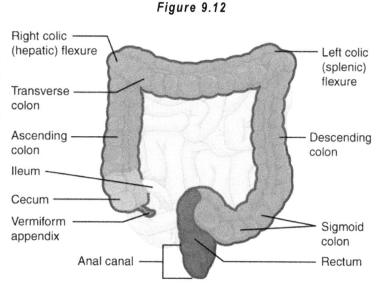

Figure 9.12

The large intestine includes the cecum, the appendix and the colon (Figure 9.12). The colon is divided into regions based on their anatomical positions in the body. The ascending colon starts in the lower right quadrant and the fecal matter ascends into the upper right quadrant. The transverse colon crosses just inferior to the liver and stomach and crosses from the right upper quadrant to the upper left quadrant. The descending colon descends to the lower left quadrant is continuous with the sigmoid colon which creates an S-shaped wave before fecal matter enters the rectum. All regions of the colon are specialized for absorption of water and electrolytes and the storage of waste.

The entire colon is lined with simple tubular glands that contain a large percentage of goblet cells (Figure 9.13). The goblet cells secrete large amounts of mucous in response to tactile stimulation. As chyme moves through the colon, more water is absorbed and the liquid chyme becomes a semisolid feces. The mucous lubricates the fecal matter and prevents abrasion of the simple columnar epithelium lining the lumen of the colon.

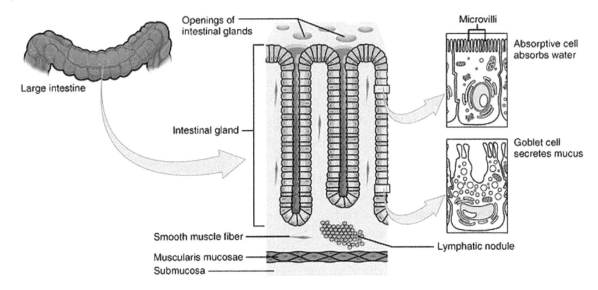

Figure 9.13

The epithelial cells of the colon are also specialized for water and ion absorption (See Figure 9.14). The rate of water absorption is linked to the movement of Na^+ ions from the lumen to the interstitial space. On the basal surface of the epithelial cells, the Na^+/K^+ pump moves Na^+ ions out of the cytosol. Recall that the Na^+/K^+ pump is an electrogenic pump and will generate a strong electro-chemical gradient for Na^+ entry into these cells. On the apical surface, Na^+ channels allow the inward movement of Na^+ which creates an osmotic gradient and allows for the movement of water into the cells through aquaporin channels. In general, there is more water movement in the proximal region of the large intestine (the ascending colon) compared to the more distal segments (the descending and sigmoid colon).

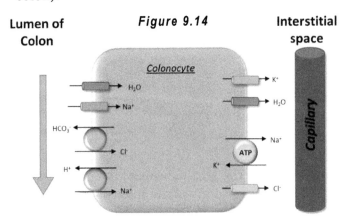

Lumen of Colon

Figure 9.14

Interstitial space

Movement of fecal matter in the large intestine is accomplished by large peristaltic waves that propel the fecal matter over large distances throughout the colon. These large waves are called mass movements and a single wave can run the entire length of the colon. These mass movements propel fecal matter toward the rectum. These waves are more common after eating and only occur a few times in a single day. When food enters the stomach this stimulates the stomach muscles to contract and create strong mixing waves in the stomach. Sensory receptors from the stomach and from the duodenum can initiate a reflex that creates the mass movements in the colon. The nervous signals originate in the stomach and move to the large intestine by way of enteric nerves that travel through mesenteries. The large mass movement ensures that as more food is being pushed into the system, there is room at the end of the system for more incoming chyme.

Elimination

Semi-solid feces are eliminated from the body by the defecation or elimination reflex. When the rectum is empty, the internal anal sphincter is in a contracted state and the external anal sphincter is relaxed. As mass movements of the colon push fecal matter from the colon into the rectum, the wall of the rectum gets stretched and initiates a reflex and causes the internal sphincter to relax and the external sphincter to contract. Somatic, conscious control over the external sphincter allows one to relax the external sphincter and increase pressure in the abdominal cavity to consciously push fecal matter out of the rectum. Parasympathetic contraction of the rectal wall aids in the elimination reflex.

Digestion and Absorption

Digestion or the breakdown of ingested material occurs in most areas of the GI tract. Mechanical digestion starts in the mouth with mastication and the ripping of food particles into small pieces as well as the salivary secretions which starts the chemical digestion of carbohydrates. In the stomach, mechanical digestion continues with mixing waves and chemical digestion of proteins begins with the enzyme, pepsin. The majority of digestion of all types of nutrients, however, occurs in the small intestine where absorption of nutrients also occurs. The epithelial cells lining the lumen of the small intestine, the enterocytes, contain specific enzymes and transporters necessary for digestion and absorption of the essential nutrients. The large intestine continues to absorb water and ions, and form a semi-solid waste product for elimination.

Proteins and amino acids

The chemical digestion of protein starts primarily in the stomach (~10-20% of protein digestion occurs). Parietal cells secrete HCl which denatures or unfolds proteins exposing the peptide bonds of proteins. Pepsin from the parietal cells work optimally at low pH (~3) and break the peptide bonds of proteins to create large polypeptides. Once chyme moves from the stomach into the small intestine, proteolytic digestion continues but at a higher pH. Pepsin is no longer active, but various proteolytic enzymes are secreted by the pancreas and proteolytic enzymes are found on the surface of the microvilli extending the length of the small intestine. Two categories of proteolytic enzymes can be found in the small intestine, endopeptidases and exopeptidases. Exopeptidases are enzymes that specifically break bonds on the ends of peptide chains producing single amino acids and di- and tri-peptides. Endopeptidases break bonds in the centers of the peptide chains and produce peptides of various lengths. Some enodpeptidases are specific to bonds between specific amino acids. The peptidases found on the microvilli of enterocytes, break small peptides into single amino acids for transport across the enterocytes that are lining the lumen of the small intestine.

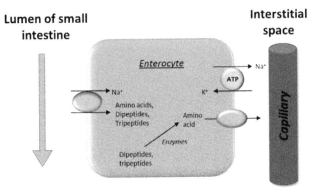

Figure 9.15

Absorption of amino acids, dipeptides and tripeptides occur using a secondary active transport mechanism (Figure 9.15). Co-transporters on the apical surface of enterocytes transport amino acids along with Na⁺ ions. The gradient for Na⁺ is established by the Na⁺/K⁺ pump which actively pumps Na⁺ out of the cell into the lumen of the small intestine. This creates a strong driving force for Na⁺ entry

into the cell and the Na⁺ can then be used by the cotransporters. In the cytosol of the enterocytes, dipeptides and tripeptides are enzymatically degraded to single amino acids which move across the basal surface by facilitated transport. The amino acids move into the interstitial space and get picked up by a capillary network that supplies each villus.

Carbohydrates and sugars

Carbohydrates comprise about half the American diet. The carbohydrates we consume are largely starches, a common polysaccharide found in plants. Other common carbohydrates in the human diet includes sucrose (table sugar) and lactose (milk sugars). Cellulose and other complex polysaccharides from plants, the fiber, passes through the small intestine largely undigested and enters the large intestine where bacteria which reside in the colon can partially digest the large polysaccharides for their own use. In the small intestine, complex sugars (polysaccharides and disaccharides) are metabolized to simple sugars (monosaccharides); glucose, fructose and galactose which are absorbed across the epithelial cells.

Chemical digestion of carbohydrates starts in the mouth by the presence of salivary amylase. Very little digestion occurs do to the short time that food spends in the oral cavity. Once food moves into the stomach, carbohydrate digestion slows way down due to the low pH and the inactivation of salivary amylase. Once chyme enters the small intestine, carbohydrate digestion once again is activated. Pancreatic secretion of amylase and the presence of specific

Figure 9.16

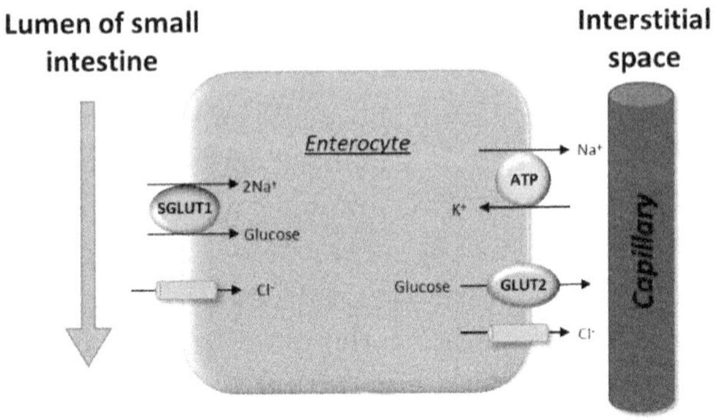

membrane bound disaccharidases such as lactase, sucrase, maltase and isomaltase on microvilli break specific complex sugars into simple sugars. Most simple sugars cross the epithelium using a secondary active transport mechanism (Figure 9.16). The Na^+/K^+ pump on the basolateral surface pump three Na^+ ions out of the cell for every two K^+ ions that move in and create a low Na^+ concentration inside epithelial cells. Glucose transport across the apical surface occurs using the Na^+-glucose cotransporter (SGLT1) and 1 molecule of glucose is co-transported with $2Na^+$ ions. Facilitated transport mechanisms transport simple sugars across the basal surface such as the glucose transporter (GLUT2) into the interstitial space and capillaries of the villi. Some simple sugars, like fructose, use facilitated diffusion on both the apical (GLUT5) and the basal surface.

Fats and lipids

Chemical digestion of fats and lipids occurs primarily in the small intestine. The enzyme lipase is the primary enzyme involved in the metabolism of triglycerides, phospholipids, steroids, and cholesterol. There are minute amounts of lipase found in saliva (lingual lipase) and in the stomach (gastric lipase) however, the activity of these enzymes is not sufficient for adequate lipid digestion. The majority of the lipase comes from the pancreas and is secreted into the first portion of the small intestine when chyme enters into the duodenum. In addition, to enzymes, bile is also secreted from the gall bladder into the duodenum. Together, lipase and bile are needed for adequate digestion of fats.

Most people are aware that oil (fats and lipids) and water do not mix well. The role of bile is to emulsify or adequately mix the fats with water. Bile salts do not chemically digest fats, but mechanically breaks large fat droplets into smaller fat droplets. Bile salts allow aqueous substances such as the lipases in water to come into contact with the fats. Lipase enzymatically breaks the bonds of fatty acids and glycerol (See

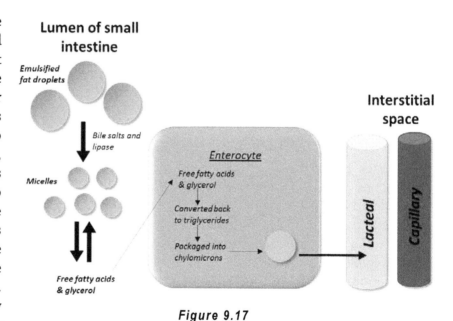

Figure 9.17

Figure 9.17). Once these chemical bonds are broken, bile salts are also important in the formation of micelles. Micelles are loosely organized structures which contain free fatty acids, glycerol and bile salts. Free fatty acids and glycerol are lipid soluble and move from high concentration to low concentration and move into the cytoplasm of enterocytes. Within enterocytes, fatty acids and glycerol are recombined in the smooth ER.

Triglycerides, phospholipids, and cholesterol are packaged with proteins into a specific type of lipoprotein, a chylomicron. The chylomicrons are large structures that are released by exocytosis into the interstitial space. In fact, they are so large that they do not fit between the fenestrae of the capillary endothelium and cannot enter capillaries. They can however, fit into the leaky lymphatic ducts and pass into a centrally located lymphatic duct running in each villus called a lacteal. The central lacteal is the site of absorption of chylomicrons. Eventually the lymphatic system drains into the venous side of the circulation and gets picked up by cells of the liver, the hepatocytes.

In blood, all lipids and fats are transported in combination with proteins and form a structure called a lipoprotein, in order to make the lipids and fats soluble in water. There are different types of lipoproteins which are produced by different tissues and cells and secreted into the blood. The lipoproteins vary in density and size based on the relative contribution of their lipid to protein ratios. Chylomicrons are manufactured by enterocytes in the small intestine and are a type of very low-density lipoprotein and contain mostly lipids with a small amount of protein. Chylomicrons are primarily picked up by cells in the liver, the hepatocytes where nutrients are stored and can be converted to various types of nutrients based on the needs of the body. The liver hepatocytes produces two types of lipoproteins, very low density lipoproteins (VLDLs) and low density lipoproteins (LDLs). The VLDLs contain large amounts of triglycerides which are primarily destined for storage in adipose tissue. LDLs contain relatively large amounts of cholesterol and are the primary route of cholesterol and phospholipids from the liver to the cells of the body. All cells in the body require cholesterol and lipids for normal function. When cells need more cholesterol and lipids, they can upregulate the number of LDL membrane receptors at the surface of the plasma membrane. LDL receptors are found in small pits on cells and when LDLs bind to the receptors, it activates a process to internalize the LDL by endocytosis. As the cells metabolic demands are met, the number of surface receptors is downregulated.

High-density lipoproteins (HDLs) primarily transport small amounts of lipids from cells back to the liver and to steroid producing cells to aid in the synthesis of steroid hormones. LDLs are considered the "bad" cholesterol structures and the HDLs are considered the "good" cholesterol structures. The reason for the designation has to do with excess numbers of LDLs. Normal LDLs are required for normal cellular function. However, when cells contain adequate amounts of cholesterol and the receptors for LDLs are downregulated, this can result in an increased number of circulating LDLs. LDLs contain high amounts of cholesterol which can then stick to walls and help in the formation of plaques on arteries.

Other nutrients

Other types of miscellaneous nutrients are also digested and absorbed in the small intestine. For example, nucleic acids are broken into their nucleotide components. Various ions (Na^+, K^+, Ca^{2+}, Mg^{2+}, etc...), vitamins, and trace elements (iron, iodide, etc...) are also required nutrients and are absorbed across the wall of the small intestine. Recall that the parietal cells in the stomach secrete intrinsic factor. Intrinsic factor binds to vitamin B12 in the small intestine (the high pH of the stomach decreases the affinity for binding).

Receptors for intrinsic factor-vitamin B12 complex are found in the latter portion of the small intestine, the ileum and vitamin B12 is absorbed. Vitamin B12 is necessary for cellular mitosis and can result in pernicious anemia or a reduction in the number of red blood cells produced in the body.

Water

The digestive tract plays a major role in the control of fluid and ion homeostasis, second only to the kidneys. The water that enters the digestive tract comes from the diet (~1.5-2L/day) and from secretions of the digestive tract itself (~7L/day) (Figure 9.18).

33) In the mouth, water is secreted with saliva to help liquefy the food (~1.5/day).
34) Secretions in the stomach help to create a liquid chyme that is acidic and contains enzymes for protein digestion (~1.5-2L/day).
35) The small intestine secretes ions and water to neutralize the acid from the stomach and maintain the liquid nature of chyme which helps aid in the process of digestion and absorption (1.5-2L/day).
36) The gall bladder secretes alkaline bile to aid in lipid digestion and neutralize acidic chyme (500-1000ml/day).
37) Secretions from the pancreas also neutralize the acidic chyme and contains many different types of enzymes used for digestion of proteins, carbohydrates and lipids (~1-1.5L/day).

Most of the total water is absorbed in the small intestine (~6.7L). Water can move across the epithelium of the small intestine either between cells (paracellular) or through cells (transcellular). Water moves simply by osmotic gradients and can move in either direction; into the interstitial space or into the lumen. In a normal, healthy digestive tract, as numerous solutes, amino acids, simple sugars and chylomicrons make their way across the epithelium, the bulk flow of water is from the lumen into the interstitial space through aquaporin channels.

Water is also absorbed in the large intestine (~1.4L/day) and the liquid chyme becomes a semisolid feces.

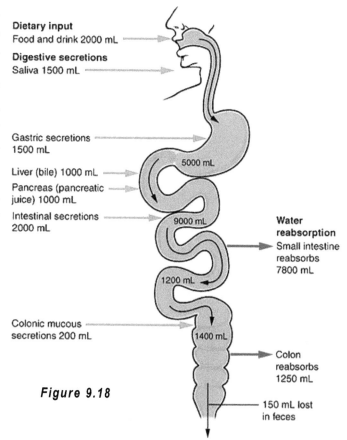

Dietary input
Food and drink 2000 mL

Digestive secretions
Saliva 1500 mL

Gastric secretions 1500 mL

Liver (bile) 1000 mL
Pancreas (pancreatic juice) 1000 mL
Intestinal secretions 2000 mL

Colonic mucous secretions 200 mL

5000 mL
9000 mL
1200 mL
1400 mL

Water reabsorption
Small intestine reabsorbs 7800 mL

Colon reabsorbs 1250 mL

150 mL lost in feces

Figure 9.18

Accessory Organs of the Digestive System

The liver, gall bladder and pancreas are considered the accessory organs of the digestive system and contribute critical components to the small intestine that are needed for the digestion of nutrients. In terms of digestion, the liver produces bile which is the stored in the gall bladder and the pancreas produces an alkaline solution containing enzymes. Secretion of these substances is under hormonal and neural regulation and occurs when chyme enters the duodenum.

Liver

The liver sits in the upper right quadrant of the peritoneal cavity just inferior to the diaphragm. The liver is the second largest organ in the body (behind skin) and is the largest gland in the body. The liver receives all of the blood that passes through the intestines by way of the hepatic portal vein and contains the absorbed nutrients (amino acids and simple sugars) as well as any other substances that may have passed through the intestine such as toxins and drugs. The liver is a major site in the body for the storage and interconversion of nutrients. Lipids make their way to the liver in the form of chylomicrons which enter the body via the lymphatic system and subsequently arrive in the liver via the arterial system. The liver has many functions including, but not limited to,

38) storage and interconversion of nutrients which can be used for basic metabolic functions (i.e., glycogen synthesis and gluconeogenesis)

39) phagocytosis and destruction of old red blood cells and recycling of their products,

40) detoxification of metabolic waste products and ingested toxins, poisons, and drugs,

41) production and release of bile into the gall bladder and duodenum to aid in digestion of fats and lipids,

42) synthesis of many blood proteins including clotting factors and

43) the synthesis of lipoproteins to transport lipids to cells.

The liver is organized into anatomical structural units called classic liver lobules (Figure 9.19). The classic lobules are polygonal structures that are distinct entities in some species and contain large connective tissue septa which delineate the boundaries of the lobules. However, in humans (and pigs) there is less connective tissue and the boundaries of the lobules are less distinct. A classic lobule is comprised of cords of cells called hepatocytes which are separated by capillaries. The hepatocytes are rectangular and stacked on top of each other much like the bricks of a house. The capillaries are called sinusoids (large capillaries) which are lined with a very leaky epithelium which are held together with a fine reticular network. The epithelium contains endothelial cells as well as a specialized resident macrophage called a Kupffer cell. Under the capillary endothelium, there is a space of Disse which allows the plasma to filter between the epithelial cells and come into direct contact with the hepatocytes. This allows the hepatocyte to absorb and release nutrients, detect toxins and poisons, and secrete substances directly into the blood. Each lobule is supplied with 3-6 portal triads. Each triad contains three vessels, 1) a branch of the hepatic portal vein, 2) a hepatic arteriole and 3) a bile duct. The blood from the hepatic portal vein and the hepatic arteriole empty into the sinusoids together and becomes mixed blood. The mixed blood flows from the periphery of the lobule towards the center bathing the Kupffer cells and hepatocytes before emptying into a central vein located in the center of the lobule.

Another way to organize the liver is based on the function of the liver in respect to blood flow. The anatomical distribution of blood flow causes blood to flow away from one side of the polygonal shape towards the center veins of the two lobules situated on each side, and forms a diagonal-shaped structure (or two triangles with their bases set up next to each other). This diagonal shaped structure is called the hepatic acinus of Rappaport (Figure 9.20). The

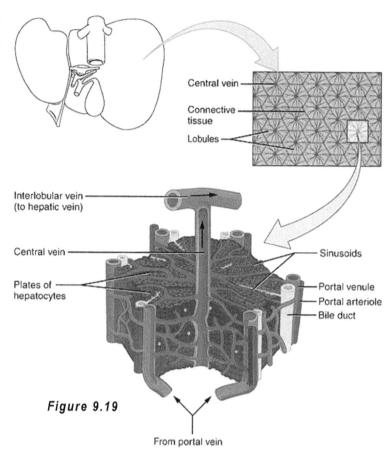

Figure 9.19

hepatic acinus of Rappaport is separated into 3 zones. As blood is dumped into the sinusoids it first passes through zone 1, then zone 2 and finally zone 3 before emptying into the central vein. As blood passes into zone 1, the cells in this region will be in contact with the blood first. The hepatocytes in this region will be very active in absorbing nutrients or they will be the first cells to be involved with detoxifying po isons or drugs. For example, after a large meal, the cells in zone 1 would be the first cells to come in contact with the glucose-rich blood. These cells would take up lots of glucose and store it in the form of glycogen. Zone 2 would be the middle zone and even less glucose would be taken up. Finally, the blood that passes through zone 3 next to the central vein may even possibly be within normal blood glucose range and may not store extra glucose. In the case of poisons, areas of zone 1 would be the first cells to come into contact with potential toxins and may even damage or kill the hepatocytes. Examination of the cellular structure within the context of the acinus of Rappaport can help physicians determine liver function.

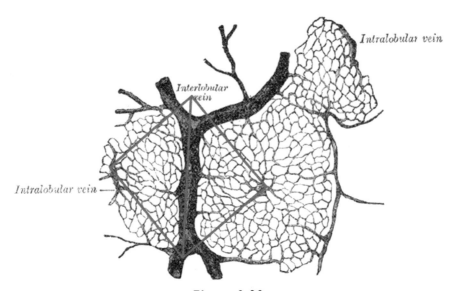

Figure 9.20

The liver hepatocytes have many cellular functions. The hepatocytes absorb lipids and carbohydrates and store them as triglycerides and glycogen. The storage of nutrients allows the liver to help regulate normal nutrient levels during times of fasting. For example, when blood glucose levels fall between meals, the hormone glucagon triggers the cells to break down the glycogen and release glucose into the blood. The hepatocytes can also convert triglycerides and amino acids into new glucose molecules via gluconeogenesis. The hepatocytes also take up and store many vitamins, trace elements, and convert lipids into lipoproteins for release and transport to cells. The liver hepatocytes also provide the blood with many of its protein components. Albumin, prothrombin, fibrinogen, clotting factors and even some precursor peptide hormones such as angiotensinogen are synthesized and released by hepatocytes. Unlike lipids and carbohydrates, the proteins that are produced by hepatocytes are not stored, but rather secreted continuously as they are produced.

Kupffer cells are a special type of macrophage that line the sinusoids of the liver lobules. Kupffer cells are responsible for the detection and destruction of foreign substances in the blood. The cells take up foreign substances by endocytosis and enzymatically degrade and destroy the material. The Kupffer cells also detect old or abnormal red blood cells and remove them from the circulation. The red blood cells are enzymatically destroyed and many of the components are recycled or reused. Bilirubin, a by-product of the breakdown of red blood cells which contain the heme groups of the hemoglobin molecules are recycled along with iron. The globin molecules are broken down to single amino acids to support the construction of new proteins. The hepatocytes or the bone marrow can pick up the iron and free bilirubin. Cells in the bone marrow use the recycled bilirubin and iron to make new red blood cells. In the liver, free bilirubin and iron can also be picked up by the hepatocytes. Up to 25% of the iron in the body is stored in the liver. The liver conjugates the bilirubin and is used as a component of bile which is used in digestion of fats.

Bile is produced and secreted by hepatocytes into small ducts called bile canaliculi which form a small network within the cords of hepatocytes. The bile canaliculi drain into the bile ducts of the portal triad, and eventually, the bile drains into the hepatic duct. The hepatic duct connects to the gall bladder via the cystic duct and bile is stored in the gall bladder for regulated release (see below). The hepatic duct continues from the liver as the common bile duct to join the pancreatic duct at the junction of the duodenum. Bile contains water, electrolytes, bicarbonate ions, bile acids, cholesterol and conjugated bilirubin. Bile is involved in the emulsification of lipids in the small intestine. Emulsification is a form of mechanical digestion in which large lipid droplets are separated to form small lipid droplets. This increases the surface area of the lipids and allows the enzymes to contact the lipids for chemical digestion.

During the intestinal phase of gastric secretions, chyme from the stomach is emptied into the duodenum. Increase in lipid concentration is sensed by neuroendocrine cells in the duodenum and trigger the release of the hormone CCK. Bile secretion is under the regulation of the hormone CCK. CCK stimulates hepatocytes to produce and secrete bile (and release bile from the gall bladder, see below). The hormone secretin is also released when chyme enters the duodenum. Secretin is released from neuroendocrine cells which sense a decrease in pH. In the liver, the hormone secretin stimulates the hepatocytes to produce and release more bicarbonate ions into bile.

Gall bladder

The gall bladder is a small pear-shaped organ with a large hollow core and is attached to the inferior aspect of the liver. The primary function of the gall bladder is to concentrate and store bile for release into the duodenum. Concentration of bile occurs through an active Na^+ transport mechanism which moves Na^+ across the epithelial cells of the gall bladder with the aid of the Na^+/K^+ pump which creates an osmotic gradient and causes water to follow. When chyme enters the duodenum, CCK is released from neuroendocrine cells. CCK acts on receptors in the smooth muscle of the gall bladder and causes the organ to constrict. This pushes bile from the gall bladder into the cystic duct, through the common bile duct and past the hepatopancreatic duct to enter the duodenum at the hepatopancreatic ampulla. There is a tight sphincter where the hepatopancreatic duct enters the duodenum called the Sphincter of Oddi which regulates secretions from the pancreas and gall bladder. The Sphincter of Oddi relaxes in response to CCK receptor activation. This allows secretions from the gall bladder to enter the duodenum.

Bile secretion is also under neural control mechanisms. Release of chyme into the duodenum stretches the walls and activates vagal sensory afferents. These vagal afferents project to the brainstem and initiate a vago-vagal reflex. Vagal motor fibers also innervate the gall bladder and cause contraction leading to bile release.

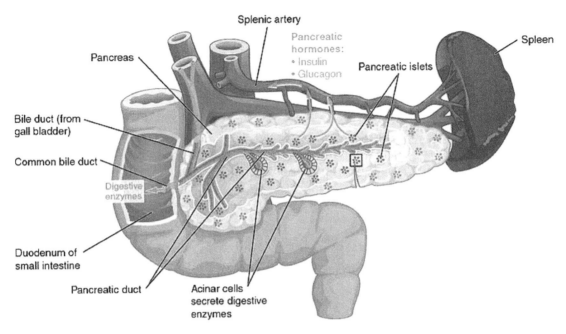

Figure 9.21

Pancreas

The pancreas sits just posterior and inferior to the stomach. The pancreas is a large gland with both exocrine and endocrine functions. The endocrine functions arise from structures within the pancreas called the islets of Langerhans. The cells of the islets of Langerhans release hormones into the interstitial space and make their way into capillaries and are involved with the regulation of blood glucose levels and will be covered in Chapter 10. The majority of the pancreatic tissue is dedicated to its exocrine function and plays an important role in digestion (Figure 9.21). The pancreas is made up of small acinar structures that are connected to a series of increasingly larger ducts that ultimately lead to two openings in the duodenum, the hepatopancreatic ampulla and the minor pancreatic duct. The cells lining the acini are triangular shaped and contain zymogen granules filled with pancreatic enzymes. The pancreas secretes many different types of enzymes involved in the digestion of proteins (trypsinogen, chymotrypsinogen, carboxypeptidase, ribonuclease, deoxyribonuclease), carbohydrates (amylase), and fats (lipase). Enzymatic release is stimulated in response to CCK which is released from neuroendocrine cells lining the duodenum. CCK acts on receptors located on the acinar cells which trigger the exocytosis of the zymogen granules and the release of enzymes into the ducts. The first small duct connected to the acini is called the intercalated duct and it is lined with a simple cuboidal epithelium that secretes a bicarbonate-rich serous fluid. The cells of the intercalated duct are stimulated by the hormone secretin. When chyme enters the duodenum, CCK and secretin are both released. These hormones inhibit gastric secretions, but promote secretions in the duodenum.

CHAPTER 9 SUMMARY

➢ Most digestive systems contain 1) an opening or receiving end, 2) conducting and storage compartments, 3) a digestive and absorption region, 4) a water absorbing area and 5) and exit or elimination region.

➢ The GI tract is lined with a similar tubular structure throughout its entirety. The lumen is lined with an epithelium sitting on a basement membrane, a lamina propria and a muscularis mucosa. The submucosa sits underneath and it enclosed by the muscularis externa (at least two layers of smooth muscle, an inner circular and an outer longitudinal muscle).

➢ The enteric nervous system innervates the GI tract and consists of a submucosal plexus and a myenteric plexus.

➢ Food is mechanically digested by structures in the mouth. Salivary amylase is secreted (under parasympathetic control, VII and IX) along with saliva into the bolus of food and begins the chemical digestion of starches.

➢ Swallowing is initiated by a voluntary phase and is followed by a pharyngeal and esophageal phases.

➢ A bolus of food enters the stomach and mixes with secretions. Secretions come from two cells found in the gastric glands. Parietal cells pump H^+ ions into the lumen followed by Cl^- due to electrical gradients. Chief cells secrete pepsinogen, an inactive precursor to pepsin, an enzyme that breaks peptide bonds.

➢ Gastric secretions are regulated in three phases; a cephalic phase, a gastric phase and an intestinal phase.

➢ The cephalic phase of gastric secretions are triggered by thoughts of food, emotions, smell, and taste. Inputs stimulate vagal efferents which innervate the parietal and chief cells and enhance secretions. This prepares the stomach for incoming food.

➢ The gastric phase is triggered by food placed in the stomach. Distension of smooth muscle activates stretch receptor feedback loops (short and long) which enhances gastric secretions. The hormone gastrin is released from neuroendocrine cells. Gastrin stimulates both parietal and chief cells as well as the release of histamine from another neuroendocrine cell type. Histamine has the greatest effect and enhances gastric secretions.

➢ The intestinal phase is triggered by chyme released into the duodenum. Distension of the duodenum and stimulation of chemosensors inhibit gastric secretions. Neural feedback loops from mechanoreceptors inhibit secretions via long and short neural loops. Neuroendocrine cells release CCK and secretin into the interstitial space. These hormones inhibit the parietal and chief cells and decrease secretions.

➢ The small intestine is specialized for the digestion and absorption of nutrients. Surface area is greatly increased by the presence of microvilli, villi and plica circularis.

➢ The large intestine is specialized for the absorption of fluid and ions.

➢ Proteins are degraded into single amino acids with enzymes that are released from the pancreas as well as membrane bound enzymes on the intestinal epithelium. Movement of amino acids is coupled to the movement of Na^+ across the apical surface of cells and facilitated diffusion on the basal surface.

➢ Carbohydrates are broken down into simple sugars by enzymes released by the pancreas as well as membrane bound enzymes on the intestinal epithelium. Movement of simple sugars are also coupled to the movement of Na^+ across the apical surface of enterocytes.

➢ Fats and lipids are mechanically broken down into smaller droplets with bile that is secreted by the gall bladder. This increases the surface area of the lipids and allows interactions to occur with the enzymes that are released by the pancreas and membrane bound enzymes. Free fatty acids and glycerol interact with bile salts to form micelles in the lumen and can freely dissociate and move through cell membranes. Inside enterocytes, free fatty acids and glycerol are reassembled into lipids and are mixed with proteins to form chylomicrons.

➢ The liver has many functions including 1) storage and interconversion of nutrients, 2) destruction of old red blood cells, 3) detoxification of toxic substances, 4) production and release of bile, 5) synthesis of blood proteins and clotting factors, and 6) synthesis of lipoproteins.

➢ The gall bladder stores and concentrates bile. CCK release during the intestinal phase causes contraction of the gall bladder and releases bile when chyme enters the duodenum.

➢ The exocrine pancreas produces and secretes enzymes in a bicarbonate rich solution. Secretin stimulates intercalated cells to secrete bicarbonate secretion and CCK stimulates acinar cells to secrete enzymes. Secretions are stimulated during the intestinal phase when chyme enters the duodenum.

References and Suggested Readings

Clevers HC, Bevins CL. 2013. Paneth cells: maestros of the small intestinal crypts. *Annual Reviews of Physiology* 75:289-311.

Furness JB. 2000. Types of neurons in the enteric nervous system. *Journal of the Autonomic Nervous System* 81:87-96.

Laforenza U. 2012. Water channel proteins in the gastrointestinal tract. *Molecular Aspects of Medicine* 33:642-650.

Ma T, Verkman AS. 1999. Aquaporin water channels in gastrointestinal physiology. *Journal of Physiology* 517(2):317-326.

Moog, F. 1981. The lining of the small intestine. *Scientific American*. 245(5):154-176.

Phillips RJ, Powley TL. 2007. Innervation of the gastrointestinal tract: patterns of aging. *Autonomic Neuroscience: Basic and Clinical* 136:1-19.

Sandle GI. 1998. Salt and water absorption in the human colon: a modern appraisal. *Gut* 43:294-299.

Schubert ML. 2008. Gastric secretion. *Current Opinions in Gastroenterology* 24:659-664.

Schultz SG. 2007. From a pump handle to oral hydration therapy: a model of translational research. *Advances in Physiological Education* 31:288-293.

Wood JD, Alpers DH, Andrews PLR. 1999. Fundamentals of Neurogastroenterology. *Gut* 45:II6-II1

Chapter 10: Endocrinology

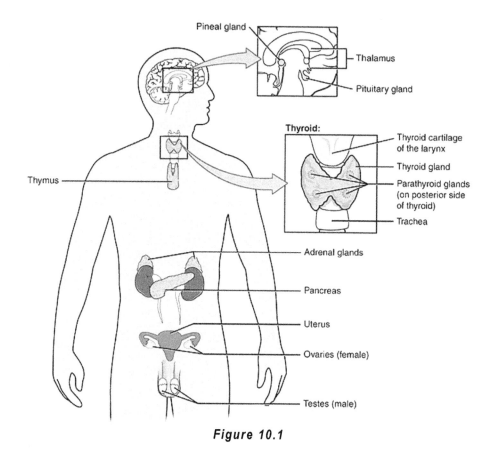

Figure 10.1

Simple cellular communication evolved in the smallest of multicellular organisms. Individual cells secrete substances or signals into the body which can then influence cells at distant locations. This system of cellular communication is called an endocrine system and the signals are called hormones. In larger organisms, individual cells can secrete hormones as well as distinct collections of cells or glands and can even form entire organs. The hormones are secreted into the interstitial space surrounding cells and are often taken up by circulatory system to influence the activity of cells in distant locations. Any cell in the body that has a specific receptor for that particular hormone can then be affected. In this regard, the endocrine system is considered less specific compared to the neural system where a single neuron can directly influence a specific cell by the release of neurotransmitters at a synapse. In more complex organisms, cells that secrete substances called hormones can be derived from all three germ layers during development and therefore can be found in all areas of the body (Figure 10.1). Hormones influence many aspects of normal physiology from the cellular to the entire organismal level. For example, hormones can promote or inhibit growth and development of cells and tissues, they can influence differentiation of tissues, they can affect the metabolic activity of cells, they help control digestion, they help control nutrient regulation (synthesis, storage and release by various tissues), they help control blood volume and ionic homeostasis, and they help in reproduction and development of the gametes; to name just a few of the roles that hormones play in the body.

Most hormones in vertebrates are short polypeptides, but hormones can also be small proteins (e.g., insulin), amines (e.g., thyroxine, epinephrine), or lipids such as steroid hormones (e.g., cortisol, aldosterone). The cells that secrete hormones are called endocrine cells, neuroendocrine cells, or neurosecretory cells. The cells that produce hormones like peptides or proteins use the normal cellular machinery such as the rough endoplasmic reticulum and Golgi apparatus and package hormones in small vesicles. Hormone release is regulated by multiple mechanisms such as another hormone, neuronal innervation and/or the detection of specific levels of ions or nutrients. For example, the secretion of insulin from the pancreas islets of Langerhans is influenced by changes in the plasma levels of the specific nutrient, glucose. As plasma glucose increases after a meal, insulin is secreted and can act on many cells in the body to enhance the transport of glucose into cells. This will in turn decrease plasma glucose and insulin secretion rates decrease. Yet, another example of a negative feedback mechanism. Some hormones like epinephrine and norepinephrine are secreted in response to neural signaling. In times of stress or exercise, sympathetic activity increases. Sympathetic stimulation of adrenal medullary chromaffin cells causes the release of epinephrine and norepinephrine into the general circulation. Circulating epinephrine and norepinephrine can bind to adrenergic receptors in the body such as in the heart and causes an increase in the heart rate and the force of contraction. Finally, some hormone secretion rates are regulated by other hormones. For example, the hypothalamus in the brain contains many neurosecretory cells which secrete a variety of hormones which directly influence the release of hormones from the anterior pituitary gland. These so-called releasing hormones are released from specialized nerve endings next to capillary networks. The hormones diffuse from the interstitial space to enter the capillaries and enter the circulation to affect cells in the anterior pituitary. Some of these cells also secrete hormones which then target other distant tissues.

The total effect that hormones have on tissues is dependent on the amount of hormones released into the blood. Low concentrations of hormones create a weak response and greater concentrations of hormones have a stronger response. This is in contrast to the neuronal system in which neurons regulate their effect by the frequency of action potential stimulation. Low frequency of action potentials results in a weak response whereas a high frequency of action potentials cause a strong response. Most hormones are released in cyclic patterns and the amounts of hormone in the blood increase and decrease in a rhythmic pattern. Many hormones are released in patterns that coincide with circadian rhythms, with food intake or with activity levels to some degree and are often influenced by negative feedback mechanisms. Some hormones are released in much longer cycles, such as the female reproductive hormones which have a 28 day+ pattern of release.

Hormones are distributed rather quickly throughout the body because they are transported through the blood circulation. Hormones can travel through the blood freely dissolved in plasma or bound to blood proteins. As free hormones, they are free to filter into the interstitial space of tissues and bind to specific membrane bound proteins and have an effect on target tissues. The amount of free hormone is regulated by the law of mass action and move by simple concentration gradients. Some hormones travel in blood bound to proteins. Some of these proteins are specific binding proteins and carry a specific hormone such as the thyroxine binding globulin (TBG) whereas some hormones bind non-specifically to blood proteins such as albumin. When hormones are in a bound state, they cannot be degraded very easily and they are not excreted readily by the renal system. But in order to have an effect they need to detach from the binding proteins and become freely dissolved hormones to pass into tissues. As free molecules, hormones tend to be quickly degraded or they may be excreted in urine or feces.

Some hormones are released in an acute situations, like epinephrine and the response to the hormone is fast. These hormones have a short half-life. Half-life is the term that is applied to the time that half the amount of hormone is degraded or removed from the system. Chronically regulated hormones, such as thyroid hormones have a long half-life and they stay around in the body for relatively long periods of time. This is primarily because much of the hormone is bound to circulating blood proteins and cannot be degraded easily.

In tissues, hormones bind to specific receptors. Hormones that are proteins and peptides bind to membrane bound G-proteins coupled receptors (GPCR) and steroid hormones can easily diffuse through the membranes to bind to receptors located in the cell cytoplasm or nucleus. In general, these different types of hormones have different cellular responses (See Table 10.1). Peptide hormones are simply several amino acid residues in length and they are produced by many different endocrine tissues. Many of these peptide hormones are produced in cells as a much larger precursor protein called a preprohormone or simply prohormones and are stored in exocytic vesicles. Cleavage of prohormones by enzymes release small peptides which can have multiple actions on cells. Stimulation of the hormone producing cell by a ligand usually triggers increased production of the hormone as well as exocytosis and release of the hormone into the interstitial space and general circulation. The hormones bind to a GPCR located on a cell membrane and initiate an intracellular signaling cascade to affect target cells.

Table 10.1. Differences between steroid hormones and peptide or amine hormone

Property	Steroid Hormones	Peptide or amine hormones
Storage sites	NONE (except thyroid follicle)	Secretory vesicles
Interaction with cell membrane	Diffusion through cell membrane	Binds to receptor located on cell membrane
Receptor	In cytoplasm or nucleus	GPCR on cell membrane
Action	Regulation of gene transcription (primarily) – long term cellular response	Signal transduction cascade affects cellular processes – usually relatively quick cellular response
Response time	Hours to days	Seconds to minutes

Steroid hormones are made only in four organs, the adrenal cortex, the ovaries, the testes and the placenta. The adrenal cortex produces glucocorticoids (primarily cortisol), mineralocorticoids (primarily aldosterone), and androgens. The gonads also produce steroid hormones. The female ovary (and placenta) produces multiple estrogens and progestins and the male testes produces androgens, primarily testosterone. Most of the secretion of steroid hormones is regulated by other hormones which come primarily from the pituitary gland. In general, the steroid hormones are released from the cell directly and are not stored intracellularly in vesicles. The concentration of steroid hormones in blood is regulated by modifying the production of the hormone. Once the hormones are produced by a cell, they are released into the blood and most of the hormone binds to proteins since they are not very soluble in plasma. The receptors for steroid hormones are found inside cells. The receptors can be found in the cytoplasm or often inside the nucleus (See Figure 2.19). Those receptors that are located in the cytoplasm will translocate to the nucleus after binding to the hormone to affect gene transcription. The nuclear receptors are often part of the machinery that regulates transcription of genes and can either turn on or off transcription. Activation of these types of cellular responses have relatively long acting consequences on cellular function.

Hormone responses can also be regulated based on the number of receptors on cells. Individual cells can change the number of receptors by either upregulation or downregulation of receptors. Cells maintain housekeeping duties on a regular basis and will degrade and replace membrane proteins. The rate of replacement can vary. An increase in the rate of synthesis will result in a greater number of proteins inserted into the membrane and is called up-regulation. In addition, cellular activation can stimulate exocytosis and the insertion of more receptors. A decrease in the rate of synthesis or endocytosis of membrane receptors is called downregulation. Specific stimuli (from hormones or neuronal inputs) can increase or decrease the number of receptors which will increase or decrease the responsiveness of cells to hormone release.

Under some conditions, many hormones are released at the same time and can work together to accomplish a similar or synergistic response. For example, hormone integration occurs during exercise to cause an increase in the available glucose for the working muscles and enhance glucose uptake. Epinephrine from the adrenal medulla and cortisol from the adrenal cortex enhance the release of glucose into the circulation and insulin from the pancreas enhances cell to increase the uptake of glucose from blood. Together, these hormones increase glucose availability to working muscles during exercise.

Some hormonal actions can antagonize each other and are often released at opposite times in a cyclic pattern. For example, insulin and glucagon have opposite effects on the liver and influence plasma glucose levels. Insulin is released after meals and acts on cells to increase the uptake of glucose and in some cells such as the liver hepatocytes and skeletal muscle glucose uptake is increased as well as the storage of glucose as glycogen. Glucagon, however, is released during times of fasting and causes hepatocytes to stimulate glycogenolysis to increase the release of stored glucose and stimulates gluconeogenesis or the production of new glucose for release. In this case, the amount of hormone released is dependent upon the amount of circulating plasma glucose.

Hypothalamic-Pituitary System

The hypothalamic-pituitary or hypothalamo-hypophyseal system has a large influence on many bodily functions. The system involves many hormones that are released from both the hypothalamus and the pituitary gland and these hormones influence nearly every tissue in the body. The pituitary gland is a small glandular tissue connected to the hypothalamus via the infundibular stalk (See Figure 10.2). During development, the pituitary gland is formed from two separate tissues. The ectoderm that originates in the mouth region (Rathke's pouch) is glandular and migrates upward to develop into the anterior pituitary. The posterior pituitary originates from a portion of the hypothalamus that extends downward and is neural in origin. Together, these two portions come together and form a single pituitary gland which sits in the sella turcia of the sphenoid bone. Because these tissues originate from different primary tissue types, the anterior pituitary and the posterior pituitary are structurally organized in distinct entities and each section works separately. In general, the posterior pituitary is made of neurons with their cell bodies located in the hypothalamus. They release neurohormones from their end terminals in the posterior pituitary and function similar to a typical neuron. The anterior pituitary releases 9 types of different hormones and their release is under the regulation of a group of regulatory hormones that are released from other hypothalamic neurons which then travel via a circulatory portal vessel to reach the anterior pituitary.

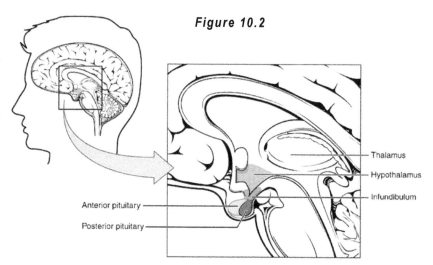

Figure 10.2

Thalamus

Hypothalamus

Infundibulum

Anterior pituitary

Posterior pituitary

Posterior pituitary (neurohypophysis)

The posterior pituitary is comprised of neural tissue. The neural tissue or neurohypophysis can be separated into 3 distinct regions, the median eminence, the infundibular stalk and the pars nervosa. The pars nervosa forms the posterior lobe of the pituitary gland. In general, the cell bodies of neurons originate in the hypothalamus with their axons extending down through the median eminence and infundibular stalk to enter the lobe of the posterior pituitary (See Figure 10.3, on the next page). The cell bodies of two types of magnocellular neurons are located within two distinct nuclei within the hypothalamus, the supraoptic and paraventricular nuclei. Each type of magnocellular neuron produces a different neurohormone. The hormones oxytocin and vasopressin (anti-diuretic hormone,

ADH) are produced in the cell bodies of magnocellular neurons, packaged into vesicles and transported down the axon to be stored in specialized neural endings called Herring bodies located in the posterior pituitary. When these neurons are stimulated, action potentials propagate down the axon and open voltage-gated Ca^{2+} channels which initiate exocytosis and the release of neurohormones. The hormones are released into the interstitial space and diffuse into capillaries to enter the general circulation. This allows the hormones to interact with specific receptors on target tissues at distant locations.

Figure 10.3

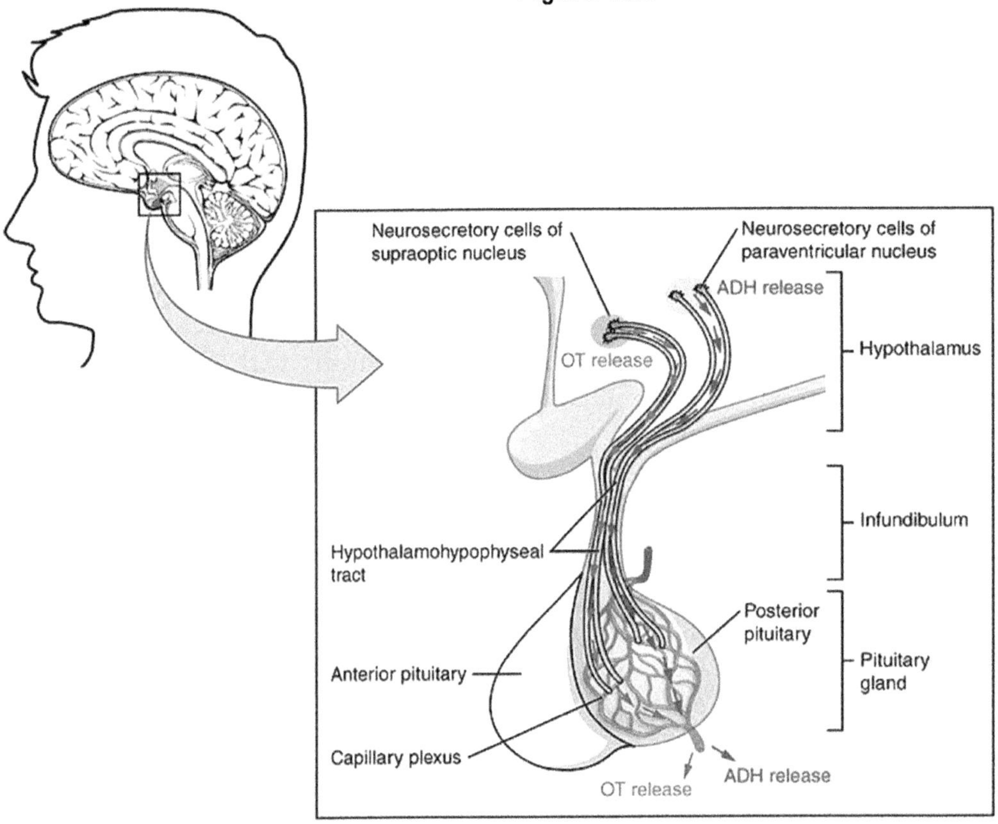

Oxytocin

One hormone that is released from the posterior pituitary is oxytocin. Oxytocin is a small peptide that is synthesized in the cell bodies of neurons and packaged as an inactive prohormone in vesicles. Within vesicles, multiple enzymatic reactions occur to produce the final active oxytocin peptide (9 amino acids) which is released by exocytosis. The majority of the oxytocin neurosecretory cells are located in the paraventricular nucleus, however, a small number of oxytocin containing neurons are also located in a concentrated region of the dorsolateral portion of the supraoptic nucleus. Oxytocin hormone is well-known for its actions in females during parturition. After birth, oxytocin is involved with milk letdown during breast-feeding. As an infant suckles on the breast tissue, mechanosensory neurons located in the nipple get activated. These sensory neurons increase the number of action potentials fired and project through a spinal reflex to the hypothalamus to stimulate the magnocellular oxytocin neurons. The magnocellular neurons fire action potentials and release oxytocin from the posterior pituitary into the general circulation. Oxytocin acts on

G-protein coupled receptors located on the myoepithelial cells underlying the epithelial glandular tissue of breasts and promote the release of milk from the mammary glands. As the infant continues to suckle, this produces a positive feedback mechanisms to release more oxytocin to promote milk letdown. Once the infant stops suckling, the feedback mechanism is turned off.

Oxytocin also acts on the smooth muscle cells in the uterus to induce uterine contractions and the dilation of the cervix during birth. After birth, oxytocin continues to stimulate the uterus smooth muscle cells and aids in reducing the size of the uterus. Oxytocin is also released from the pituitary gland in both males and females at times other than parturition and appears to play a role in the development of relationship bonding; both between males and females as well as between parents and children. In this regard, the hormone is known as the "cuddling" or "love" hormone and plays roles in creating healthy emotional bonds between individuals, as well as the development of romantic relationships. Oxytocin has also been shown to be involved with the development of trust between individuals.

Vasopressin

The second hormone that is released from the posterior pituitary is vasopressin (arginine vasopressin, AVP) which is also called anti-diuretic hormone (ADH). AVP is involved in the regulation of blood volume and therefore blood pressure. Special osmoreceptors are located in a region of the hypothalamus which line the anterior wall of the third ventricle. Special sensory neurons in this region, the lamina terminalis, are outside of the blood brain barrier and make intimate contact with arterial plasma. They are sensitive to changes in plasma osmolarity as well as to circulating angiotensin II hormone. Increases in plasma osmolarity stimulate the neurons of the lamina terminalis which project directly to AVP neurons. AVP magnocellular neurons are found in the supraoptic nucleus and scattered with the oxytocin magnocellular neurons in the paraventricular nucleus. These neurons produce and package AVP in vesicles in the cell body and vesicles are transported down to the specialized nerve terminals in the posterior pituitary for storage in the Herring bodies. Neurons of the lamina terminalis respond to increased plasma osmolarity (dehydration) and stimulate AVP neurons which then release AVP into the circulation. AVP acts on G-protein coupled receptors (vasopressin 2 receptor, VP2) located on the kidney collecting tubules. Activation of the VP2 receptor stimulates Gs and activates adenylyl cyclase. Increases in intracellular cAMP lead to the insertion of aquaporin 2 channels in the apical membrane via exocytosis of vesicles. This leads to the enhanced reabsorption of water and a subsequent increase in blood pressure. The hormone angiotensin II also directly stimulates receptors on the neurons in the lamina terminalis. This also causes increased release of AVP and enhanced water reabsorption from the kidney tubule. This results in an increase in blood volume and therefore blood pressure.

Anterior pituitary (Adenohypophysis)

The anterior pituitary is derived from epidermal tissue. The majority of the anterior pituitary is called the pars distalis and is the region that produces most of the hormones released from the anterior pituitary. The pars intermedia is a small region that sits between the pars distalis and the pars nervosa and in some species this is a distinct region and in others, like humans, simply blends with the pars distalis. A small amount of tissue extends upward and surrounds a portion of the infundibular stalk and is called the pars tuberalis. The anterior pituitary is under hormonal control of hypothalamic hormones (See Figure 10.4, on the next page). Small parvocellular hypothalamic neurons from multiple hypothalamic nuclei secrete releasing hormones which stimulate target cells of the anterior pituitary. There are 5 different types of cells that can be found in the anterior pituitary; somatotrophs, thyrotrophs, corticotrophs, gonadotrophs, and lactotrophs. Hormones from the hypothalamus bind to specific G-protein coupled receptors located on these cells and either stimulate or inhibit the release of nine different major hormones from the anterior pituitary (Table 10.2).

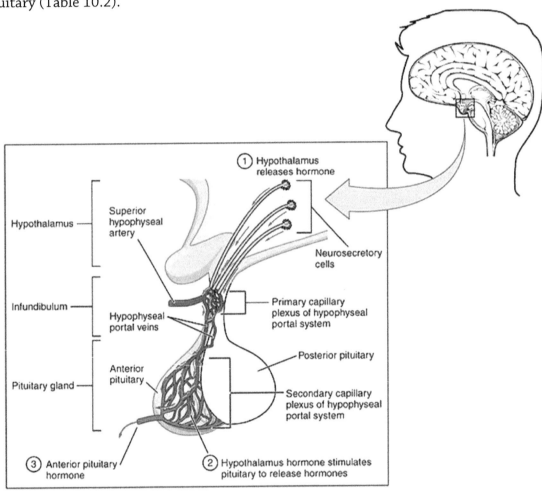

Figure 10.4

Table 10.2. List of the hypothalamic releasing hormones and their effect on the anterior pituitary.

Hypothalamic Hormone	Anterior Pituitary Hormone	Effector (tissue and basic action)
Growth Hormone Releasing Hormone (GHRH) Growth Hormone Inhibiting Hormone (GHIH) or somatostatin	Growth Hormone (somatotropin)	Acts on most cells to stimulate growth
Thyrotropin Releasing Hormone (TRH)	Thyroid Stimulating Hormone (TSH)	Acts on most cells to stimulate metabolic activity
Corticotropin Releasing Hormone (CRH)	Adrenocorticotropic Hormone	Acts on adrenal cortex. Main role is to stimulate the release of cortisol which acts on most cells to enhance uptake of glucose and stimulate cellular activity
	Melanocyte Stimulating Hormone (MSH)	Stimulates melanocytes to increase melatonin synthesis
	β-Endorphins	Acts on neurons and decreases pain threshold
	Lipotropins	Acts on adipocytes and stimulates release and breakdown of lipids
Gonadotropin Releasing Hormone (GnRH)	Follicle Stimulating Hormone (FSH)	In females: stimulates follicular growth and maturation of oocyte in the ovary In males: stimulates spermatogenesis
	Luteinizing Hormone (LH)	In females: stimulates ovulation In males: stimulates production and release of testosterone.
Prolactin Releasing Hormone Prolactin Inhibiting Hormone	Prolactin	Acts on mammary glands to promote the synthesis of milk proteins.

The blood circulation that supplies the anterior pituitary is unique and helps to transport hormones from the hypothalamus to the anterior pituitary. The hypothalamic hypophyseal portal system is comprised of two capillary beds connected with portal veins. The primary capillary bed is located in the median eminence, a region of the neurohypophysis that attaches at the base of the hypothalamus. Parvocellular neurons of the hypothalamus release hormones into the interstitial space near the primary capillary bed and the hormones move by simple diffusion into the capillary. The primary capillary bed connects to portal veins which drain through the infundibular stalk to join a secondary capillary bed located in the anterior pituitary. The releasing hormones diffuse out of the secondary capillary bed and can act on receptors located on the cells of the anterior pituitary gland. So in terms of the regulation of the anterior pituitary, we have two categories of hormones; the hormones that released from the hypothalamus (the releasing hormones) and the hormones that are released from the anterior pituitary (Table 10.2).

Growth Hormone

In the hypothalamus, parvocellular neurons are found in several nuclei including the arcuate and the periventricular nuclei. Growth hormone releasing hormone (GHRH) and growth hormone inhibiting hormone (GHIH or somatostatin) are released in opposite cyclic patterns throughout the day; when GHRH levels increase the amount of somatostatin secretion decreases and vice versa. Secretion rates vary depending on the developmental status, the nutritional status and the wake/sleep state or the amount of activity (i.e., exercise) of an individual. GHRH is synthesized by parvocellular neurons located primarily in the arcuate nucleus and released from neurons in the median eminence to enter the primary capillary bed. GHRH diffuses out of the secondary capillary bed in the anterior pituitary and binds to G-protein coupled receptors on somatotrophs. Stimulation of somatotrophs instigate the release of growth hormone (GH) from the anterior pituitary. Growth hormone then enters the circulation via the secondary capillary bed to target distant tissues.

Growth hormone can be found in all vertebrates, even the most primitive vertebrates, and even invertebrates contain very similar hormones that share a high degree of homology to GH. In general, GH is a very basic hormone which stimulates cells to divide and increase in size, it increases the utilization of amino acids and increases the amount of available glucose and fatty acids (See Figure 10.5, on the next page). The hormone helps regulate basic cellular metabolism and helps regulate nutrient levels in the blood both after a meal and during times of fasting. In this regard, it is not surprising that a similar hormone is found throughout the animal kingdom. During human development, growth hormone is particularly important in promoting bone and cartilage growth and too little hormone released can cause dwarfism and too much hormone can result in gigantism.

Figure 10.5

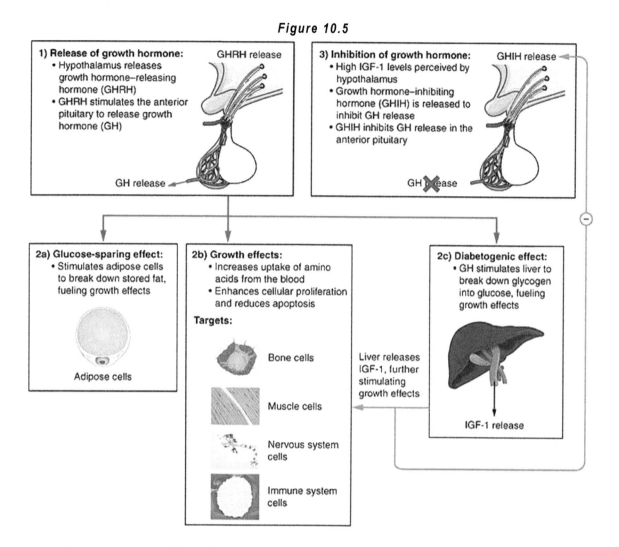

Somatostatin inhibits the release of GH from the anterior pituitary. Somatostatin is also produced by parvocellular neurons located in the periventricular nucleus and arcuate nucleus of the hypothalamus. They also release somatostatin into the primary capillary bed located in the median eminence and the hormone migrates down the portal vessels to enter the anterior pituitary. In the anterior pituitary, somatostatin inhibits the release of GH from the somatotrophs. In addition, there is evidence that the parvocellular neurons also project directly to the neurons that secrete GHRH and inhibit them directly.

The somatostatin parvocellular neurons are stimulated by high levels of GH and thus constitute a negative feedback loop; when GH levels are high, the levels of GHRH decrease and when the GH levels are low, the level of GHRH increases. GH can inhibit the release of GHRH, but can also stimulate the release of somatostatin. GH also stimulates another class of neurons in the arcuate nucleus that contain neuropeptide Y (NPY). Release of NPY also increases the release of somatostatin and decreases the release of GHRH. This negative feedback loop helps to maintain an oscillating range of GH values in the blood throughout the day.

Thyroid Stimulating Hormone

The thyroid gland is under the regulation of thyroid stimulating hormone (TSH). Thyroid hormone is released from the thyroid gland in response to activation by TSH. Thyroid hormone affects the normal metabolism rates of nearly all cells in the body; it can alter the rate of nutrient utilization, the activity of the Na^+/K^+ pump, and the activity of the mitochondria. Thyroid hormone is critically important for normal growth and development and without sufficient amounts can result in severe developmental disorders such as mental retardation and abnormal musculoskeletal growth. Levels of circulating plasma thyroid hormones are regulated by hormones released from the hypothalamic-pituitary system.

In the hypothalamus, parvocellular neurons of the paraventricular nucleus synthesize thyrotropin releasing hormone (TRH) and release the hormone into the primary capillary bed. TRH travels through the portal veins to enter the anterior pituitary to bind to G-protein coupled receptors on thyrotrophs. Stimulated thyrotrophs release thyroid stimulating hormone (TSH) which exit via the secondary capillary bed to enter the general circulation. TSH binds to receptors located on follicular cells of the thyroid gland to stimulate the release of thyroid hormone (T3 and T4) (see below for more detail). Thyroid hormone also triggers a negative feedback mechanism and regulates the amount of circulating thyroid hormone in a narrow range; increases in thyroid hormone cause a decrease in the release of TRH and TSH and when thyroid hormone levels begin to decrease the levels of the TRH and TSH begin to increase. Receptors for thyroid hormone are located on both hypothalamic parvocellular neurons and the thyrotrophs of the anterior pituitary. Activation of these receptors inhibit the transcription, translation and release of TRH and TSH.

Adrenocorticotropic Hormone (and related hormones)

Adrenocorticotropic hormone (ACTH) is released by the anterior pituitary and regulates the secretion of cortisol from the adrenal cortex. Cortisol is released in response to both emotional and physical stressors and is one of the components that underlie the "fight or flight" response along with inputs from the sympathetic nervous system. In general, cortisol acts to maintain adequate glucose and nutrient levels in the blood between meals or during times of need. Stressors initiate neural impulses that originate in many regions of the brain. Some of these impulses project to the paraventricular nucleus of the hypothalamus and stimulate parvocellular neurons to release corticotropin releasing hormone (CRH) into the median eminence. CRH is carried via the hypothalamic-hypophyseal portal system to enter the anterior pituitary. CRH binds to G-protein coupled receptors (CRH-R1) located on the plasma membrane of corticotrophs to stimulate the synthesis and secretion of ACTH. Stressors also stimulate magnocellular neurons in the paraventricular nucleus that release AVP. Receptors for AVP are also found on the corticotrophs and this enhances the secretion of ACTH. When AVP is released without CRH, they do not have a large effect on corticotrophs and their main role is in the kidney and is involved water homeostasis. Receptors for ACTH are located in the adrenal cortex and activation of the G-protein coupled receptors cause the secretion of the hormone cortisol into the general circulation (see below for more detail). Cortisol has a negative feedback mechanism and inhibits the release of CRH and ACTH (Figure 10.6).

ACTH is synthesized in corticotrophs from a large precursor molecule called proopiomelanocortin (POMC). Cleavage of POMC gives rise to multiple hormones that can be released by corticotrophs including ACTH, α-melanocyte stimulating hormone (α-MSH), β- and γ-lipotrophins, and β-endorphin. When CRH and AVP are released due to signals that arise due to stressors, ACTH is the major hormone that is released along with some β-endorphins and γ-lipotrophins. CRH can also bind to melanotrophs lwocated in the pars intermedia. In these cells, POMC is cleaved to α-MSH and corticotrophin-like intermediate peptide (CLIP). α-MSH binds primarily to receptors on melanocytes to stimulate melanin production. CLIP appears to act on neural tissues, but its function is not well known.

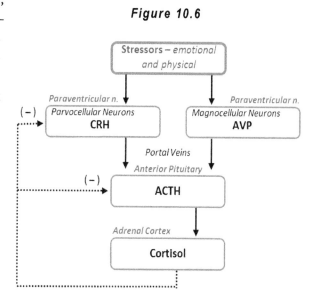

Figure 10.6

Follicle Stimulating Hormone (FSH) and Luteinizing Hormone (LH)

The gonadotropins FSH and LH are released from the anterior pituitary in response to gonadotropin-releasing hormone (GnRH). Gonadotropins are hormones that exert specific actions on the gonadal tissue in both males and females. FSH and LH are both produced by gonadotrophs of the anterior pituitary. They are packaged in separate vesicles and are differentially regulated. In general, the frequency of pulses of GnRH influence which hormone is released; fast pulses of GnRH preferentially cause the release of LH and slow pulses of GnRH preferentially stimulate the release of FSH. The hormones are named after their specific actions in the female reproductive organs. In females, FSH stimulates follicular growth in the ovary (see below for more detail). As the follicles grow, they begin to secrete estrogen which exerts a positive feedback mechanism and induces the release of more FSH. FSH also causes the follicular cells to upregulate the number of LH receptors. As the levels of estrogen continue to elevate, it induces a large output of LH. The LH binds to the follicular cells and stimulates ovulation. After ovulation, the follicular cells enter the luteal phase and begin secreting higher amounts of the hormone progesterone. Progesterone inhibits the release of GnRH, FSH and LH. If pregnancy does not occur, the corpus luteum begins to atrophy and the progesterone and estrogen levels begin to fall. This releases the inhibition and GnRH secretion begins to elevate again. The entire cycle lasts ~28 days in the female reproductive system.

In males, FSH stimulates the Sertoli cells in the testes to promote spermatogenesis and release the hormone inhibin (see below for more details). LH stimulates the interstitial cells to secrete testosterone which enhances spermatogenesis. Testosterone and inhibin play a negative feedback role and inhibit the release of FSH and LH. These hormones are also released in a cyclic pattern in males but in a short time scale, hours/days.

Prolactin

Prolactin is involved in the letdown of milk. The secretion of prolactin is under the regulation of prolactin releasing hormone and prolactin inhibiting hormone (dopamine). An infant suckling on the nipples induces the release of PRH (along with oxytocin) which stimulates the release of prolactin from the anterior pituitary. Prolactin increases the production of milk by the mammary glands. Prolactin secretion also inhibits the release of GnRH and prevents pregnancy. If regular, daily breast feeding occurs this will inhibit the formation of new follicular growth and ovulation in a lactating female. It is known as the "natural contraception" after the birth of a newborn infant. It however, is not perfect in all individuals.

Thyroid Gland

The thyroid gland is the largest endocrine gland in the human body. In general, thyroid hormones are involved in the regulation of cellular metabolism. Thyroid hormone enhances carbohydrate, lipid and protein metabolism in every cell and increases total metabolic rate. Thyroid hormones can activate futile pathways to create heat and maintain constant body temperature. The thyroid gland is a single gland with two large lobes that are connected across the anterior aspect of the trachea by an isthmus and sits just below the larynx. The tissue is comprised of many round structures called follicles that are lined with a simple cuboidal epithelium which surround a center filled with colloid. The interstitial tissue between the follicles contains a rich vascular capillary bed and parafollicular cells which are involved in calcium homeostasis.

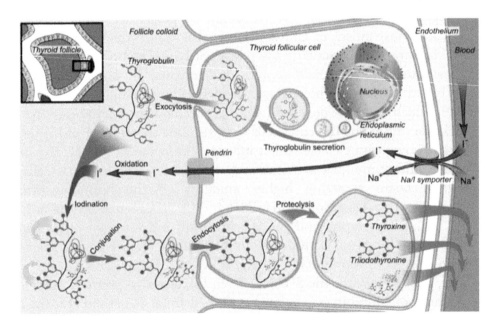

Figure 10.7

Thyroid hormones are produced and secreted by the follicular cells and are under the regulation of the hypothalamic-pituitary system. Plasma iodide (I⁻) is "trapped" by follicular cells and I⁻ is actively transported into follicular cells using a Na^+/I^- cotransporter located on the basolateral surface of follicular cells (Figure 10.7). Iodide is oxidized to iodine (I_2) in the cytoplasm and moves into the lumen of the follicle. Thyroperoxidase in the follicular lumen aid in the attachment of I_2 to the tyrosine residues of thyroglobulin molecules forming monoiodothyronine (MIT) and diiodothyroninine (DIT). Thyroglobulin protein is produced by the endoplasmic reticulum of the follicular cells, packaged in vesicles by the Golgi apparatus and secreted into the lumen of the follicles. Within the follicles, the iodinated tyrosine molecules are conjugated; an MIT and a DIT form triiodothyronine (T3) and two DITs combine to form tetraiodothyronine (T4). Upon stimulation, the follicular cells initiate endocytosis of thyroglobulin and form intracellular vesicles which fuse with lysosomes. Proteolytic enzymes cleave T3 and T4 from the thyroglobulin molecule. T3 and T4 are lipid soluble and diffuse down its concentration gradient out the basolateral surface of the follicular cells and bind to proteins in the blood, including a special binding protein produced by the liver called thyroxine binding globulin (TBG). The thyroid gland is unique among the endocrine glands because it stores a large quantity of hormone outside of its gland in blood bound to protein and in the form of T4.

The thyroid gland releases two hormones; T4 (~90%) and T3 (~10%), however, T3 is the more potent and active form of the hormone. T3 and T4 can both enter cells by diffusion and once in the cytoplasm T4 gets converted to T3 by an enzyme, deiodinase. Type 1 deiodinase is found in liver and kidneys and is responsible for converting most of the T4 to T3 which can then influence nearly every tissue in the body. Type 2 deiodinase is commonly found in the heart, skeletal muscle, brain, adipose tissue and the thyroid gland and converts T4 to T3 for local use in those tissues.

Once inside the cell, the hormone translocates to the nucleus where T3 binds to thyroid hormone receptors and forms the thyroid response element to initiate gene transcription. Activation of thyroid receptors regulates many genes related to basic metabolism and growth such as the Na^+/K^+ ATPase, gluconeogenic enzymes, respiratory enzymes, and β adrenergic receptors. Basic carbohydrate metabolism (gluconeogenesis and glucogenolysis), lipid metabolism (lipogenesis and lipolysis) and protein metabolism are all enhanced by thyroid hormones. Thyroid hormones also upregulate the number of adrenergic receptors on target tissues and increase the effect of epinephrine on target tissues. Without thyroid hormone, epinephrine would only have a weak response. This process or phenomenon is called permissiveness and is when one hormone is required for the action of another hormone.

The level of thyroid hormones (T3 and T4) in the blood is regulated by hormones secreted by the hypothalamic-pituitary system. Within the hypothalamus, parvocellular neurons of the arcuate nucleus release thyrotropin releasing hormone (TRH) into the primary capillary bed located in the median eminence. TRH acts on receptors located on thyrotrophs in the anterior pituitary which then secrete TSH. TSH acts on the TSH receptor (a GPCR coupled to Gs) on follicular cells and enhances the synthesis and secretion of T3 and T4 from the thyroid gland. Increases in circulating T3 and T4 inhibit the production of TSH.

A decrease in the production of thyroid hormones below normal leads to a general decrease in metabolic rate and weight gain, poor muscle development, poor hair growth and an increase in infection rates. During development, hypothyroidism can be devastating and can result in mental retardation and abnormal growth of the body. During hypothyroidism, a goiter can form and is simply an enlarged thyroid gland. The most common cause of goiter formation is the reduction of iodide in the diet which prevents the formation of thyroid hormone. The follicular cells, however, continue to get stimulated by TSH and synthesize thyroglobulin and form colloid. Since the thyroid hormones do not increase in the blood, TSH levels continue to be released. This continues to stimulate the thyroid gland which results in an increase in the size of the gland and goiter.

Increased production of thyroid hormones can result in hyperthyroidism. Hyperthyroidism causes dramatic increases in metabolic rate, increased body temperature, sweating and warm skin, increased heart rate and blood pressure increase and they become hyperactive. People with hyperthyroidism have an increased appetite but continue to decrease in weight because the tissues are so active.

The thyroid gland also contains parafollicular cells which are involved with the regulation of Ca^{2+} along with the hormone parathyroid hormone. Parafollicular cells sense increases in extracellular Ca^{2+} concentrations. The hormone calcitonin is released and acts on G-protein coupled receptors located on osteoclasts and inhibit their activity. Bone degradation is slowed which causes less release of Ca^{2+} into the circulation and thus reduces plasma Ca^{2+}. This hormone is not as critical for Ca^{2+} homeostasis as the parathyroid glands.

Parathyroid Glands

Ca^{2+} plays a critical role in many cellular processes and affects normal physiological functions. Recall that Ca^{2+} is involved in exocytosis and therefore is involved in the secretion of neurotransmitters, hormones and any secretory pathway that utilizes exocytosis. Ca^{2+} is also involved with action potential generation and the contraction of skeletal, cardiac and smooth muscles, and Ca^{2+} is involved in the activation and inactivation of many enzymes. Therefore, the extracellular concentration of Ca^{2+} is tightly regulated within a very narrow range.

Phosphate also plays important physiological functions. Phosphate ions are a component of ATP and is critical for normal cellular function. ATP is used to phosphorylate proteins and is involved in the activation and inactivation of protein function. Phosphate levels in blood are not as tightly regulated as Ca^{2+}. In the body, Ca^{2+} and phosphate are intimately linked due to their chemical interactions and storage in bone. Ca^{2+}, phosphate and O_2 form hydroxyapatite, a molecule which gives bone its characteristic hard structure. The major hormone involved in the regulation of Ca^{2+} and phosphate concentration in the extracellular fluid is parathyroid hormone, however, two other hormones, vitamin D (calcitriol) and calcitonin, also help to control extracellular Ca^{2+} levels.

The parathyroid glands are typically 2 pairs of small clusters of cells that are located posterior to each lobe of the thyroid gland (See Figure 10.8, on the next page). The parathyroid gland is made of a homogeneous groups of chief cells that secrete parathyroid hormone in response to lowered plasma Ca^{2+} levels. Chief cells have Ca^{2+} sensing receptors located in their plasma membranes. Ca^{2+} binds to the receptors and activates a G_q protein pathway and leads to a decrease in the synthesis and release of PTH. If Ca^{2+} levels decrease in the extracellular space, then the number of Ca^{2+} sensing receptors that get activated decreases. This leads to a disinhibition and the amount of PTH synthesis and release goes up. PTH influences Ca^{2+} regulation in three tissues, the bone, kidneys and intestines. In the bone, PTH increases the activity of osteocytes. Increased enzymatic degradation of bone by osteocytes releases Ca^{2+} and phosphate into the circulation. In the intestines, PTH (along with Vitamin D) increases absorption of Ca^{2+} and phosphate. In the kidneys, PTH increases Ca^{2+} reabsorption. The excess phosphate that is released from bone or absorbed in the intestine is filtered in the glomerulus and will be excreted in urine. If too much Ca^{2+} and phosphate are found circulating in blood together, these can combine and form hydroxyapatite crystals in the tissues.

Figure 10.8

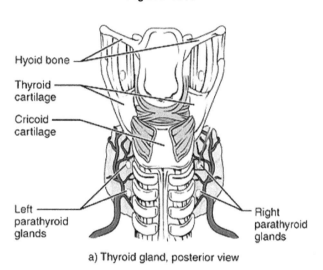

a) Thyroid gland, posterior view

Vitamin D acts as a hormone in the body, activating cytosolic and nuclear receptors to affect gene transcription. The synthesis of vitamin D starts in skin. Sunlight acts on melanocytes in the epidermis to produce 7-dehydrocholesterol which is converted to cholecalciferol (vitamin D3) for release. Vitamin D3 also enters the body by ingestion of fish and meats and other supplements. In the liver, vitamin D3 is converted to the prohormone calcidiol and circulated to the kidneys which convert inactive calcidiol to the active form of vitamin D (calcitriol). Vitamin D aids in Ca^{2+} absorption from the intestines and enhances Ca^{2+} in the blood.

Pancreas – Islets of Langerhans

The majority of the pancreas functions as an exocrine gland and plays a role in secreting a solution rich in bicarbonate ions and enzymes. Scattered within the exocrine glands are small islands of endocrine cells called islets of Langerhans which are particularly important in the regulation and homeostasis of blood glucose. Like all endocrine glands they are surrounded by a rich capillary source which aids in the movement of hormones into the general circulation so that they can easily reach their distant target tissues. Within the islets of Langerhans, there are at least 5 types of distinct cells, of which each secretes a different hormone.

The most common type of cell in the islets of Langerhans is the beta (β) cell which respond to increased extracellular glucose levels. After meals, when absorption of nutrients increases, the β cells respond by secreting the hormone insulin. In general, insulin promotes the uptake of nutrients by cells of the body. At rest, the β cells have a negative resting membrane potential. As the extracellular concentration of glucose increases, it is transported into the β cell via the GLUT1 transporter (in humans) which is constitutively expressed on the cell membrane. The cells break down the glucose which results in higher concentrations of intracellular ATP. The excess ATP binds to an ATP-sensitive K^+ channel and causes it to close resulting in cellular depolarization (less K^+ leaks out of the cells). As the cells depolarize, voltage-gated Ca^{2+} channels open and the influx of Ca^{2+} initiates exocytosis and the release of insulin. Insulin moves into the capillaries and circulates throughout the body. Insulin binds to an insulin receptor, a membrane bound, tyrosine kinase receptor which phosphorylates the tyrosine residues of certain proteins in cells. This leads to an upregulation of the number of glucose transporters and facilitates the uptake and storage of glucose in cells. Some cells, like liver, skeletal muscle and adipose tissue are particularly sensitive to insulin and upregulation of the GLUT4 transporter is upregulated which results in the uptake and storage of large quantities of glucose (Figure 10.9).

The alpha (α) cells in the islets of Langerhans are sensitive to low blood glucose concentrations and secrete the hormone glucagon to activate the release of glucose into the blood. The α cells are under strong regulatory control by the autonomic nervous system. Increases in sympathetic activity stimulate α cells to release glucagon into the blood. Glucagon acts on GPCRs to increase the activity of glycogen phosphorylase to break down glycogen to glucose and release glucose into the blood during times when the body needs extra energy.

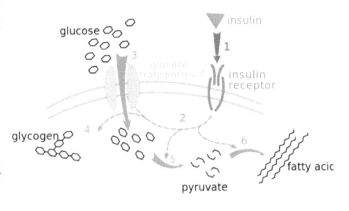

Figure 10.9

Delta (δ) cells are another cell that releases somatostatin. Somatostatin works in a paracrine fashion to inhibit the alpha and beta cells and decrease the secretion of insulin and glucagon. Delta cells are primarily under the control of parasympathetic nervous system. ACh is released from vagal efferents and binds to M3 receptors on the delta cells. This activates the secretion of somatostatin and the inhibition of alpha and beta cells.

At least two other types of hormone secreting cells can be found in the pancreatic islets of Langerhans. PP-cells secrete pancreatic poly-peptide and another cell has recently been found to secrete ghrelin. Pancreatic poly-peptide is generally involved with the auto-regulation of pancreatic function, both the exocrine and endocrine pancreas are affected. In general, pancreatic poly-peptide is secreted after high protein meals or during fasting or exercise. The hormone stimulates pancreatic enzyme secretions from the exocrine pancreas. Ghrelin is a hormone that is released just prior to food intake. It is linked to increased appetite. Most sources of ghrelin come from cells in the stomach lining, but a small percentage comes from other locations including the islets of Langerhans.

Adrenal Gland

The adrenal glands are found retroperitoneal and sit just superior to the kidneys. The adrenal glands are endocrine glands which secrete many types of hormones from their outer cortex as well as their inner medulla (Figure 10.10). The secretion of adrenal hormones is under many different regulatory control mechanisms.

The inner medulla consists of chromaffin cells interspersed between a rich capillary bed. The chromaffin cells are a modified post-ganglionic neurons of the sympathetic nervous system. During times of stress and exercise, sympathetic activation increases. Pre-ganglionic sympathetic neurons synapse onto the chromaffin cells and release ACh which cross the synaptic cleft to activate nACh receptors. The cells depolarize and open voltage-gated Ca^{2+} channels. The influx of Ca^{2+} causes vesicular release of epinephrine and norepinephrine into the interstitial space and the neurohormones enter the general circulation. Epinephrine and norepinephrine can bind to any type of adrenergic receptor in the body. In terms of the cardiovascular effect, adrenal medulla stimulation causes an increase in heart rate, stroke volume and total peripheral resistance which all lead to an increase in mean arterial pressure. Epinephrine prepares the body for activity. In terms of metabolic activity, epinephrine increases the available glucose by acting on liver hepatocytes, it increases the metabolism of adipose tissue and causes vasodilation of blood vessels in skeletal and cardiac muscles.

The adrenal cortex consists of three distinct layers of tissue which are involved in the synthesis and release of many different types of hormones. The outermost layer is called the zona glomerulosa due the clustering of cells into ball-like structures and this region secretes various mineralocorticoids. The middle layer is called the zona fasciculata and secretes the glucocorticoids and the innermost layer is called the zona reticularis and secretes androgens. All of the steroid hormones are synthesized from cholesterol that is primarily derived from LDLs. The cells of the adrenal cortex express LDL receptors in coated pits and endocytose LDLs. ACTH released from the anterior pituitary stimulates the cells of the adrenal cortex to upregulate the number of LDL receptors.

Cells of the zona glomerulosa synthesize and release aldosterone, the primary mineralocorticoid. These cells are responsive to the hormone angiotensin II as well as to changes in extracellular K^+ concentration. During conditions of low blood pressure, renin is released from the juxtaglomerular cells in the kidney and converts angiotensinogen to angiotensin I. Eventually angiotensin I is converted to angiotensin II in the lungs and can act on target tissues to increase blood pressure. One target tissue is the zona glomerulosa. These cells contain receptors for angiotensin II which is a GPCR which stimulates the synthesis and release of aldosterone. In smooth muscles this leads to increased smooth muscle contraction and in the kidneys, aldosterone acts primarily on the principal cells of the distal convoluted tubule to increase the reabsorption of Na^+. The cells of the zona glomerulosa are also sensitive to changes in extracellular K^+. Recall that the principal cells in the kidney tubule use a Na^+/K^+ exchanger and secretes K^+ ions. This mechanism is involved in the homeostasis of K^+ independent of changes in blood pressure.

The cells of the zona fasiculata are the most sensitive to ACTH. When ACTH is released from the anterior pituitary, it stimulates the cells of the zona fasiculata to release cortisol. ACTH binds to GPCRs on the plasma membrane and stimulate G_s. Activation of adenylyl cyclase leads to increases in cAMP which leads to the production of cortisol from cholesterol. Since cortisol is also a steroid hormone and is lipid soluble, it is released as it is produced. Cortisol is considered a glucocorticoid because it primarily affects glucose metabolism in the body. In general, cortisol is released during times of stress, physical activity and even when blood glucose levels are reduced. Cortisol increases the release of glucose from the liver, heart rate, blood pressure, and the release of fatty acids from adipose tissue.

The zona reticularis or the innermost layer of the adrenal cortex is involved in the secretion of androgenic hormones. The effects of the androgenic hormones are generally weak in adult humans and probably play a more important role during development of fetal tissues. During puberty, these hormones lead to some changes such as the growth of axillary and pubic hair in the female.

Figure 10.10

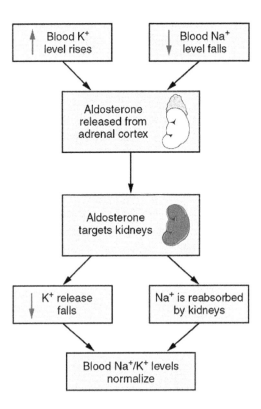

Gonadal hormones

In general, gonadal hormones play important roles in promoting spermatogenesis in males, the production of the male gametes, the sperm, and the promotion of oogenesis in females, the stimulation of follicular growth and ovulation. Gonadal hormones play important roles in the regulation of the sexual act and promote erection in males. In addition, the gonadal hormones play important roles in the regulation of reproductive functions and the secretion of additional hormones involved with reproductive physiology. And finally, gonadal hormones play important roles during conception and pregnancy in females. In both males and females, hormones released from the anterior pituitary, FSH and LH play important pivotal roles in gonadal function.

Male reproductive physiology

During development in male tissues, the presence of specific genes on the Y chromosome (SRY gene) initiate the development and differentiation of primordial gonadal tissue into the testes (Figure 10.11). The testes contain the primordial germ cells along with Sertoli cells and Leydig cells within the seminiferous tubules of the testes. The Sertoli cells secrete Müllerian inhibiting substance which causes the Müllerian ducts to regress. The Leydig cells secrete testosterone which promotes the development and differentiation of the Wolffian ducts to form the male reproductive tubular structures (the epididymis, ductus deferens, seminal vesicles and the ejaculatory ducts). This also leads to the formation of the penis, scrotum and prostate glands.

Figure 10.11

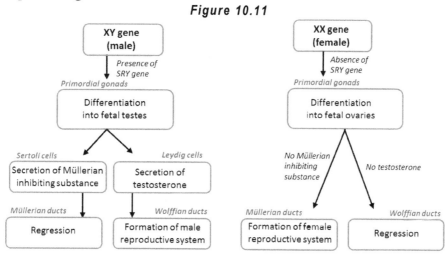

Puberty is the age at which humans develop the ability to reproduce. Around the time of puberty, the hypothalamic neurons begin to secrete GnRH. During adolescence, small amounts of testosterone that is released from the zona reticularis of the adrenal cortex inhibits hypothalamic production of GnRH. At puberty, the sensitivity of these neurons to testosterone decreases and they begin to secrete GnRH. Pulses of GnRH from the hypothalamus stimulate gonadatrophs to release FSH and LH from the anterior pituitary (See Figure 10.12). In general, FSH promotes the production of sperm and stimulates Sertoli cells, and LH stimulates testosterone release from Leydig cells. Testosterone, in turn, stimulates Sertoli cells in the somniferous tubules and inhibits the release of GnRH, FSH and LH. The seminiferous tubules are lined with spermatogonia on the basement membrane surrounded by Sertoli cells (See Figure 10.13). FSH stimulates spermatogenesis. The spermatogonia first undergo mitosis and form two daughter cells, a spermatogonium to replace itself on the basement membrane and a primary spermatocyte. The Sertoli cells form tight junctions with each other and form a tight barrier which separates the inside of the lumen from interior of the body. The primary spermatocytes can permeate this barrier, after which they begin to enlarge and undergo meiosis (Figure 10.13). The first stage of meiosis forms two secondary spermatocytes. Each secondary spermatocyte undergoes the second stage of meiosis forming a total of 4 spermatids. The spermatids that form are initially a small round cell, however, they begin to differentiate and form a spermatozoa with a distinctive head, mid-piece and tail region. This process takes about 74 days.

Figure 10.12

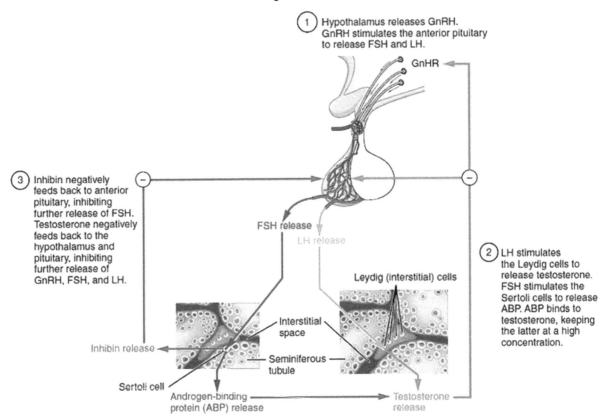

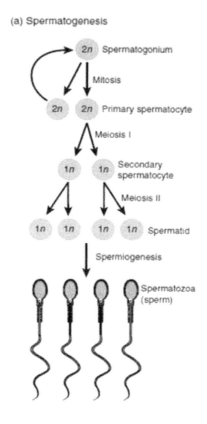

(a) Spermatogenesis

Figure 10.13

Sertoli cells play important roles in regulating spermatogenesis. They form the tight junctions and prevent immune cells from reacting to sperm cells. They are stimulated by testosterone which is released from the Leydig cells found in the interstitial spaces between the seminiferous tubules. The Sertoli cells synthesize and secrete various hormones including inhibins, small amounts of androgens and estrogen. Inhibins play a role in inhibiting FSH release from the anterior pituitary (Figure 10.12). In general, Sertoli cells stimulate, support, and nourish the developing spermatozoa.

The Leydig cells are found in the interstitial spaces between the seminiferous tubules. Leydig cells respond to LH and release testosterone. During fetal development testosterone release is important in the development of the male genital system and initiates descent. At birth, testosterone levels decrease until puberty. At puberty, testosterone release increases and is important in the generation of the male sexual characteristics. For example, testosterone causes the enlargement and differentiation of the male genitals and ductal system, stimulation of hair growth particularly on the genital, axillary, and facial regions, hypertrophy of the larynx which leads to a deeper sounding voice and increases metabolic rate and stimulates growth.

Spermatozoa are released into the lumen of the seminerferous tubule and are moved via the ciliary action of the Sertoli cells. They move into a network of collecting tubules called the rete testis before entering the epididymis via the efferent ductules (Figure 10.14). The epididymis is a long winding tubule that collects alongside the testis and is stored for release. The spermatozoa that enter the epididymis are non-motile but continue to mature and develop motility. Although sperm gain the ability to be motile they are inhibited by specific proteins that are secreted by the epithelial cells. The spermatozoa migrate through the epididymis and into the ductus deferens. Spermatozoa can be stored for many weeks in the male reproductive system.

Figure 70.14

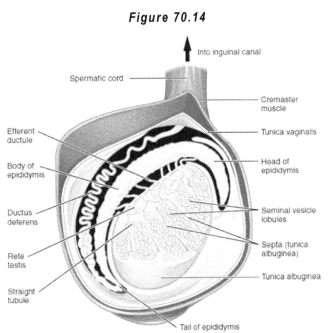

There are three glands that secrete fluids which comprise the majority of semen. The seminal vesicles are found surrounding the ejaculatory duct. These alkaline secretions contain fibrinogen and comprise ~60% of the total semen volume. The prostate gland produces about 30% of the total semen volume. The prostate gland which contains an alkaline secretion with many clotting factors as well as fibrinolysin. The bulbourethral glands (or Cowper's glands) contribute ~5% of the semen volume. This is an alkaline mucus secretion. The alkaline nature of semen helps to neutralize the acidic pH of the female vagina.

The male sexual act requires testosterone to initiate and maintain proper physiology and behavior. The male sex act is a complex series of events that cause the erection of the penis, secretion of fluid and mucus, emission and finally ejaculation. The inputs that initiate the male sex act begin from mechanoreceptor activation originating directly from the penis or from descending pathways that can originate from multiple brain regions. Thoughts, emotions and sensory inputs that originate from various inputs such as the visual and olfactory centers can initiate the sex act and initiate erection. These sensory inputs increase the activity of neurons that innervate the smooth muscle of arterioles that innervate the penile tissue.

Within the penis, there are special cavernous sinusoidal tissues called the corpus cavernosum and the corpus spongiosum. The parasympathetic neurons release ACh which binds to muscarinic receptors and activate Gs causing cause vasodilation of the smooth muscle. In addition, nitric oxide is released from the presynaptic terminals. Nitric oxide diffuses through the tissues and activates guanylyl cyclase in the smooth muscle cells. This also promotes relaxation of the smooth muscle. Vasodilation of this special vasculature results in the sinusoids filling with blood. As this occurs, it presses on the veins leaving the erectile tissue and causes the corpus cavernosum and corpus spongiosum to engorge with blood, resulting in the enlargement and hardening of the penis (Figure 10.15). This process is called erection.

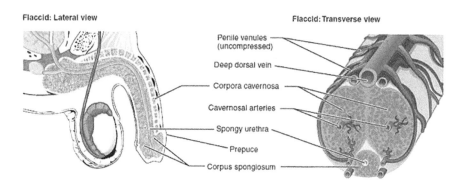

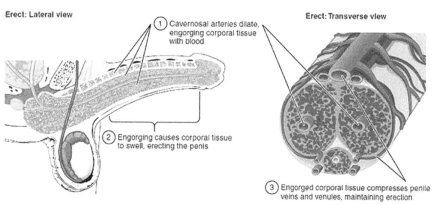

Figure 10.15

As the sexual inputs increase in intensity, sympathetic centers in the spinal cord are initiated which stimulate emission and ejaculation. Inputs that arise from the lower thoracic spinal cord project to the male reproductive organs and cause stimulation of the ductus deferens. In addition, the bulbourethral glands, the prostate glands and the seminal vesicles are stimulated and release their secretions. This results in the accumulation of spermatozoa and fluid in the urethra. This process is called emission.

Ejaculation is the propulsion of the fluid out of the penile tissue. Emission, of the movement of fluid into the urethra results in the stimulation of mechanosensory stretch receptors. A reflex is initiated which results in sympathetic constriction of the internal sphincter of the urinary bladder to prevent the mixing of urine and semen, and a combination of sympathetic and somatic motor output that causes the propulsive rhythmic contractions that force the semen out of the urethra. Semen is deposited in the female copulatory organ, the vagina for reproduction. Approximately 75-400 million sperm are released during ejaculation, however, many do not survive in the female reproductive organs.

Female reproductive physiology

During female early development, the lack of specific genes (found on the Y chromosome) lead to the formation and development of the female reproductive organs (Figure 10.16). The primordial gonadal tissue forms into the ovarian tissue and contains the primordial germ cells. The Müllerian ducts form the uterus, uterine tubes and vagina. The absence of testosterone results in the regression of the Wolffian ducts and the absence of male genital components (refer back to Figure 10.11). During early development of the female ovaries, the oocytes develop and enter the first stage of meiosis and are arrested in prophase. The oocytes remain at this stage until puberty.

In females, small amounts of androgens secreted from the adrenal cortex also inhibit the release of GnRH.

Figure 10.16

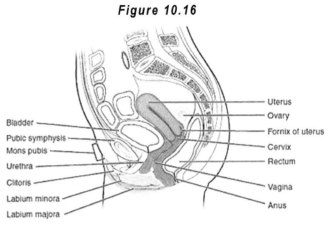

(a) Human female reproductive system: lateral view

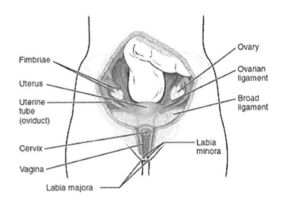

(b) Human female reproductive system: anterior view

At puberty, the hypothalamic neurons begin to secrete pulses of GnRH which stimulates the release of FSH and LH from the anterior pituitary. In females, FSH is responsible for the stimulation of follicular growth in the ovaries. The events that occur in the ovary can be divided into two phases, the follicular phase in which the follicles develop and the luteal phase in which the corpus luteum develops.

Within the ovary, primordial follicles are the oocytes that are arrested in the first meiotic division and are surrounded by granulosa cells. At the beginning of one ovarian cycle, approximately 10-20 primordial follicles begin to develop (Figure 10.17). The oocyte begins to enlarge and the granulosa cells begin to proliferate and form primary follicles. The oocyte and granulosa cells secrete a thick proteinaceous layer surrounding the oocyte called the zona pellucida which is surrounded by a thick layer of granulosa cells. Eventually the granulosa cells begin to secrete a fluid which collects into spaces called antrum. This is the formation of secondary follicles. Finally the antrum coalesce into a single large follicular antrum with the oocyte pulled off to one side and forms the mature follicle. At this stage the oocyte finishes the first stage of meiosis and a single small cell, called a polar body is produced. Usually only one follicle reaches the mature stage. The mechanism is not clear, but it appears that the follicles that are in the most advanced stages cause the inhibition of growth of nearby follicles which ultimately results in only one follicle reaching the mature stage. The dying cells undergo atresia and are called atretic follicles.

Figure 10.17

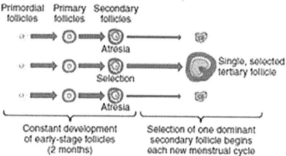

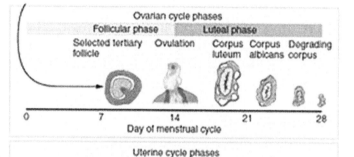

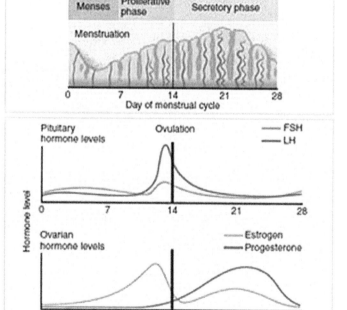

Ovulation is triggered by a surge in LH. LH is necessary for ovulation and the release of the oocyte from the ovary. LH also causes changes in the granulosa and theca cells. Theca cells begin to secrete androgens which are taken up by the granulosa cells and converted to estrogen and progesterone and form a structure called the corpus luteum. Before ovulation, estrogen is secreted in greater quan tities and after ovulation progesterone is secreted in greater quantities. If fertilization does not take place, the corpus luteum begins to atrophy and degenerates forming scar tissue or the corpus albicans.

At the same time as events occur in the ovary, separate events are occurring in the uterus (refer to Figure 10.17). Day 1 of the female reproductive cycle is the first day of menstruation or menses and coincides with the start of the follicular phase. During this period, the inner functional layer of the endometrium is sloughed off. Then the endometrium begins to grow or proliferate. This is triggered by the estrogen that is secreted from the developing follicles. After ovulation, the corpus luteum begins to secrete higher amounts of progesterone which triggers the endometrium to enter the secretory phase. The lining of the endometrium is preparing for possible implantation of a blastocyst. If fertilization does not occur, then the corpus luteum begins to atrophy around 12 days after ovulation and the amount of progesterone decreases and the endometrium begins to atrophy and die. This leads to menses and the cycle starts over.

In general, the female cycle lasts 28 days. The first 14 days include the follicular phase of the ovarian cycle and menses and the proliferative phases of the uterine cycle. This period starts at the onset of menses and runs until ovulation occurs. The last 14 days include the luteal phase of the ovarian cycle and the secretory phase of the uterine cycle. This period starts at ovulation and ends when menses occurs. The last 14 days rarely varies in length and in most females run 13-14 days. The first portion of the female cycle, the time at the onset menses until ovulation varies quite a bit. The menstrual cycles in humans can vary from 21-45 days in length. This is due to changes in the first portion of the cycle.

If the oocyte is fertilized, this typically occurs within 12-24 hours after ovulation. The oocyte is in the ampulla region of the uterine tube during this time. A zygote is formed and the cells begin to divide. As they divide they form a structure called the blastocyst which secretes a hormone called human chorionic gonadotropin (hCG). The corpus luteum is sensitive to hCG and induces further growth of the corpus luteum during pregnancy. The corpus luteum continues to secrete greater and greater amounts of progesterone which maintain the endometrial lining and keep it intact during pregnancy.

The opening to the uterus is called the cervix. This region of the uterus secretes a thick mucus and forms a barrier to sperm and bacteria. Around the time of ovulation, as LH levels surge, this causes the secretions to become thinned which allow sperm entry over a period of several days.

CHAPTER 10 SUMMARY

➢ Hormones are substances released from endocrine glands. They move into the circulation and affect target tissues at distance locations.

➢ Most hormones are peptides and are stored in intracellular vesicles. These hormones bind to GPCR located on cell membranes to initiate relatively quick cellular responses.

➢ Some hormones are steroids and are lipid soluble molecules which are produced on demand. They act on intracellular receptors which regulate gene transcription. These responses cause relatively long term cellular responses.

➢ The hypothalamic pituitary system influences many aspects of normal physiology.

➢ The pituitary is comprised of two distinct regions, the anterior pituitary and the posterior pituitary.

➢ Magnocellular neurons in the supraoptic and paraventricular nucleus of the hypothalamus send axons down the infundibular stalk to the posterior pituitary.

➢ Vasopressin is released from the posterior pituitary in response to decreased blood osmolarity. Vasopressin acts on receptors in the kidney tubule and causes an upregulation in the number of aquaporin channels. This increases water reabsorption.

➤ Oxytocin is released from the posterior pituitary in response to an infant suckling on the nipples. Oxytocin acts on myopithelial cells in the breast mammary glands and causes milk letdown.

➤ The anterior pituitary is under regulation of regulating hormones from parvocellular neurons in the hypothalamus.

➤ Growth hormone from the anterior pituitary stimulates cells to divide and increase in size and number and help regulate basic cellular metabolism and nutrient levels.

➤ Thyroid stimulating hormone from the anterior pituitary stimulates the thyroid gland to release thyroid hormone (T3 and T4). Thyroid hormone is critical for normal cell metabolism and growth and development.

➤ Adrenocorticotropic hormone from the anterior pituitary stimulates the adrenal cortex to release the steroid hormone, cortisol. Cortisol is released in response to emotional and physical stressors and enhances glucose availability.

➤ Follicle stimulating hormone and luteinizing hormone from the anterior pituitary gland regulate reproductive organs.

➤ Prolactin from the anterior pituitary is involved with the letdown of milk during breast feeding.

➤ The parathyroid glands are involved in the regulation of calcium homeostasis. Parathyroid hormone stimulates osteoclasts in bones to release calcium into the blood, stimulates the kidney to increase calcium reabsorption, and increased calcium absorption in the intestines.

➤ The pancreas contains both exocrine and endocrine glands. The endocrine glands are the islet of Langerhans. Insulin is released in response to elevated blood glucose and enhance the uptake and storage of nutrients. Glucagon is released in response to lowered blood glucose levels and enhances the release of stored glucose.

➤ The adrenal gland releases many different hormones. The adrenal medulla is under neural control of the sympathetic nervous system. The adrenal medullary chromaffin cells release epinephrine and norepinephrine into the blood. These neurohormones bind to adrenergic receptors preparing the body for physical exercise.

➤ The adrenal cortex releases multiple steroid hormones including the mineralocorticoids, glucocorticoids and androgens.

> The adrenal cortex releases aldosterone in response to low blood pressure or in response to high K^+ concentrations. In the kidney, aldosterone upregulates the number of Na^+/K^+ exchanger and Na^+ is reabsorbed and K^+ is secreted.

> Spermatogenesis is under the regulation of the anterior pituitary hormone FSH and LH stimulates the release of testosterone.

> In females, FSH stimulates follicular growth in the ovaries and LH stimulates ovulation.

References and Suggested Readings

Bluet-Pajot, MT, Epelbaum J, Gourdji D, Hammond C, Kordon C. 1998. Hypothalamic and hypophyseal regulation of growth hormone secretion. *Cellular and Molecular Neurobiology* 18(1):101-123.

Chiamolera M, Wondisford FE. 2009. Thyrotropin-releasing hormone and the thyroid hormone feedback mechanism. *Endocrinology* 150(3):1091-1096.

Gylfe E, Gilon P. 2013. Glucose regulation of glucagon secretion. *Diabetes Research and Clinical Practice* 103:1-10.

Hartenstein V. 2006. The neuroendocrine system of invertebrates: a developmental and evolutionary perspective. *Journal of Endocrinology* 190: 555-570.

Ishunina TA, Swaab DF. 1999. Vasopressin and oxytocin neurons of the human supraoptic and paraventricular nucleus; size changes in relation to age and sex. *The Journal of Clinical Endocrinology and Metabolism* 84(12):4637-4644.

McKinley MJ, Mathai ML, McAllen RM, McClear RC, Miselis RR, Pennington GL, Vivas L, Wade JD, Oldfield BJ. 2004. Vasopressin secretion: osmotic and hormonal regulation by the lamina terminalis. *Journal of Neuroendocrinology* 16:340-347.

Minami S, Kamegai J, Sugihara H, Suzuki N, Wakabayashi I. 1998. Growth hormone inhibits its own secretion by acting on the hypothalamus through its receptors on neuropeptide Y neurons in the arcuate nucleus and somatostatin neurons in the periventricular nucleus. *Endocrine Journal* 45:S19-S26.

Møller N, Jørgensen JOL. 2009. Effects of growth hormone on glucose, lipid, and protein metabolism in human subjects. *Endocrine Reviews* 30(2):152-177.

Nillni EA. 2010. Regulation of the hypothalamic thyrotropin releasing hormone (TRH) neuron by neuronal and peripheral inputs. *Frontiers in Neuroendocrinology* 31:134-156.

Yang SN, Shi Y, Yang G, Li Y, Yu J, Berggren PO. 2014. Ionic mechanisms in pancreatic β cell signaling. *Cell and Molecular Life Sciences* 71:4149-417.

Credits

Chapter 2

1. Anatomy and Physiology, OpenStax College, 2013. Copyright © Rice University (CC by 3.0).
2. Anatomy and Physiology, OpenStax College, 2013. Copyright © Rice University (CC by 3.0).
3. Anatomy and Physiology, OpenStax College, 2013. Copyright © Rice University (CC by 3.0).
4. Anatomy and Physiology, OpenStax College, 2013. Copyright © Rice University (CC by 3.0).
5. Anatomy and Physiology, OpenStax College, 2013. Copyright © Rice University (CC by 3.0).
6. Anatomy and Physiology, OpenStax College, 2013. Copyright © Rice University (CC by 3.0).
7. Anatomy and Physiology, OpenStax College, 2013. Copyright © Rice University (CC by 3.0).
8. Anatomy and Physiology, OpenStax College, 2013. Copyright © Rice University (CC by 3.0).
9. Anatomy and Physiology, OpenStax College, 2013. Copyright © Rice University (CC by 3.0).
10. http://commons.wikimedia.org/wiki/File:Major_events_in_mitosis.svg, National Institutes of Health, 2006. Copyright in the Public Domain.
11. Anatomy and Physiology, OpenStax College, 2013. Copyright © Rice University (CC by 3.0).
12. Anatomy and Physiology, OpenStax College, 2013. Copyright © Rice University (CC by 3.0).
13. Mariana Ruiz Villarreal, http://commons.wikimedia.org/wiki/File:Desmosome_cell_junction_en.svg. Copyright in the Public Domain.
14. Mariana Ruiz Villarreal, http://commons.wikimedia.org/wiki/File:Adherens_Junctions_structural_proteins.svg. Copyright in the Public Domain.
15. Mariana Ruiz Villarreal, http://commons.wikimedia.org/wiki/File:Gap_cell_junction-en.svg. Copyright in the Public Domain.
16. Mariana Ruiz Villarreal, http://commons.wikimedia.org/wiki/File:Cellular_tight_junction-en.svg. Copyright in the Public Domain.
17. Jawahar Swaminathan and MSD Staff at European Bioinformatics Institute, http://commons.wikimedia.org/wiki/File%3APDB_1hi9_EBI.jpg. Copyright in the Public Domain.
18. Anatomy and Physiology, OpenStax College, 2013. Copyright © Rice University (CC by 3.0).
19. Anatomy and Physiology, OpenStax College, 2013. Copyright © Rice University (CC by 3.0).
20. Anatomy and Physiology, OpenStax College, 2013. Copyright © Rice University (CC by 3.0).
21. Mariana Ruiz Villarreal, http://commons.wikimedia.org/wiki/File:Osmotic_pressure_on_blood_cells_diagram.svg. Copyright in the Public Domain.
22. Anatomy and Physiology, OpenStax College, 2013. Copyright © Rice University (CC by 3.0).
23. Mariana Ruiz Villarreal, http://commons.wikimedia.org/wiki/File:Exocytosis_types.svg. Copyright in the Public Domain.
24. Anatomy and Physiology, OpenStax College, 2013. Copyright © Rice University (CC by 3.0).
25. Bensaccount, http://commons.wikimedia.org/wiki/File:LGIC.png. Copyright in the Public Domain.
26. Bensaccount, http://commons.wikimedia.org/wiki/File:G-protein-coupled_receptor.png. Copyright in the Public Domain.

Chapter 3

1. Anatomy and Physiology, OpenStax College, 2013. Copyright © Rice University (CC by 3.0).
2. Anatomy and Physiology, OpenStax College, 2013. Copyright © Rice University (CC by 3.0).
3. Anatomy and Physiology, OpenStax College, 2013. Copyright © Rice University (CC by 3.0).
4. Andrew c, http://commons.wikimedia.org/wiki/File:Neuron_with_oligodendrocyte_and_myelin_sheath.svg. Copyright in the Public Domain.
5. Roadnottaken, http://commons.wikimedia.org/wiki/File:Myelinated_neuron.jpg. Copyright in the Public Domain.
6. Anatomy and Physiology, OpenStax College, 2013. Copyright © Rice University (CC by 3.0).
7. Anatomy and Physiology, OpenStax College, 2013. Copyright © Rice University (CC by 3.0).
8. Mariana Ruiz Villarreal, http://commons.wikimedia.org/wiki/File:Connexon_and_connexin_structure.svg. Copyright in the Public Domain.
9. Anatomy and Physiology, OpenStax College, 2013. Copyright © Rice University (CC by 3.0).
10. Copyright © Danko Dimchev Georgiev (CC BY-SA 3.0) at http://commons.wikimedia.org/wiki/File:Exocytosis-machinery.jpg.

11. Anatomy and Physiology, OpenStax College, 2013. Copyright © Rice University (CC by 3.0).
12. Anatomy and Physiology, OpenStax College, 2013. Copyright © Rice University (CC by 3.0).
13. Takuma-sa, http://commons.wikimedia.org/wiki/File:NAchR-2BG9_default.png. Copyright in the Public Domain.
14. Shao, http://commons.wikimedia.org/wiki/File:N-ACh_receptor-scheme.jpg. Copyright in the Public Domain.
15. NEUROtiker, http://commons.wikimedia.org/wiki/File:L-Tyrosin_phys.svg. Copyright in the Public Domain.
16. Codc, http://commons.wikimedia.org/wiki/File:L-Dopa.svg. Copyright in the Public Domain.
17. Harbin, http://commons.wikimedia.org/wiki/File:Dopamine2.svg. Copyright in the Public Domain.
18. Edgar181, http://commons.wikimedia.org/wiki/File:Norepinephrine_structure.png. Copyright in the Public Domain.
19. Roland Mattern, http://commons.wikimedia.org/wiki/File:Epinephrine.svg. Copyright in the Public Domain.
20. Edgar181, http://commons.wikimedia.org/wiki/File:1-methyltryptophan.svg. Copyright in the Public Domain.
21. Harbinary, http://commons.wikimedia.org/wiki/File:5-hydroxytryptophan.png. Copyright in the Public Domain.
22. Meodipt, http://commons.wikimedia.org/wiki/File:2-Methyl-5-hydroxytryptamine.png. Copyright in the Public Domain.
23. Anatomy and Physiology, OpenStax College, 2013. Copyright © Rice University (CC by 3.0).
24. Anatomy and Physiology, OpenStax College, 2013. Copyright © Rice University (CC by 3.0).
25. Anatomy and Physiology, OpenStax College, 2013. Copyright © Rice University (CC by 3.0).
26. Anatomy and Physiology, OpenStax College, 2013. Copyright © Rice University (CC by 3.0).
27. Anatomy and Physiology, OpenStax College, 2013. Copyright © Rice University (CC by 3.0).
28. Mysid, http://commons.wikimedia.org/wiki/File:Gray769-en.svg. Copyright in the Public Domain.
29. Mysid, http://commons.wikimedia.org/wiki/File:Gray770-en.svg. Copyright in the Public Domain.
30. Anatomy and Physiology, OpenStax College, 2013. Copyright © Rice University (CC by 3.0).
31. Anatomy and Physiology, OpenStax College, 2013. Copyright © Rice University (CC by 3.0).
32. Anatomy and Physiology, OpenStax College, 2013. Copyright © Rice University (CC by 3.0).
33. Gray696, http://commons.wikimedia.org/wiki/File:Gray696.svg. Copyright in the Public Domain.
34. Anatomy and Physiology, OpenStax College, 2013. Copyright © Rice University (CC by 3.0).
35. Anatomy and Physiology, OpenStax College, 2013. Copyright © Rice University (CC by 3.0).

Chapter 4

1. Anatomy and Physiology, OpenStax College, 2013. Copyright © Rice University (CC by 3.0).
2. Copyright © Thomas.haslwanter (CC BY-SA 3.0) at
   http://commons.wikimedia.org/wiki/File:Skin_proprioception.svg.
3. Anatomy and Physiology, OpenStax College, 2013. Copyright © Rice University (CC by 3.0).
4. Anatomy and Physiology, OpenStax College, 2013. Copyright © Rice University (CC by 3.0).
5. Anatomy and Physiology, OpenStax College, 2013. Copyright © Rice University (CC by 3.0).
6. Anatomy and Physiology, OpenStax College, 2013. Copyright © Rice University (CC by 3.0).
7. Anatomy and Physiology, OpenStax College, 2013. Copyright © Rice University (CC by 3.0).
8. Copyright © BruceBlaus (CC by 3.0) at
   http://commons.wikimedia.org/wiki/File:Blausen_0389_EyeAnatomy_02.png.
9. Anatomy and Physiology, OpenStax College, 2013. Copyright © Rice University (CC by 3.0).
10. Anatomy and Physiology, OpenStax College, 2013. Copyright © Rice University (CC by 3.0).
11. Copyright © Ahnode (CC BY-SA 3.0) at http://commons.wikimedia.org/wiki/File:Cone_scheme_ru.svg.
12. Copyright © Distorted (CC BY-SA 3.0) at http://commons.wikimedia.org/wiki/File:Cone_cell.svg.
13. Anatomy and Physiology, OpenStax College, 2013. Copyright © Rice University (CC by 3.0).
14. Anatomy and Physiology, OpenStax College, 2013. Copyright © Rice University (CC by 3.0).
15. Anatomy and Physiology, OpenStax College, 2013. Copyright © Rice University (CC by 3.0).
16. Copyright © Thomas.haslwanter (CC BY-SA 3.0) at
   http://commons.wikimedia.org/wiki/File:HairCell_Transduction.svg.
17. Anatomy and Physiology, OpenStax College, 2013. Copyright © Rice University (CC by 3.0).
18. Anatomy and Physiology, OpenStax College, 2013. Copyright © Rice University (CC by 3.0).

Chapter 5

1. Anatomy and Physiology, OpenStax College, 2013. Copyright © Rice University (CC by 3.0).
2. Anatomy and Physiology, OpenStax College, 2013. Copyright © Rice University (CC by 3.0).
3. Louisa Howard, http://commons.wikimedia.org/wiki/File:Human_skeletal_muscle_tissue_2_-_TEM.jpg. Copyright in the Public Domain.
4. Heinte, http://commons.wikimedia.org/wiki/File:Muskelfibrille_(Sarkomer).PNG. Copyright in the Public Domain.
5. Anatomy and Physiology, OpenStax College, 2013. Copyright © Rice University (CC by 3.0).

6. Anatomy and Physiology, OpenStax College, 2013. Copyright © Rice University (CC by 3.0).
7. Anatomy and Physiology, OpenStax College, 2013. Copyright © Rice University (CC by 3.0).
8. http://commons.wikimedia.org/wiki/File:Electron_micrograph_of_neuromuscular_junction_(cross-section).jpg, National Institutes of Health, 2006. Copyright in the Public Domain.
9. Anatomy and Physiology, OpenStax College, 2013. Copyright © Rice University (CC by 3.0).
10. Anatomy and Physiology, OpenStax College, 2013. Copyright © Rice University (CC by 3.0).
11. Anatomy and Physiology, OpenStax College, 2013. Copyright © Rice University (CC by 3.0).
12. Copyright © Polarlys (CC BY-SA 3.0) at http://commons.wikimedia.org/wiki/File:Muskulatur_-_Einzelzuckung.png.
13. Copyright © Polarlys (CC BY-SA 3.0) at http://commons.wikimedia.org/wiki/File:Muskulatur_-_unvollstaendiger_Tetanus.png.
14. Copyright © Polarlys (CC BY-SA 3.0) at http://commons.wikimedia.org/wiki/File:Muskulatur_-_vollstaendiger_Tetanus.png.
15. Anatomy and Physiology, OpenStax College, 2013. Copyright © Rice University (CC by 3.0).
16. Anatomy and Physiology, OpenStax College, 2013. Copyright © Rice University (CC by 3.0).
17. Anatomy and Physiology, OpenStax College, 2013. Copyright © Rice University (CC by 3.0).
18. Anatomy and Physiology, OpenStax College, 2013. Copyright © Rice University (CC by 3.0).
19. Anatomy and Physiology, OpenStax College, 2013. Copyright © Rice University (CC by 3.0).
20. Anatomy and Physiology, OpenStax College, 2013. Copyright © Rice University (CC by 3.0).

Chapter 6

1. Anatomy and Physiology, OpenStax College, 2013. Copyright © Rice University (CC by 3.0).
2. Copyright © Patrick J. Lynch (CC by 2.5) at http://commons.wikimedia.org/wiki/File%3AHeart_circulation_diagram.svg.
3. Copyright © ZooFari (CC BY-SA 3.0) at http://commons.wikimedia.org/wiki/File%3AHeart_anterior_large.jpg.
4. Henry Vandyke Carter / Huckfinne, http://commons.wikimedia.org/wiki/File:Gray1216_modern_locations.svg. Copyright in the Public Domain.
5. Anatomy and Physiology, OpenStax College, 2013. Copyright © Rice University (CC by 3.0).
6. Anatomy and Physiology, OpenStax College, 2013. Copyright © Rice University (CC by 3.0).
7. Anatomy and Physiology, OpenStax College, 2013. Copyright © Rice University (CC by 3.0).
8. Anatomy and Physiology, OpenStax College, 2013. Copyright © Rice University (CC by 3.0).
9. Anatomy and Physiology, OpenStax College, 2013. Copyright © Rice University (CC by 3.0).
10. Anatomy and Physiology, OpenStax College, 2013. Copyright © Rice University (CC by 3.0).
11. Copyright © DanielChangMD (CC BY-SA 2.5) at https://commons.wikimedia.org/wiki/File:Wiggers_Diagram.svg.
12. Anatomy and Physiology, OpenStax College, 2013. Copyright © Rice University (CC by 3.0).
13. Anatomy and Physiology, OpenStax College, 2013. Copyright © Rice University (CC by 3.0).
14. Anatomy and Physiology, OpenStax College, 2013. Copyright © Rice University (CC by 3.0).
15. Anatomy and Physiology, OpenStax College, 2013. Copyright © Rice University (CC by 3.0).
16. Anatomy and Physiology, OpenStax College, 2013. Copyright © Rice University (CC by 3.0).
17. Anatomy and Physiology, OpenStax College, 2013. Copyright © Rice University (CC by 3.0).
18. Anatomy and Physiology, OpenStax College, 2013. Copyright © Rice University (CC by 3.0).

Chapter 7

1. Mariana Ruiz Villarreal, http://commons.wikimedia.org/wiki/File:Respiratory_system_complete_en.svg. Copyright in the Public Domain.
2. Anatomy and Physiology, OpenStax College, 2013. Copyright © Rice University (CC by 3.0).
3. Anatomy and Physiology, OpenStax College, 2013. Copyright © Rice University (CC by 3.0).
4. Anatomy and Physiology, OpenStax College, 2013. Copyright © Rice University (CC by 3.0).
5. Anatomy and Physiology, OpenStax College, 2013. Copyright © Rice University (CC by 3.0).
6. Anatomy and Physiology, OpenStax College, 2013. Copyright © Rice University (CC by 3.0).
7. Anatomy and Physiology, OpenStax College, 2013. Copyright © Rice University (CC by 3.0).
8. Anatomy and Physiology, OpenStax College, 2013. Copyright © Rice University (CC by 3.0).
9. Anatomy and Physiology, OpenStax College, 2013. Copyright © Rice University (CC by 3.0).
10. Anatomy and Physiology, OpenStax College, 2013. Copyright © Rice University (CC by 3.0).
11. Anatomy and Physiology, OpenStax College, 2013. Copyright © Rice University (CC by 3.0).
12. Anatomy and Physiology, OpenStax College, 2013. Copyright © Rice University (CC by 3.0).

Chapter 8

1. Anatomy and Physiology, OpenStax College, 2013. Copyright © Rice University (CC by 3.0).
2. Anatomy and Physiology, OpenStax College, 2013. Copyright © Rice University (CC by 3.0).
3. Anatomy and Physiology, OpenStax College, 2013. Copyright © Rice University (CC by 3.0).
4. Anatomy and Physiology, OpenStax College, 2013. Copyright © Rice University (CC by 3.0).
5. Anatomy and Physiology, OpenStax College, 2013. Copyright © Rice University (CC by 3.0).

Chapter 9

1. Mariana Ruiz Villarreal, http://commons.wikimedia.org/wiki/File:Digestive_system_diagram_en.svg. Copyright in the Public Domain.
2. Anatomy and Physiology, OpenStax College, 2013. Copyright © Rice University (CC by 3.0).
3. Copyright © Boumphreyfr (CC BY-SA 3.0) at http://commons.wikimedia.org/wiki/File:Neural_control_gut.png.
4. Anatomy and Physiology, OpenStax College, 2013. Copyright © Rice University (CC by 3.0).
5. Anatomy and Physiology, OpenStax College, 2013. Copyright © Rice University (CC by 3.0).
6. Anatomy and Physiology, OpenStax College, 2013. Copyright © Rice University (CC by 3.0).
7. Anatomy and Physiology, OpenStax College, 2013. Copyright © Rice University (CC by 3.0).
8. Copyright © Boumphreyfr (CC BY-SA 3.0) at http://commons.wikimedia.org/wiki/File%3AGastric_gland.png.
9. Anatomy and Physiology, OpenStax College, 2013. Copyright © Rice University (CC by 3.0).
10. Anatomy and Physiology, OpenStax College, 2013. Copyright © Rice University (CC by 3.0).
11. Anatomy and Physiology, OpenStax College, 2013. Copyright © Rice University (CC by 3.0).
12. Anatomy and Physiology, OpenStax College, 2013. Copyright © Rice University (CC by 3.0).
13. Anatomy and Physiology, OpenStax College, 2013. Copyright © Rice University (CC by 3.0).
14. Henry Gray / Henry Vandyke Carter, Anatomy of the Human Body, 1918. Copyright in the Public Domain.
15. Anatomy and Physiology, OpenStax College, 2013. Copyright © Rice University (CC by 3.0).

Chapter 10

1. Anatomy and Physiology, OpenStax College, 2013. Copyright © Rice University (CC by 3.0).
2. Anatomy and Physiology, OpenStax College, 2013. Copyright © Rice University (CC by 3.0).
3. Anatomy and Physiology, OpenStax College, 2013. Copyright © Rice University (CC by 3.0).
4. Anatomy and Physiology, OpenStax College, 2013. Copyright © Rice University (CC by 3.0).
5. Anatomy and Physiology, OpenStax College, 2013. Copyright © Rice University (CC by 3.0).
6. Mikael Häggström, http://commons.wikimedia.org/wiki/File%3AThyroid_hormone_synthesis.png. Copyright in the Public Domain.
7. Anatomy and Physiology, OpenStax College, 2013. Copyright © Rice University (CC by 3.0).
8. XcepticZP, http://commons.wikimedia.org/wiki/File:Insulin_glucose_metabolism_ZP.svg. Copyright in the Public Domain.
9. Anatomy and Physiology, OpenStax College, 2013. Copyright © Rice University (CC by 3.0).
10. Anatomy and Physiology, OpenStax College, 2013. Copyright © Rice University (CC by 3.0).
11. Anatomy and Physiology, OpenStax College, 2013. Copyright © Rice University (CC by 3.0).
12. Anatomy and Physiology, OpenStax College, 2013. Copyright © Rice University (CC by 3.0).
13. Anatomy and Physiology, OpenStax College, 2013. Copyright © Rice University (CC by 3.0).
14. Anatomy and Physiology, OpenStax College, 2013. Copyright © Rice University (CC by 3.0).
15. Anatomy and Physiology, OpenStax College, 2013. Copyright © Rice University (CC by 3.0).

CPSIA information can be obtained
at www.ICGtesting.com
Printed in the USA
LVOW02s2155290816

502357LV00005B/11/P